Source maps

Base map

Compilation at drafting scale.
Black and white or multicolor.

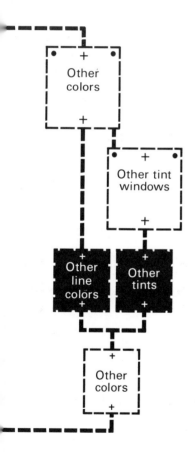

Traced from compilation, one separation
per color. Include symbols and type.

Traced from line separations, one window
per tint. Solid black or red original.

Reduced to final (printed) size.
Aligned by register marks.

Negatives combined (double-burned).

Indicates pin-register.

Indicates register marks.

Prentice-Hall, Inc.
Englewood Cliffs, New Jersey 07632

John Campbell

University of
Wisconsin-Parkside

Introductory Cartography

Library of Congress Cataloging in Publication Data

Campbell, John, (date)
  Introductory cartography.

  Includes bibliographies and index.
  1. Cartography. I. Title.
GA105.3.C35 1984   526   83–15990
ISBN 0-13-501304-6

Dedicated to the memory of
Willis R. Heath

Editorial/production supervision: Maria McKinnon
Interior and cover design: Judith A. Matz
Manufacturing buyer: John Hall
Cover art by: Hazel Campbell

© 1984 by Prentice-Hall, Inc., Englewood Cliffs, New Jersey 07632

10 9 8 7 6 5 4 3 2 1

ISBN 0-13-501304-6

Prentice-Hall International, Inc., *London*
Prentice-Hall of Australia Pty. Limited, *Sydney*
Editora Prentice-Hall do Brasil, Ltda., *Rio de Janeiro*
Prentice-Hall Canada Inc., *Toronto*
Prentice-Hall of India Private Limited, *New Delhi*
Prentice-Hall of Japan, Inc., *Tokyo*
Prentice-Hall of Southeast Asia Pte. Ltd., *Singapore*
Whitehall Books Limited, *Wellington, New Zealand*

Summary Contents

Complete Contents

Preface

This book reflects the experiences accumulated during thirty years of working with maps—in the map library, the drafting room, the darkroom, and the classroom. It is my hope that reading it will help others to enjoy maps and mapping as much as I have.

The book is conceived as the text for a general, introductory course in cartography—the type of course that is a vital component of many undergraduate geography programs. The usual content of this type of course has conditioned the structure of the book. At the same time, the interests, needs, and capabilities of the students who are typically enrolled have influenced the manner in which the material is presented.

The sequence in which topics are discussed is directly related to the order in which the basic cartographic tasks are accomplished. Such matters as the determination of the size and shape of the earth and the problems involved in using map projections to record that information on flat paper are discussed first. An account of how information about the distribution of features on the earth's surface is obtained through surveying, aerial photography, and other forms of remote sensing is provided next. This is followed by a description of the preparation of the drawings, scribings, other materials, and of the processes used in the reproduction of maps, which leads to an explanation of how the printing of multiple copies of single-color and multicolor maps is accomplished. Finally, following an exploration of the problems and methods involved in the presentation of statistical information, the methods and equipment involved in the increasingly important use of computer-assisted cartographic techniques are explained.

The goals of students who enroll in the introductory cartography course differ rather markedly: some of them will have no further formal contact with cartography, others are aspiring cartographers who will take extensive additional training in the field, and many will fall somewhere between the two extremes. The book meets the needs of all these students by providing a general introductory overview of the field. The approach taken throughout is primarily descriptive and virtually non-mathematical, with each aspect of the map production process discussed in logical sequence. Excessive detail is avoided, but the level of information is sufficient for a basic understanding and provides a basis for further, productive study. Building on the groundwork provided, students can readily begin to expand the scope of their studies by making use of the Suggested Readings at the end of each chapter.

ACKNOWLEDGMENTS

Many people have contributed to the process of creating this book—some directly and some indirectly. The following list names some of the most important contributors, although there are undoubtedly others who may be inadvertently overlooked. Those whose names are listed will realize what their contributions have been. I wish to share with them whatever success the book may achieve.

Therefore, I wish to thank Robert P. Hinkle, G. Donald Hudson, Malcolm M. Micklewright, and Leonard Sczygiel. In addition, John C. Sherman has, over many years, provided counsel, advice, and inspiration; Morgan D. Thomas has provided the encouragement and motivation I have often needed. Alan E. Guskin and Lorman A. Ratner, as well as other colleagues at the University of Wisconsin–Parkside, have provided significant help in many ways, much of which directly aided in this project. I also wish to acknowledge the vital support provided by my family and, especially, by my wife, Hazel. Without her loving encouragement the project would have never been undertaken or completed.

I wish to acknowledge the considerable help provided by the following reviewers: John C. Sherman, University of Washington; Mark Stephen Monmonier, Syracuse University; Jack F. Williams, Michigan State University; Jon Kimerling, Oregon State University; Thomas K. Poiker and R. B. Squirrell C.C., Fraser University; Kenneth A. Erickson, University of Colorado; Kresho Frankich, British Columbia Institute of Technology; and Norah Henry, S.U.N.Y., Binghamton. Their thoughtful comments have significantly improved many aspects of the final manuscript. Betsy Perry and her colleagues at Prentice-Hall have provided generous professional support throughout the process of creating this book. Finally, many persons assisted the project by providing illustrative materials and information; their help is also appreciated.

Blame for any of the book's shortcomings should be ascribed to no one but the author.

J. C.

Introduction

CARTOGRAPHY AND MAPS

This book is about *cartography,* the art and science of making maps. Before we begin the main portion of the book, which discusses the myriad details involved in making maps, we should pause for a moment and consider a most basic question: "What is a map?" The simplest answer to this question is the popular conception that "a map is a bird's-eye view of a portion of the earth's surface." This answer is partially true. Even the most "realistic" map, however, does not show the earth exactly the way a bird sees it, and many maps present invisible or abstract information that even the most perceptive bird could never see.

Despite its partial truth, the "bird's-eye view" definition does not tell us very much about the role that maps play in human affairs. This is an important shortcoming because cartographers should produce maps that are as useful as possible. For this reason, a definition based on the function of maps is likely to be both more accurate and more useful.

The underlying basic function of maps is to serve as a means of communication—to provide information about how various phenomena are arranged on the surface of the earth. It is this role that provides a tie between the maps of the past and the maps of today. Maps have been in use since at least 3000 B.C. In that era, maps showing the extent of Mesopotamia were scratched into the surface of clay tablets. Today, maps take many forms; they are often printed in multiple colors by high-speed presses, or are stored in the memory banks of computers, and the topics they depict range from the topography of the ocean floor to the pattern of crime rates in a particular city. Today, as in ancient Mesopotamia, the communication function is present.

A functional definition, then, says that "a map is a device for storing and communicating information about the physical and social phenomena that are distributed over the earth's surface." Thus, a map acts as a data storage and retrieval system for spatial information. Once the information is symbolized, plotted, and reproduced, it remains stored until the map user consults it and interprets its contents.

Maps perform many specific functions, ranging from navigational or engineering applications to the presentation of pictorial views of the terrain or statistical information. The role of the cartographer consists of gathering, organizing, and processing the information that will be included on these various maps. This is done by incorporating the information into a worksheet that establishes the map's layout and design. Along with this worksheet, the cartographer establishes specifications for the production and reproduction of the finished map. In order to prepare these two basic documents adequately, the cartographer must draw on information obtained from a number of sciences.

Basic map information is of two types. One type is provided by workers in the field of geodesy, surveying, and photogrammetry and consists of information about the earth and its physical characteristics. The cartographer must have enough knowledge of these contributing fields to understand the information they supply and to utilize it to provide the map framework.

The other type of information is about the distribution of phenomena on the earth and may consist of any of a myriad of topics. Physical and natural scientists provide information about natural phenomena. Social scientists produce censuses and other social, economic, and political studies that provide information that may be usefully displayed and more easily interpreted when it is in map form. Again, cartographers need to know how to convert such information into a map format.

In carrying out these tasks, the cartographer is *not* a geodesist, surveyor, or photogrammetrist, and *not* a biologist, geologist, sociologist, economist, political scientist, or any of the other specialists. However, he or she must understand enough about the information generated by workers in contributing fields to be able to present it effectively. In order to design a map that is an effective graphic communication device, the cartographer must also understand how information is transmitted and assimilated. Thus, cartography's theories and techniques can be applied to the infinite number of subject data types that can and have been mapped.

Finally, the cartographer must understand the technical processes involved in producing and reproducing maps—the steps by which the map is brought into being. Knowledge of the applications and limits of different materials and techniques is required in order to carry out these steps and to understand what is feasible and how to do it. The cartographer must also communicate what is wanted to the specialists involved in doing the actual drawing or printing; this is crucial to producing the desired final product.

MAP CATEGORIES

Many cartographers feel that it is useful to classify maps into two broad types: *reference* (or topographic) and *thematic* (or special-purpose) maps.[1] Definitions vary but, according to this scheme, maps that show only the locational characteristics of hydrography and topography are classified as reference maps. This category is often extended to include maps that show the location of settlements, roads, political

[1]A useful summary of the issues, and a bibliography for further reading, is provided by Barbara Bartz Petchenik, "From Place to Space: The Psychological Achievement of Thematic Mapping," *The American Cartographer*, 6, no. 1 (April 1979), 5–12.

boundaries, and other cultural features. In contrast, maps that present information regarding the variation from place to place in the essentially limitless range of mappable topics are called thematic maps.

One reason for differentiating maps into these two types is to emphasize that some maps consist of two major elements: the background, or base map, and the information regarding the particular topic that is being presented. The map background for thematic maps, then, is based either directly or indirectly on information obtained from reference maps. The special information, which is drawn from existing maps, statistical tables, or other sources, is plotted on the base, using appropriate symbols. Generally, the creation of thematic maps involves a process of *compilation,* which consists of the assembly and manipulation of a variety of source materials, including existing base maps, to produce a new product.

One problem with dividing maps into reference and thematic types is that there is no clear-cut dividing line between the two. Although it is apparent that there are significant differences in content and appearance between a large, detailed topographic map that covers only a few square kilometers of the earth's surface, and a small, page-size atlas map that shows the distribution of climatic types over an entire continent, many maps combine features of both of the extreme types. It is not clear, therefore, how to define the differences between the types in a useful way. It may be argued, furthermore, that the term ''thematic'' is misleading, because every map has a ''theme.'' The theme of a topographic map, for example, is the distribution of the physical features that it shows. In addition, many definitions of thematic maps imply that they are statistical in nature, which is not necessarily true.

The classification of maps into reference and thematic types only indirectly affects the organization pattern of this book. The techniques and concepts presented are generally useful for mapping the variations from place to place in all types of phenomena, whether the maps are called reference maps or thematic maps.

ORGANIZATION OF THE BOOK

The foregoing discussion provides the basis for the organization of this book, which is designed to provide an introductory overview of the cartographic processes. It describes the basic compilation, design, production, and reproduction techniques involved in the creation of maps.

Because cartography touches on many fields of expertise, a great variety of topics must be discussed. For this reason, the book is primarily descriptive. The amount of detail about each topic is limited; in general, only enough is presented to introduce the basic concepts involved. Processes and techniques are described but technical information, such as exact processing times, specific chemical names, and so on, is not included. The reason for this is that most readers need to have basic information about the many topics, along with insights into how the processes described relate to the cartographic task, but do not require the level of detail that would be included in a technical handbook or a specialized treatise. Once this initial survey is absorbed, these topics may be studied in much greater detail; references to more specialized works are provided so that interested readers can pursue the various subjects further.

The information-gathering phase of the cartographic process is described first. We begin with a description of the size and shape of the earth, including a discussion of the methods used for taking its measurements. This is followed by a description of the concepts involved in the creation and use of map projections, as well as a summary of the principal characteristics of some of the best-known projections. Triangulation and surveying are discussed next because these techniques provide the locational framework for the construction of maps. Once this framework is established, a great variety of information can be plotted against it. In addition, the use of aerial photographs and other remote sensing techniques in the gathering and plotting of detail is described.

Following the survey of the information-gathering processes, we turn our attention to the compilation, production, and reproduction of maps. Approaches to map compilation and generalization are considered first. As these steps constitute the encoding phase of the communication process, the goal here is to assist in the creation of attractive map layout and design. We then review the techniques involved in the production and reproduction of maps. First, drafting and scribing techniques are treated. Then, reproduction processes are described, working from the basic techniques and materials involved in single-color reproduction to the more complex approaches required for adding gray values and colors.

The final section deals with two special topics. It begins with a discussion of the special considerations related to the creation of maps that fall toward the thematic end of the reference-thematic continuum. The goal here is to provide an understanding of the problems involved in selecting appropriate symbols, and to describe some basic ways of effectively mapping quantitative information about points, lines, areas, and surfaces. Finally, because the use of computers in various aspects of the mapping processes is increasing rapidly, an overview of the application of computer-assisted techniques is provided.

It may be reassuring to some to note that the small amount of mathematics involved is kept at an extremely simple level and is explained as it is encountered.

Suggested Readings

KEATES, JOHN S., *Understanding Maps*. New York: John Wiley & Sons, A Halsted Press Book, 1982.

MCCLEARY, GEORGE F., JR., "How to Design an Effective Graphics Presentation," in *How to Design an Effective Graphics Presentation,* Harvard Library of Computer Graphics, 1981 Mapping Collection, vol. 17, 15–64. Cambridge, Mass.: Harvard University, Laboratory for Computer Graphics and Spatial Analysis, 1981. The topics covered in this chapter are discussed on pp. 15–19.

PETCHENIK, BARBARA BARTZ, "From Place to Space: The Psychological Achievement of Thematic Mapping," *The American Cartographer,* 6, no. 1 (April 1979), 5–12.

ROBINSON, ARTHUR H., and BARBARA BARTZ PETCHENIK, *The Nature of Maps, Essays toward Understanding Maps and Mapping*. Chicago, University of Chicago Press, 1976.

1

The Earth:
The Object
to be Mapped

The earth itself is the subject of the cartographic processes described in this book. This initial chapter, therefore, deals with the basic characteristics of our home planet.

Knowledge of the size and shape of the earth is provided by the practitioners of the science of *geodesy*. Geodesists make and analyze precise measurements of time, distance, the location of stars, the pull of gravity, and other factors. The end products of their work—including the determination of the earth's size and shape, as well as the precise location of certain points on the earth's surface—are used by surveyors and cartographers as the basis for the production of maps. The short presentation in this chapter provides a background understanding of some selected, basic aspects of geodesy. The discussion avoids mathematics and omits the complexities that would be of concern to a practicing geodisist; it is intended only to provide a logical point of beginning for the discussion of the mapping process.

In this era of extraterrestrial exploration, it is interesting to note that the principles employed in mapping the earth are equally applicable to the mapping of the moon, Mars, Venus, or any similar body. Because the principal focus of most cartographic work is on the earth, the presentation here focusses on earthbound mapping.

SHAPE AND SIZE

Shape

Human beings have long been curious about the shape of the earth and, over the centuries, have subscribed to various notions about its form. These have included the Babylonian belief that the earth was a flat disc, floating on the surface of the ocean; Aristotle's concept that it was a perfect sphere, floating in space; and the modern understanding that it is basically spherical, but somewhat flattened and rather lumpy.

Sphere Aristotle's view, which was based on the philosophical ideal that man's abode should be a "perfect" sphere, was essentially correct; the earth is close to a spherical shape.[1] In order to make our maps more accurate representations of the

---

[1] A perfect sphere is a round body whose surface is at all points equidistant from its center.

earth, however, it is necessary to confirm this abstract, philosophical view with concrete evidence, and to acquire more detailed knowledge of the earth's exact shape.

One simple and convincing piece of concrete evidence is based on what is seen by a stationary observer who watches a ship sail away toward the horizon. The observer would note the important fact that the image of the ship does not simply become progressively smaller in size as the ship becomes more distant; in addition, the lower portion of the ship's hull disappears over the horizon first and the upper portion of the mast disappears last (Fig. 1.1). This sequence of events can only be due to the fact that the ship is moving away over a downward-curving surface. Furthermore, because this phenomenon is consistent regardless of the direction of the ship's movement, the curvature must exist in all directions; only a spherically shaped earth provides an adequate explanation for such consistent observations.

An observer in the Northern Hemisphere, traveling north or south over the earth's surface, sees a second piece of evidence. At each new location, the elevation of Polaris above the horizon is seen to change. Because Polaris is almost directly in line with the earth's axis of rotation, when the observer is at the pole the star is directly overhead; as the observer moves toward the equator, Polaris appears to move lower in the sky, closer to the horizon (Fig. 1.2). Again, this phenomenon always occurs, regardless of the original location of the observer, and it is also observed in relation to other stars in both the Northern and Southern Hemispheres. Because the observed amount of change in elevation is related in a uniform way to the difference in the observer's latitude, it can be satisfactorily explained only if the observer is assumed to be moving over a continuously curved, spherical surface.

A third piece of evidence is the fact that, during lunar eclipses, the earth always casts a circular shadow on the moon. Although a properly aligned disk could also cast a circular shadow, only a sphere always casts such a shadow regardless of its position. Once again, therefore, the evidence for a spherical earth is very strong.

Although all these clues have been noted over long periods of time and have led to general acceptance of the idea of a spherical earth, later developments have added three other clues. First, when telescopes allowed the other planets to be observed it was noted that they are all spherical in shape. Astronomers reasoned, by analogy, that the earth should be similarly shaped. Second, it is known that the pull of gravity is very close to being equal everywhere on the surface of the earth. This indicates that the surface is everywhere approximately the same distance from the center of the earth's mass, which is only possible on the surface of a virtually spherical shape. Finally, in this era of space flight, direct observational and photographic evidence has effectively removed any lingering doubts regarding the earth's basically spherical shape.

Figure 1.1 Successive telescopic views of a ship receding over the horizon.

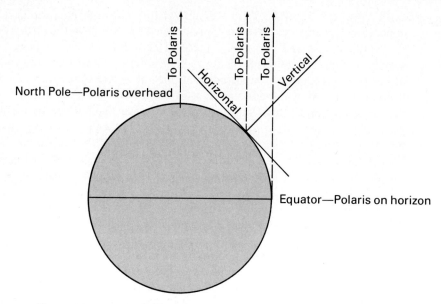

Figure 1.2 The angle between Polaris and the horizon varies as the observer moves north or south.

The circumnavigation of the globe, first accomplished by Magellan's crew in 1519–22, provided supplementary direct evidence that the earth is a solid object. Although this did not necessarily prove that the earth is a sphere (a similar feat would have been possible if, for example, the earth was shaped like a cylinder), experience with repeated circumnavigations in many directions, as well as with navigation in general, has effectively shown that the assumption of a spherical shape best fits the evidence.

Ellipsoid Although the earth clearly has a basically spherical shape, it has been theorized, since Isaac Newton first proposed the idea around 1670, that its precise shape departs from a pure spherical form. The source of this deviation is the centrifugal force generated by the rotation of the earth on its axis. As it rotates at a regular angular velocity, the portions close to the equator move at a greater speed than do the portions closer to the poles. There is, therefore, greater centrifugal force near the equator and an equatorial bulge in the earth's shape results. At the same time, the less rapidly spinning material in the polar areas is subject to a lesser centrifugal force and thus is pulled closer to the center of the earth, creating a flattening near the poles. The net result of these forces is an earth that is shaped like an *ellipsoid*, which is the three-dimensional figure obtained by rotating an ellipse about its shorter axis (Fig. 1.3).

It is very reasonable to theorize that the overall shape of the earth is that of an ellipsoid, but it is necessary to take measurements in order to determine its exact shape. The necessary measurements were first completed during the period from 1735 to 1743 when two expeditions were sent out for the purpose by the French

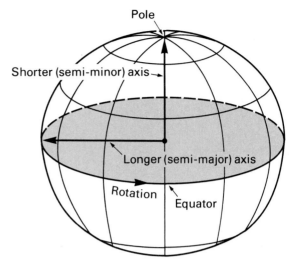

Figure 1.3   An ellipsoid is formed by rotating an ellipse on its shorter axis.

Royal Academy of Sciences. One of these expeditions worked at the Arctic Circle in Lapland (now Finland), and the other worked at the equator in colonial Peru (now Ecuador). The members of these expeditions carried out careful field measurements of the length of a degree of latitude—north-south position—at their respective locations.

At the starting point of each survey the angle of elevation of a selected star was measured. The instrument used for this purpose was a *theodolite,* a telescope that can be precisely leveled, using a bubble level (Fig. 1.4). The telescope can then be rotated so that vertical angles can be read with great accuracy. After the first angle was measured, the theodolite was moved a precisely measured distance along a direct north-south line and the angle of elevation of the same star was again measured. The difference between the two angles represented the angular difference between the starting and ending points (Fig. 1.5). The measured distance between the two points was then divided by the angular difference between them and the result was the length of a degree of arc at that latitude. When the two sets of measurements were compared it was found that a degree of arc in the northern latitudes was substantially longer than a degree of arc near the equator.

The significance of the differences in the length of a degree of arc is that the length is directly related to the radius of the body on whose surface it lies. The longer degree of arc in the polar regions indicated a larger radius there than in the equatorial regions, which reflects an ellipsoidal shape (Fig. 1.6). The findings of the expeditions, therefore, were sufficient to substantiate the theoretical view that the earth is flattened at the poles, and thus has a longer radius there, and bulges at the equator.[2]

[2]The term *oblate spheroid* is sometimes used to describe the ellipsoid. The name means that the figure of the earth is approximately spherical, but has a slightly smaller diameter from pole to pole than it does at the equator.

Figure 1.4 A theodolite is used for measuring vertical angles. (Courtesy of The Lietz Co.)

Figure 1.5 Observation of the angle between the horizon and a given star, taken from two different observation points, to determine the length of a degree of arc.

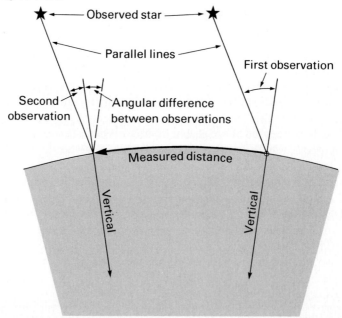

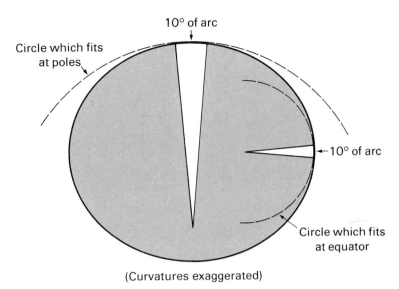

Figure 1.6   The length of a degree of arc is greater toward the poles, indicating a larger radius there.

Geoidal surface   If the earth's composition were uniform, an ellipsoid would accurately represent its shape. As a matter of fact, however, its shape is further influenced by the differential pull of gravity on different portions of its surface. The shape that results from this differential pull of gravity is called the *geoid*. The surface of the geoid is a theoretical surface on which the potential of the gravity force of the earth is equal at all points. The pull of gravity is also perpendicular to the surface of the geoid.

In order to understand the definition of the geoid assume for a moment that the earth is completely water-covered; that it has no tidal action and, therefore, that no shifts occur in the level of the ocean's surface; that it does not rotate on its axis; and that the composition of its crust is completely uniform. In this situation gravity would uniformly pull the water toward the center of the earth. Even if there were initially some higher or lower points on the surface, the water would flow away from the high points toward the low points. The final result would be a smooth and continuous surface, equidistant from the center of the earth at all points, and with an equal pull of gravity everywhere on the surface. Under these circumstances the geoid would be perfectly spherical.

The earth, of course, does not have all of the characteristics described in the previous paragraph. First, it rotates on its axis; the resulting bulge at the equator and flattening at the poles has already been described. Moreover, the composition and density of its crust varies from place to place. This results in a commensurately greater or lesser gravitational pull at various points. Because of these variations in gravity, the geoidal surface is not a perfect ellipsoid. It is therefore necessary to observe and measure it in order to determine its shape, as will be described. Finally, the earth is only partially water-covered, and the water is subject to tidal action, so the measurement of the geoid is further complicated even in the water-covered areas.

The process of determining the surface of the geoid begins along the line of contact between the land and the water. If there were no tides, this line would be constant and would directly represent the line of contact between the geoidal surface and the topographic surface. Because elevation differences do occur, due to tidal action, the tidal level is measured hourly over a long period of time. This information is used to calculate the average surface level, called *mean sea level,* which is then taken as the level of the geoid (see Chapter 3).

The extension of the geoidal surface into land areas requires additional observational techniques. What is desired is a determination of the elevation at which the gravitational pull is equal to what it would be at the surface of the ocean. If, for example, it were possible to extend water-filled sea-level canals into the interior of the continents without affecting water levels in the oceans, the level of the geoid could be directly observed. In the absence of such direct methods, careful observations are taken using special instruments such as gravimeters. These instruments are used to measure the differential pull of gravity at various points on the earth's surface. When this difference in pull is known, it is possible to calculate the elevation difference that would be necessary to bring the gravitational pull to the theoretical norm and, thereby, to establish the level of the geoid.

Because of the varying density of the earth's crust and the presence of relief features, which vary in mass, the geoid has a rather lumpy shape, with a greater bulge in the Southern Hemisphere than in the Northern Hemisphere. It has even been characterized as having a pear shape, although that description tends to exaggerate the amount of deviation from the ellipsoidal form.

Applications   The nature of the three representations of the shape of the earth—the sphere, the ellipsoid, and the geoid—has been described. Each of them, in sequence, represents a more realistic representation of the actual shape of the earth. It is important to realize that different applications may require, or allow, the adoption of one or another of these representations.

Because it is the most accurate of the three figures of the earth, the geoid is used for purposes such as geodetic control surveys (see Chapter 3). Measurements taken on the earth's surface are obtained by the use of instruments whose orientation is governed by the pull of gravity. Plumb bobs, for example, are used to define the vertical and are subject to this influence. Instruments that use bubble levels to establish the horizontal also respond to the pull of gravity. This means that all horizontal, vertical, and angular measurements are necessarily obtained with reference to the geoid.

The "lumpy" shape of the geoid makes it very difficult to deal with mathematically. In order to expedite computations and, ultimately, the construction of maps, measurements made on the geoid must be converted to measurements on an ellipsoid. The ellipsoid is a reasonable representation of the geoidal shape, but its surface is easier to manipulate mathematically. Also, locations on the ellipsoid have a regular and predictable relationship to one another that is the basis for the system of latitudes and longitudes.

The spherical model is used for some purposes because of its simplicity, even though we know it has shortcomings that may, in special circumstances, call for additional refinements. In the next chapter, for example, the discussion of map projections uses the spherical model because considering the ellipsoid would un-necessarily complicate the presentation. In addition, because the differences be-tween the spheroid and the geoid are quite minute, the spheroid is used in small-scale mapping—the position differences that would result from using the geoid are negligible in small-scale maps (such as typical atlas maps, which often represent a country or a continent on a single page). It must be recognized, however, that the ellipsoid is taken into account in the actual construction of large-scale projections such as are used for topographic maps.

The decision regarding which shape to use to represent the figure of the earth depends on the amount of realism and accuracy required by the task that is being accomplished. At times the simple spherical shape is sufficient; in other applications the ellipsoid must be used; in the most detailed type of work the geoid must be taken into consideration.

Size

Once the earth's shape is determined, it is important to measure its size. At first it is rather difficult to visualize how a person standing on the surface of the earth could successfully measure such an immense body. Because it is obviously imprac-tical to do any type of direct measurement, except for limited portions of the sur-face, indirect methods are utilized.

Eratosthenes' method   Eratosthenes was able to provide a very creditable measure-ment of the earth around 250 B.C. His method, which used simple instruments and basic geometry, provides a useful explanation of how the problem is approached, even today.

Eratosthenes knew that at the time of the summer solstice the noon sun was directly overhead at the town of Syene in Egypt (near present-day Aswan). His knowledge was based on the fact that, at that specific time, the sun shone directly to the bottom of a vertical well shaft situated in the town. This meant that the town was located on the Tropic of Cancer.

He also observed that, at the same time of the same day, the sun cast a shadow in the city of Alexandria, which was located north of Syene on approximately the same meridian. He knew, in addition, that the surface distance between Syene and Alexandria was 5000 stadia, although accounts differ as to whether he had the dis-tance carefully measured or whether he estimated it on the basis of travelers' re-ports.

By driving a vertical stake (called a *gnomon*) into the ground at Alexandria, he determined that the angle of the shadow it cast at noon on the day of the solstice was 7° 12′ away from the vertical. From geometry he knew that the angle between a pair of lines drawn vertically to the center of the earth from Syene and from Alexandria would, therefore, also be 7° 12′ (Fig. 1.7). Because the angle between the verticals at Syene and Alexandria amounted to 1/50 the circumference of the earth (360° ÷ 7° 12′ = 50), it was apparent that the distance between the two towns was also equal to 1/50 the earth's circumference. By multiplying 5000 stadia by 50 he obtained an estimate of 250,000 stadia for the circumference.

Some writers have equated Eratosthenes' measurement to a modern equivalent of approximately 46,250 km (28,740 mi). This is about 15 percent greater than present-day estimates of an equatorial circumference of 40,075 km (24,901) mi). Others have estimated that the measurements were in the range from 38,624 km to 40,234 km (24,000 to 25,000 mi); the latter would be extremely accurate. The problem with verifying any of these estimates is twofold: first, various accounts differ regarding the details of Eratosthenes' results and, second, the conversion factor from stadia into modern measurements is uncertain. Later investigation has also shown that the apparent accuracy of Eratosthenes' measurement was due in part to a lucky offsetting of certain errors in his measurements.

Regardless of these details of interpretation, the approach that Eratosthenes took to the problem of measuring the earth was perfectly sound and is an excellent example of the indirect methods that must be used. The major difference between his method and the methods used today is the greater accuracy of the measurements that can now be obtained and used as the basis for the computations. Modern methods often make use of the stars or artificial satellites as reference points, rather than the sun.

Figure 1.7 Eratosthenes estimated the circumference of the earth by observing the difference in angle between the rays of the sun at two points on the earth's surface.

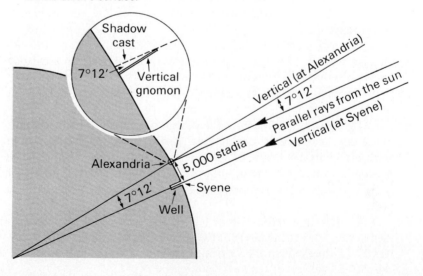

It is interesting to note that the size of the earth has also been used as a reference measurement. In 1799, for example, the French established the length of a *meter* as one ten-millionth of the then-known distance from the equator to the North Pole, measured along a meridian. A platinum bar was prepared to the length of this standard and became the prototype against which measuring devices were standardized. The prototype meter was later found to be slightly in error when compared to the actual earth measurement. Since 1960 the definition of the meter has been related to a specific number of wavelengths of the radiation of Krypton-86, under controlled conditions.

The Ellipsoid   The size and shape of an ellipse is specified in terms of its *semimajor axis* and its *flattening* [Fig. 1.8(a)]. The semimajor axis is the radius of the longest axis of the ellipse and is designated by the letter *a*. The *semiminor axis* is the radius of the shortest axis and is designated by the letter *b*. Given these two pieces of information, flattening, designated by the letter *f*, is given by the equation: $f = (a - b)/a$. This equation means that the flattening is the difference between the lengths of the semimajor and semiminor axes, taken as a proportion of the length of the semimajor axis. The resulting ratio indicates how close the ellipsoid is to being spherical. If the ratio is a large number, like $\frac{1}{2}$, the ellipsoid is very flat; if it is an extremely small number, like 1/300, the ellipsoid is very close to being a sphere [Fig. 1.8(b)].

Present-day estimates of the size of the earth are based on its ellipsoidal shape. In this case, the earth's semimajor axis is its radius at the equator and its semiminor axis is its radius along the axis of rotation, which joins the poles. Because the flat-

Figure 1.8   (a) The shape of an ellipse is determined by the relative length of the semimajor axis (*a*) and the semiminor axis (*b*). (b) The flattening ratio (*f* = (*a* − *b*)/*a*) approaches zero as the ellipse becomes closer to a circle.

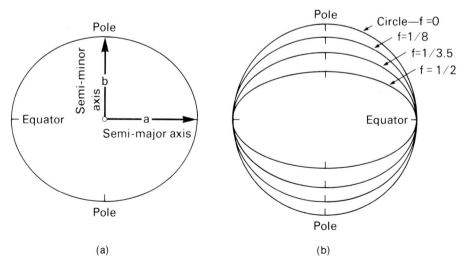

(a)   (b)

Table 1.1 **ELLIPSOIDS CURRENTLY IN USE**

Name of Ellipsoid*	Equatorial Radius (meters)	Flattening (approx.)	Some Users
Krasovsky (1938)	6,378,245	1/298	USSR
International (1924) (Hayford–1909)	6,378,388	1/297	Adopted for international use
Clarke (1880)	6,378,249	1/293	France, S. Africa
Clarke (1866)	6,378,206	1/295	North America†
Bessel (1841)	6,377,397	1/299	Japan, Germany
Airy (1844)‡	6,377,563	1/299	Great Britain
Everest (1830)	6,377,276	1/301	India
IUGG§ (1979)	6,378,137	1/298	North America‖ Adopted for international use

*Often named for the person principally responsible for the computation of the ellipsoid.

†North American Datum, 1927, originates at Meade's Ranch, Kansas, 1927–83.

‡Source: D. H. Maling, *Coordinate Systems and Map Projections* (London: George Philip and Son Limited, 1973).

§International Union of Geodesy and Geophysics.

‖North American Datum, 1983 (NAD83), beginning 1983. Data from National Geodetic Survey.

Source: Adapted from R. K. Burkard, *Geodesy for the Layman* (St. Louis, Missouri: Aeronautical Chart and Information Center, 1964); and B. Szabo, *Geodetic Datums and an Estimate of Their Accuracy*, ACIC Technical Report No. 24, Revised. (St. Louis, Missouri: Aeronautical Chart and Information Center, 1956).

tening of the earth is approximately 1/298, it is obviously very close to a spherical shape.

The shape of the geoid varies from place to place. These variations mean that differently shaped ellipsoids will fit different areas more closely; for this reason, certain ellipsoids are in use for specific parts of the world. The problems caused by the use of different ellipsoids may be reduced in the future because a worldwide ellipsoid has been adopted for international use and will be used as the basis for the *North American Datum* (NAD83) beginning in 1983. It is hoped that this will be a first step toward a worldwide standardization of the reference ellipsoid. In the meantime, the sizes and shapes of some of the ellipsoids currently in use are indicated in Table 1.1.

LOCATION

A primary requirement for setting up any extensive mapping system is a means of specifying the location of points on the earth's surface. A difficulty that must be dealt with in doing this is that a sphere, or ellipse, has a continuous surface with no edges or other natural starting points on which to base the locational system. If the earth were simply a free-floating sphere there would be no logical starting point for a reference system and any system that was established would be completely arbitrary. Fortunately, however, the earth's rotation on its axis provides an answer to this problem because the poles of rotation are fixed, identifiable points.

A *great circle* is a line created by the intersection with the surface of the earth of a plane that passes through the center of the earth. Once the *poles* are located, arcs of great circles, called *meridians* or lines of *longitude,* are drawn joining the poles [Fig. 1.9(a)]. The *equator* is then located by drawing another great circle, midway between the poles. It should be noted that the shortest segment of the great circle that passes through any two points on the earth's surface represents the shortest distance between them [Fig. 1.9(b)].

A *small circle* is a line created by the intersection with the surface of the earth of a plane that does not pass through the center of the earth. *Parallels* (lines of *latitude*) are small circles that are drawn parallel to the equator [Fig. 1.9(c)].

The equator is the starting point for the numbering system applied to the parallels. The equator, itself, is numbered 0°. The numbers increase with each degree, both north and south, until they reach a maximum value of 90° at each of the poles.

Although the poles and the equator provide a logical framework for identifying the parallels, there is no similar logical starting point for the identification of the meridians; one meridian is the same as another and any convenient starting point can be selected.

In the past, because there is no obvious initial meridian, many countries used the meridian of their national capital as the starting point for their maps. Increased trade and other contact between nations resulted in a great deal of confusion and

Figure 1.9 (a) Meridians (lines of longitude) are arcs of great circles that meet at the poles. (b) The arc of a great circle is the shortest distance between two points on the earth's surface. (c) Parallels (lines of latitude) are concentric small circles that are parallel to the equator.

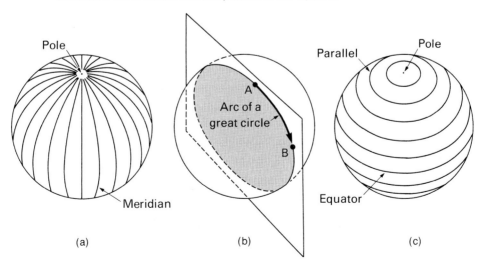

(a)   (b)   (c)

inconvenience stemming from the use of different starting points, which required conversions back and forth from one system to another. This eventually led to a general agreement that a common reference line should be selected for the convenience of all map producers and users. In 1884, the longitude of the observatory at Greenwich, England, was adopted by many nations as the starting line for longitudal measurements. This starting line is called the *prime meridian*. Although most maps produced today adhere to the convention of measuring longitude from Greenwich, exceptions to this rule may be encountered. Maps produced outside of the United States should be checked to determine whether or not they are based on the Greenwich prime meridian.

The number 0 is assigned to the longitude at Greenwich; the numbers increase each degree, both east and west, until they reach a maximum value of 180°. The 180th meridian is rather convenient because it passes through the Pacific Ocean and does not intersect many landmasses. The prime meridian, however, is not so convenient, because it passes through western Europe and northwestern Africa. This means that some locations within a single country have an east longitude and others a west longitude.

Graticule

The network of meridians and parallels on the globe is called the *graticule*. Once the graticule is established, following the pattern explained above, its characteristics can be identified and described. This is important because an understanding of the characteristics of different map projections is most usefully based on a comparison of the characteristics of the projected map graticules with those of the graticule on the globe.[3]

Assuming that the earth is spherical, the main characteristics of the graticule on its surface can be described as follows:

1. Parallels, except the equator, are complete small circles (the equator is a complete great circle).
2. Parallels are true east-west lines.
3. Parallels are equally spaced between the equator and the poles.
4. Parallels are always parallel to one another, so they are always the same distance apart.
5. Meridians are halves of great circles, stretching from pole to pole.
6. Meridians are true north-south lines.
7. Meridians are spaced farthest apart on the equator and converge to a single point at the poles.

[3]The network of parallels and meridians, whether it is projected on a map or drawn on a globe, is referred to as a *graticule*. The use of the term *grid* is reserved for the case of an arbitrary set of parallel lines used for locational purposes. A grid does not represent parallels and meridians.

8. Parallels and meridians cross one another at right angles.
9. An infinite number of parallels and meridians can be drawn.

Lengths of Degrees

Latitude   As already explained, the earth's radius is different at the polar and equatorial latitudes and there is a slight variation in the distance between parallels due to the polar flattening. The difference does not occur abruptly, however. There is, instead, a continuous change in radius as one moves from the equator to the poles. The result of this continuously changing radius is that the degrees of latitude become progressively longer near the poles. A summary of these dimensions is shown in Table 1.2 and a more complete listing is provided in Appendix A.

Longitude   Because the meridians converge toward the poles, the length of a degree of longitude is a maximum at the equator and a minimum at the poles. At 60°, for example, the length of a degree of longitude is one-half the length of a degree at the equator.[4] Some of the representative distances are shown in Table 1.3 and a more complete listing is included in Appendix A.

Table 1.2   LENGTH OF DEGREES OF LATITUDE*
GEODETIC REFERENCE SYSTEM 1980 ELLIPSOID[†]

Lat.	Km	Statute Miles	Nautical Miles
0	110.574	68.708	59.705
5	110.583	68.713	59.710
10	110.608	68.728	59.724
15	110.649	68.754	59.746
20	110.704	68.788	59.776
25	110.773	68.831	59.813
30	110.852	68.881	59.856
35	110.941	68.935	59.903
40	111.035	68.994	59.954
45	111.132	69.054	60.006
50	111.229	69.115	60.059
55	111.324	69.173	60.110
60	111.412	69.228	60.158
65	111.493	69.278	60.201
70	111.562	69.321	60.239
75	111.618	69.356	60.269
80	111.660	69.382	60.292
85	111.685	69.398	60.305
90	111.694	69.403	60.310

*Length of a degree of arc centered on the latitude named.
[†]The ellipsoid has the following parameters: $a = 6378137.000$; $f = 298.2572221$.

Source: Computed from data supplied by National Geodetic Survey.

[4]Because of the trigonometric relationships involved, longitude varies as the cosine of the latitude and the cosine of 60° is 0.5.

Table 1.3   LENGTH OF DEGREES OF LONGITUDE*
GEODETIC REFERENCE SYSTEM 1980 ELLIPSOID†

Lat.	Km	Statute Miles	Nautical Miles
0	111.319	69.171	60.108
5	110.899	68.909	59.881
10	109.639	68.127	59.201
15	107.551	66.829	58.073
20	104.647	65.025	56.505
25	100.950	62.727	54.509
30	96.486	59.954	52.099
35	91.288	56.724	49.292
40	85.394	53.061	46.109
45	78.847	48.993	42.574
50	71.696	44.550	38.713
55	63.994	39.764	34.554
60	55.800	34.673	30.130
65	47.176	29.314	25.473
70	38.187	23.728	20.619
75	28.902	17.959	15.606
80	19.393	12.051	10.472
85	9.735	6.049	5.256
90	0.000	0.000	0.000

*Length of a degree of arc along the latitude named.
†The ellipsoid has the following parameters: $a = 6378137.000$; $f = 298.2572221$.

Source: Computed from data supplied by National Geodetic Survey.

Position Determination

An observer located on the earth's surface can, by astronomic observation, establish the location of that point in relation to the globe's graticule. Determining the *astronomic coordinates* of a location plays an important part in navigation as well as in the complex process of setting up a geodetic control network. In this context, astronomic observation consists of measuring the angle between a horizontal plane (or a plumb line) and a star (or the sun) and recording the precise time at which the angle is measured.

Latitude   To a present-day observer standing at the North Pole, the star Polaris appears to be almost exactly overhead.[5] Polaris is an excellent point of reference for measuring latitude throughout the Northern Hemisphere. This is true because, as will be shown, the measurement of the angle between Polaris and the observer's horizon defines the observer's astronomic latitude.

Star observation   The angle that an observer at the North Pole measures between the horizon and Polaris is 90 degrees, which is the latitude of the pole (Fig. 1.2).

[5]Polaris is not precisely over the pole, however. The angles that are measured must be corrected slightly to account for the deviation.

When an observer at the equator measures the angle, however, the star is exactly on the horizon; its elevation, therefore, is 0 degrees, which is the latitude of the equator. An observer at 45°N finds that the angle between the star and the horizon is 45° degrees, and so on, for other latitudes.

Notice that the lines in the diagram that indicate the direction to Polaris are drawn as though they were parallel. This is possible because differences of position on the earth are so slight, compared to the distance between the earth and the star, that they have no detectable effect on the angle of observation. The same is true of the sun's rays as they reach the earth—for most purposes they can be considered to be parallel.

Other stars are also used for the determination of latitude; this is obviously necessary in the Southern Hemisphere because Polaris is not in view and there is no equivalent star in alignment with the South Pole. When other stars are used, it is necessary to correct the angle of observation to take their position in the sky into account. Star catalogs, such as the *American Ephemeris and Nautical Almanac,* published by the Naval Observatory, are available to provide the necessary information.

Observation of the sun   When observation of the sun is used to determine the latitude of a position, the first piece of information that is needed is the angle between the observer's horizon and the sun. This angle, known as the altitude of the sun, is measured at noon, when the sun has reached its highest point in the sky. The highest point is determined by taking a series of readings starting slightly before noon and continuing until slightly after noon. The maximum reading is the one taken precisely at noon and is the correct altitude reading for that day.

The sun may be directly over the equator on the day the latitude measurement is undertaken. This is unlikely, however, because it is in that position only twice a year, on the dates of the *equinoxes* (March 21 or 22 and September 22 or 23). If, by chance, the observation is being taken on one of those dates, the sun's *altitude,* subtracted from 90 degrees, gives the observer's latitude [Fig. 1.10(a)].

On dates other than the equinoxes it is necessary to know the sun's *declination* in addition to its altitude. The declination is the latitude of the parallel that the sun is directly over on that particular day. The declination value is used to adjust the altitude reading in order to determine the observer's latitude. Figure 1.10(b) shows, as an example, the correction needed when the sun is overhead at 20° S latitude. The sun's declination for each day can be obtained from a nautical almanac or it can be read, less accurately, from a graph called the *analemma.*

Analemma   The analemma is a figure-eight-shaped diagram that is drawn on most globes; it stretches between the Tropic of Cancer and the Tropic of Capricorn. One function of the analemma is to indicate the parallel at which the sun is directly overhead on each day of the year. To use the analemma for this purpose the required date is located on the diagram (Fig. 1.11). The parallel that intersects the location of that date is the required parallel. For example, the date August 15 is marked on the analemma and it is apparent that the sun is directly over latitude 14° N, on that

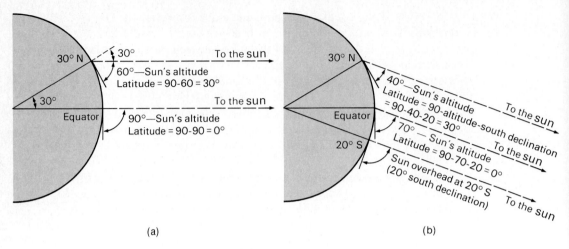

(a)   (b)

Figure 1.10 (a) On the dates of the equinox, the sun's altitude, subtracted from 90°, gives the latitude of the observation point. (b) On dates other than the equinox, the sun's declination is taken into account in the determination of latitude.

day. This information is then used as described above to adjust the altitude of the sun during the determination of latitude.

The analemma is also used to show the equation of time, which is needed for the determination of longitude. This application is described in the next section.

Longitude

The fact that the earth rotates on its axis is used as the basis for timekeeping. It is also the basis for determining longitude, because of the direct relationship between time and longitude. The *astronomic longitude* of a point is defined as the angle between the plane of the prime meridian and the plane of the meridian of the point in question.

Time and longitude Each point on the earth's surface has a *celestial meridian;* this is the imaginary meridian in the sky located vertically over the point. By definition, noon, *local apparent time,* occurs at each location on the earth's surface at the moment when the sun crosses that location's celestial meridian and reaches its highest altitude for the day. The period of time that elapses between two successive transits of the sun across the celestial meridian of a stationary observer is defined as a *solar day.*

By convention, the solar day is divided into 24 equal units of time known as hours. The hours are each further divided into 60 minutes and the minutes into 60 seconds. Each 24-hour period, therefore, is equivalent to a 360-degree rotation of the earth on its axis. Each hour, then, is equal to 15 degrees of rotation (1/24 × 360 degrees), and so on, for longer or shorter periods of time (see Table 1.4).

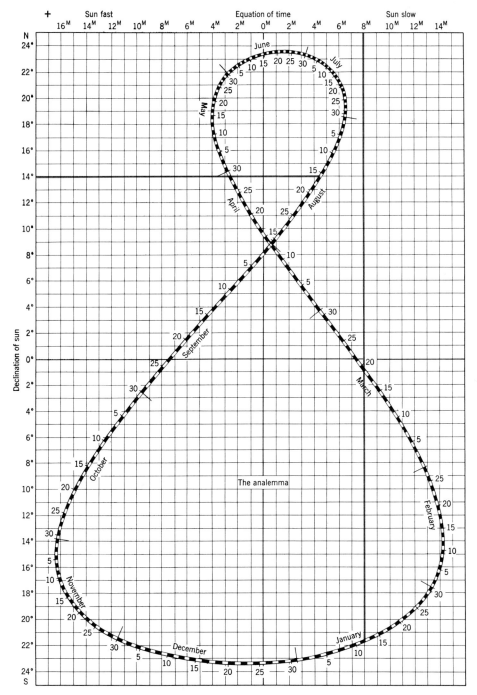

Figure 1.11 An analemma. (From A. N. Strahler, *Physical Geography*, 4th ed., copyright © 1975 by John Wiley & Sons, New York. Reproduced by permission of author and publisher.)

Table 1.4

Time Period		Angle of Rotation
24 hours	=	360°
1 hour	=	15°
1 minute	=	15′
1 second	=	15″

Time difference   Because of the relationship between time and the earth's rotation, establishing the time difference between two different locations makes it possible to determine the difference between their longitudes. Obviously, precise determination of time is required in order to establish accurate longitudes—a difference of 1 second of time is equivalent to a difference of approximately 0.464 km (0.288 statute mi or 0.251 nautical mi)[6] at the equator.

Since its introduction and refinement, the *chronometer,* which is simply an extremely accurate timepiece, has been used for determining time differences. The chronometer is set to coincide with the time at a particular reference location and is then carried to the location whose longitude is to be determined. Greenwich Mean Time (GMT) is usually used for this purpose. (The concept of mean time is explained in the section on the equation of time, below.) By observing on the chronometer the time at which local apparent noon occurs, one can determine the time difference between that location and the reference meridian at Greenwich. This time difference is then used as the basic piece of information in the determination of the difference in longitude between the two locations.

In modern times, time signals indicating GMT are transmitted by radio from carefully regulated observatories. These signals, which provide even more accurate time determinations than those available by the use of chronometers, are used in the calculation of the longitudinal location of points on the earth's surface, and for determining the location of ships and aircraft.

Longitude determination   The apparent movement of the sun through the sky is from east to west. The time difference between different locations corresponds to the rate of that movement. If, for example, the apparent solar time at an unknown location is 1700 hours and GMT is 1900 hours,[7] the time difference between the two locations is defined as plus two hours (GMT minus local time). The unknown point, therefore, is located at 30° W longitude, which is determined as follows: The longitude is west of Greenwich because the sun passed over Greenwich's celestial meridian prior to passing over the unknown location. During that two-hour period the earth rotated 30 degrees on its axis. (This rotation is the actual cause of the sun's

---

[6]A statute mile equals 1.609 km or 5280 ft, whereas an international nautical mile equals 1.852 km or 6076.1033 ft.

[7]The use of the 24-hour clock greatly simplifies the process of dealing with time differences. In the 24-hour system, for example, 0900 hours indicates 9:00 A.M., whereas 2100 hours indicates 9:00 P.M.

apparent movement.) The longitudinal distance between the two points, therefore, is also 30 degrees.

If the apparent solar time at an unknown location is 1900 hr and GMT is 1700 hr the time difference between the two locations is minus two hours and the unknown point is located at 30° E. In this case, the sun reached the unknown location two hours prior to reaching the longitude of Greenwich, and the unknown point is, therefore, east of Greenwich. The longitudinal distance between the two points, of course, is calculated in the same manner as for a point west of Greenwich.

Equation of time   The solar day is not uniform throughout the year because the earth moves through its elliptical orbit at varying speeds at different times of the year, and also because of the effect of the inclination of the earth's axis. It would be extremely inconvenient, however, to have clocks running at different speeds at different times of the year in order to accommodate to the variations in the length of the solar day. The concept of *mean solar time,* which is introduced to take these variations into account, assumes a uniform length of day based on the average rate of the sun's apparent movement around the earth. The average length of day is used to govern the timing of clocks with the result that clock time is constant year round.

The difference between the local mean time and local apparent time (or solar time) is called the *equation of time.* Because local mean time is based on an averaging concept, there are periods when local apparent time is ahead of local mean time and the equation of time is positive. Periods also occur when local apparent time is behind local mean time and the equation of time is negative. Finally, there are four dates during the year when the two times are the same.

Information regarding the equation of time for specific dates is most accurately provided in tables found in nautical almanacs. The same information can also be determined graphically, with less accuracy, by using the analemma (Fig. 1.11). This is done by locating the desired date on the diagram and extending a vertical line from that date to the horizontal time scale. The intersection of the vertical line with the time scale gives the number of minutes by which mean solar time is ahead of or behind apparent solar time.

The equation of time is used to refine the process of determining longitude. Assume, for example, that the observations in the previous example are being made on January 12. The time of apparent local noon at the observation location is determined to be 2:00 P.M. GMT. This is found by observing the time at which the sun crosses the solar meridian, using either a chronometer or a broadcast time signal. The equation of time indicates that apparent solar noon occurs 8 minutes after mean solar noon on January 12. This means that mean solar time at the observation location was 8 minutes earlier than the apparent solar time of the observation, or 1:52 P.M. GMT. The earth had, therefore, actually been rotating for one hour and 52 minutes, since noon GMT. Referring to Table 1.4, we find that the earth rotates 15 degrees in one hour and, in an additional 52 minutes, would rotate another 13 degrees (1 degree per 4 minutes). Based on this calculation, the observation site is located at 28° (15° + 13°) W longitude.

Satellite observations   Location determination has recently entered a more modern era through the introduction of navigational satellites. A combination receiver-computer on the earth's surface receives signals broadcast by these satellites. These signals are immediately converted into a digital readout of the latitude and longitude of the receiving station. The accuracy of this infomation, coupled with the speed with which it can be obtained at any time and in any weather conditions, is a major advance in the determination of location. Indeed, the same methods are sometimes used to establish survey control points (see Chapter 3).

Direction

When speaking of direction, unless otherwise specified, it is assumed that the term *north* refers to *true north,* or geographic north. True north is the direction established with reference to the graticule, using Polaris and the pole of the earth's rotation on its axis.

North is sometimes determined by the use of a compass. This direction is called *magnetic north* and is usually not identical to the direction of true north. The difference occurs because a compass is aligned with the earth's magnetic field. The compass, therefore, points toward the north *magnetic pole,* which is currently located in northern Canada, approximately 1440 km (895 statute mi) south of the pole of rotation. Unless a particular point on the earth's surface is located so that the two poles are aligned in the same direction, there is a difference between the true and magnetic north. This difference is called the *declination.* Declination is either to the east or the west, and may amount to several degrees of difference—it reaches values as high as 22° in the United States, for example.

It should be noted that declination varies from place to place mainly because of the difference in position relative to the north magnetic pole. In addition, however, the composition of the earth's crust introduces minor irregularities. Mineral deposits affect the earth's magnetic field and, therefore, the amount of declination observed. The total declination at different points on the earth's surface is determined and recorded on maps called isogonic charts. An *isogonic line* is a line that joins points of equal declination[8] (see Fig. 1.12). Using this information, it is a relatively simple matter to correct a magnetic (compass) reading and convert it to a true reading (or vice versa).

The fact that the magnetic pole is not fixed in its location also affects declination. Because the magnetic pole moves in a predictable fashion, the correction for declination must be adjusted from time to time (Fig. 1.12).

Finally, nearby magnetic substances, such as automobiles or buildings, introduce errors into magnetic compass readings. This type of error, called *compass deviation,* cannot be predicted by reference materials such as an isogonic map, so care must be taken to avoid it when compass readings are taken.

A third north can also be defined. This is called *grid north* and refers to the direction of the arbitrary grid lines that are sometimes added to maps (see for ex-

---

[8]An *agonic line* is an isogonic line of zero declination.

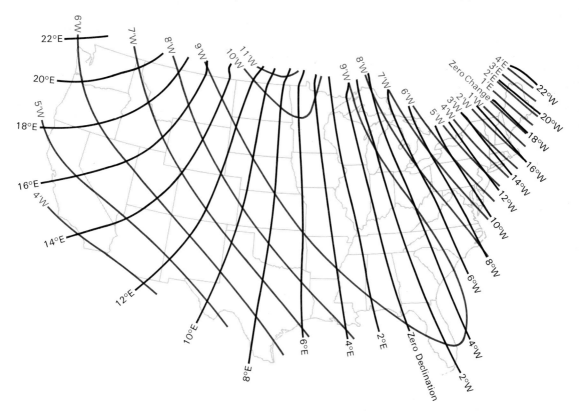

Figure 1.12 An isogonic chart. Black lines are isogonic lines, which join points of equal compass declination; the colored lines join points of equal annual change in declination. (Source: "Magnetic Declination in the United States—Epoch 1980," USGS map I-1283, 1980.)

ample, the description of the state plane coordinate system in Chapter 2). Grid north does not usually coincide with either true north or magnetic north.

Many maps include a *declination diagram*. This diagram shows the relationships between true, magnetic, and grid north (Fig. 1.13). The rate and direction of change of magnetic north is usually noted in conjunction with the declination dia-

Figure 1.13 A declination diagram from a USGS topographic map (Menan Buttes quadrangle, Idaho, 1951). The star indicates true north, GN grid north, and MN magnetic north. Angles on the diagram show only relative directions; actual angles are plotted when making adjustments.

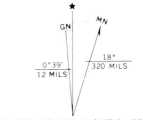

UTM GRID AND 1951 MAGNETIC NORTH
DECLINATION AT CENTER OF SHEET

gram so that the declination can be brought up to date. A declination diagram is only correct at a single point and is therefore most useful on detailed topographic maps or navigational charts that cover a relatively small portion of the earth's surface. On such maps it is usually sufficiently accurate to apply the same declination over the whole area covered by a given sheet. Maps of the type found in atlases and books, on the other hand, usually cover large areas on a small sheet of paper. This means that a number of declination diagrams would be needed to indicate the variation in declinations from one location to another. For this reason, and, more importantly, because such maps are not normally used for detailed direction finding or navigation, declination diagrams are seldom shown on small-scale maps.

Suggested Readings

BOMFORD, G., *Geodesy* (2nd ed.). Oxford: The Clarendon Press, 1962.

BURKARD, R. K., *Geodesy for the Layman*. St. Louis, Mo.: Aeronautical Chart and Information Center, 1964.

COTTER, C. H., *The Astronomical and Mathematical Foundations of Geography*. New York: American Elsevier Publishing Co., Inc., 1966.

EWING, C. E., and M. M. MITCHELL, *Introduction to Geodesy*. New York: American Elsevier Publishing Co., Inc., 1970.

GARLAND, G. D., *The Earth's Shape and Gravity*. New York: Pergamon Press, 1965.

UNITED STATES NAVAL OBSERVATORY, *The American Ephemeris and Nautical Almanac*. Washington, D.C.: U.S. Government Printing Office, issued annually. An example of an ephemeris of the sun, Polaris and other selected stars.

WILFORD, JOHN N., *The Mapmakers*. New York: Alfred A. Knopf, 1981. A nontechnical history of cartography that includes a description of the expeditions to Lapland and Peru to verify the flattening of the earth at the poles.

2

Map Projections: Establishing the Graticule

The earth has a three-dimensional, nearly spherical shape, as discussed in the previous chapter. A *globe,* which shows the correct relationships between features on the earth's surface, is therefore an ideal model of the earth. One might wonder why maps are needed at all; why not use globes to perform the functions for which we typically use maps?

Several considerations make maps a necessary supplement or replacement for globes, for many purposes. First, globes are extremely expensive to make. The processes involved are time-consuming and many of them require meticulous handwork, such as fitting and gluing numerous strips of paper, called *gores,* to the surface of the globe. As a result, good quality globes are difficult to produce in quantity and their prices tend to remain high. Second, globes are cumbersome and awkward to use. Even a classroom-size globe, typically less than a meter in diameter and showing relatively little detail, consumes a large amount of space and is ungainly to move. Third, to show any significant part of the world in detail, an extremely large globe, many meters in diameter, or at least a section of such a large globe, is required. Such globes or sections can be built but the costs and the awkwardness are multiplied many times over and storage is difficult; the number of large globes that exist is extremely limited. Plotting locations and routes on the curved surface of a globe is also much more awkward than performing the same tasks on a map and a viewer can see, at most, only a portion (slightly less than half) of the earth's surface at one time. For many purposes, therefore, the use of globes is really impractical. Finally, and perhaps most importantly, a person looking at a globe sees a *perspective* view, not an *orthographic* one (directly overhead at all points). Flat maps, which are quite easily and inexpensively produced in large quantities, and which are rather easily handled, are truly a necessity despite the shortcomings and difficulties they often present.

Once the decision is made to draw a map, there are major problems involved in representing the features that appear on the earth's surface on the flat map sheet. The source of these problems may be appreciated by simply attempting to apply a sheet of paper to a globe, so that the entire surface of the paper is touching the surface of the globe, without wrinkling the paper. The impossibility of doing this will immediately become apparent. This task is the mirror image of the *map projection* problem; the cartographer is attempting to flatten the curved surface of the globe onto a flat sheet of paper without stretching or tearing it. Both tasks are equally impossible and so map projection techniques are used to convert the three-dimensional globe to its two-dimensional representation on a map. The projection process inevitably involves accepting compromises in the characteristics of the map.

In this chapter, the general approach used in map projection is considered first, with emphasis on the relationship between the globe and the map. This introduction is followed by a discussion of the variables that are manipulated in order to otain the many possible types of projections. As illustrations, a few of the more common projections are described. A short discussion of the particular uses for various projections is presented as an aid to selecting the most suitable type of projection for particular applications. The final section of the chapter deals with two *locational grids* that are often superimposed on map projections—the state plane coordinate system and the Universal Transverse Mercator system.

SCALE

It is helpful to consider a map as a transformation from a globe which is itself a scale model of the earth. The *scale* of the globe is the ratio between measurements taken between points on its surface and measurements taken between equivalent locations on the earth. If the diameter of a globe is 1 m, for example, and the equatorial diameter of the earth is 12,756,370 m (NAD83), the scale of the globe is 1:12,756,370. The scale of the map projected from this globe will be a function of the scale of the globe. As we shall see, however, the relationship between the globe and the map varies from place to place, depending upon the particular projection being drawn. The scale of the map, therefore, is not the same at all points and the *nominal scale* is used to designate the scale of a particular map (see the section on the scale factor, below).

Once it is established, the nominal scale of a globe or a map is expressed in three different forms. These are (1) a *word statement,* (2) a *representative fraction,* or (3) a *graphic scale.* Each of these forms has certain advantages.

Word Statement

Scale may be expressed in a phrase, such as, "ten centimeters to one kilometer," which means that 10 cm on that particular map is equivalent to 1 km on the earth. An expression such as this has the advantage of relating a map distance to a recognizable distance on the earth's surface, which assists the visualization of the scale relationship.The word statement, however, is not the most easily used form for measurement purposes.

A word statement of scale that says the map is at a scale of "ten centimeters 'equals' one kilometer," is, strictly speaking, incorrect. The problem is that it is not possible for 10 cm to "equal" anything but 10 cm (or the equivalent 3.937 ft)! It is, however, possible for 10 cm to "represent" some other distance, such as 1 km. It is proper, therefore, to use a word statement that indicates the map is at a scale of "ten centimeters 'to' one kilometer."

Scale Ratio (Representative Fraction)

The scale of a map may also be expressed as the ratio between two distances: (1) the distance between two points as measured on the map, and (2) the actual distance between the same two points as measured on the earth's surface. This ratio is always presented with the map units listed first. For example, if the distance between two points on the map is 10 cm and the distance between equivalent points on the earth is 1 km (100,000 cm), the ratio between them is 10:100,000. This ratio is then reduced to 1:10,000 for listing on the map.

It is important to note that scale ratios are not expressed in terms of any specific units of measurement. This means, when such scales are used, that both sides of the ratio must be specified in the same units. If the scale is given as 1:10,000, it means that 1 cm on the map represents 10,000 cm (0.1 km) on the earth, just as 1 in. on the map represents 10,000 in. (0.158 mi) on the earth.

The scale ratio is frequently written as a fraction, called the *representative fraction* (RF for short), which is simply another way of expressing the equivalent scale ratio. A scale ratio of 1:10,000, for example, means exactly the same thing as the representative fraction 1/10,000.

Graphic Scale

Map scales are also represented in graphic form. This is done by dividing a line into units, each of which represents, at map scale, the actual distance between two points on the earth. These units are usually chosen to be easily usable, rounded numbers, such as tens or hundreds of kilometers, miles, meters, or feet. Part of the scale is often subdivided into fractional units to aid in measuring distances more precisely.

Graphic scales are especially useful for scaling actual earth distances from the map, if the projection is suitable for the purpose. This is done by using dividers (see Chapter 5) or other measuring devices to transfer the map distances to the scale. The scale is then read directly in actual earth distances. It is equally easy to reverse the process by measuring a required distance on the scale and transferring it to the map.

It is particularly helpful to use a graphic scale when a map drawing may be photographically reproduced at different sizes. This is because the scale itself is automatically enlarged or reduced, in proportion with the map, when the map is photographed. The word statement and representative fraction forms do not have this advantage and must be recomputed each time there is a change in the size of the map drawing.

Graphic scales are drawn in any one of a number of styles, as discussed in Chapter 8.

Areal Scale

The nominal scale of a map is usually defined in terms of linear dimensions. The *areal scale* of a map is defined in terms of areal units and is the square of its linear scale. An areal scale expresses the relationship between an area on the earth and the same area as represented on a map. Consider, for example, a square area on the earth's surface, bounded by edges 1 km long—that is, an area of 1 km² or 1,000,000 m². On the map (ignoring any projection distortions), this square kilometer is represented by a square bounded by edges 0.1 m long, with an area of 0.01 m². The relationship between the two areas, then, is 0.01 square units on the map to 1,000,000 square units on the ground.

Relative Scales

At times it is desirable to be able to make a general statement regarding the scale of a map without referring to a specific scale ratio or word statement. When comparing two maps, for example, it is convenient to say that "Map A is at a smaller scale than Map B." This statement conveys to the listener a feeling for the probable level of detail of the two maps, as well as the relative amount of area covered by each.

When a map of a given size covers a relatively small area of the earth's surface it is called a large-scale map. Large-scale maps, all things being equal, include a considerable amount of detail. If a map of the same size covers a large area on the earth's surface, relatively little detail can be included and the map is referred to as small-scale. For example, in the case of a map that is at a scale of 1:10,000, each unit of distance on the map represents 10,000 units on the ground. A 1:1,000,000 scale map, on the other hand, shows 1,000,000 units of distance on the ground in the same map distance. It is obvious that the 1:10,000 scale map fits the definition of a large-scale map and the 1:1,000,000 is at a small scale.

In addition to being used for comparative purposes, the terms small-, medium-, and large-scale are sometimes used as a shorthand way of referring to certain ranges of map scales. The problem with this practice is that there is no universally accepted cutoff level for the scales that should be included in each category. The following suggestions, which are used in United States Geological Survey publications, are generally acceptable, although many lists with different divisions may be found.

Topographic maps at scales of 1:25,000 or larger are classified as large-scale maps. Maps in the 1:50,000 to 1:100,000 range are considered to be intermediate-scale, whereas those in the 1:250,000 to 1:7,500,000 are small-scale. In addition, city maps, which are often called plans, may be at very large scales, such as 1:2,500, and maps in atlases, books, and reports, which may even be in the range of 1:100,000,000, or smaller, must be classified as very small-scale maps.

Because of the inconsistency in the range of scales assigned to each category by various writers, the examples in the preceding paragraph are suggestions at best. It is recommended that actual scale ranges, rather than these categories, be used to establish the scale in a particular case. The use of the terms for comparative purposes, however, such as "this map is at a larger scale than that map," is convenient and easily understood.

GLOBE CHARACTERISTICS

For some purposes it is necessary to use an ellipsoid as a representation of the figure of the earth. In this chapter, however, the earth is assumed to be a sphere and this is taken to be sufficiently accurate. This is partly because the development and use of map projections is most easily explained and understood by considering the relatively simpler sphere. At smaller map scales, taking the shape of the ellipsoid into account requires a level of accuracy that is offset by the inaccuracy inherent in making a drawing and measuring a map.[1] The distortion introduced by the normal stretching and shrinking of the paper on which the map is printed is likely to exceed the changes due to recognizing the ellipsoidal shape. It should be understood, however, that when large-scale projection systems are constructed, the shape of the ellipsoid is taken into consideration.

When features from the earth's surface are shown on a globe, their shape, the area they occupy, and the distances and directions between them are correctly shown. An ideal map projection would retain all of these characteristics and translate them to the map. The basic problem of making the transition from a three-dimensional globe to a flat map is that the process inevitably involves the loss of some globe characteristics. If a particular projection retains equal areas, for example, it cannot retain correct shape. If another projection shows correct distance, it cannot show correct area, and so on.

A globe is the only correct representation of the features on the earth's surface. Although it suffers from the handicaps mentioned at the beginning of this chapter, a globe is a useful reference tool. Comparisons between the globe and the map will assist in resolving questions regarding the characteristics of a given map projection.

Conformality

The retention of correct angles on a map is called *conformality*. The importance of this characteristic is that it allows the identification of small map features by their distinctive shape.

The requirements for conformality are that the lines of latitude and longitude must cross one another at right angles, and that the scale must be the same in all directions at any given point on the map. Both of these conditions exist on a globe.

[1] It is sometimes assumed that a point cannot be plotted with an accuracy greater than approximately 0.15 mm, regardless of the scale of the map. Measurements made from the map cannot be any more precise than this "zero dimension." Peter Richardus and Ron K. Adler, *Map Projections for Geodesists, Cartographers and Geographers* (New York: American Elsevier Publishing Co., Inc., 1972), p. 14.

In a sense, the term *conformality* is somewhat misleading because the condition can only be achieved for small areas on a map. The shape of large areas, such as continents, is different from the shape of those areas as shown on the globe, even though the shape of small areas is retained and the map is classified as conformal.

Equivalence

Equivalence is the condition in which a unit area drawn on the map always represents the same number of square kilometers on the globe's surface, regardless of where it is drawn. The retention of such areal relationships is especially important on maps used to make comparisons between the areal extent of different phenomena on the earth's surface.

In order to retain equivalence, any scale changes that occur in one direction must be offset by suitable changes in the other direction. For example, the three rectangles shown in Fig. 2.1(a) are equal in area, even though they have different dimensions.

The right-angle crossing of parallels and meridians is lost in many projections. The shape changes that this causes do not necessarily affect the ability to retain equivalence; in fact, retaining equivalence will inevitably distort shapes. The fact that different intersections of parallels and meridians need not affect area is shown by comparing the areas of the skewed quadrilaterals in Fig. 2.1(b). Even though the shapes of the figures differ, their areas are the same because their height and base dimensions are the same.

Distance

The retention of correct distance relationships requires that the length of a straight line between two points on the map represent the correct great-circle distance between them. It is possible to design maps that have this characteristic but, even on such *equidistant* maps, correct distances can only be measured from one point or, at most, two points. Distances between other points will not be correct and, indeed, may be greatly exaggerated. One should not make the mistake of thinking that mea-

Figure 2.1   (a) Each rectangle has the same area (2,025 m² at the scale selected). (b) Each quadrilateral has the same area (2,025 m² at the scale selected).

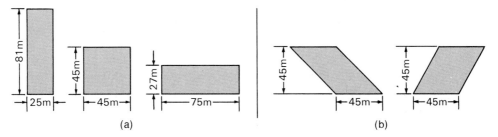

surements between any and all points, even on an equidistant map, will yield correct distances. Indeed, because of the distortions involved in almost all projections, it is not advisable to measure distances on small-scale maps, with the exceptions just noted.

Direction

If correct direction is retained, a straight line drawn between two points on the map will show the correct great-circle route between the points, as well as the correct azimuth of the line. An *azimuth* is defined by the angle formed at the starting point of a straight line, in relation to a meridian, measured in a clockwise direction from north. Although it is possible to measure an azimuth with reference to true north, magnetic north, or grid north, we shall assume a true north reference unless otherwise specified (Fig. 2.2).

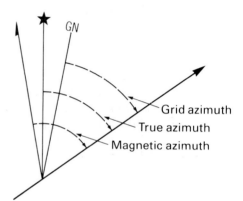

Figure 2.2 Example of differences in azimuths based on true, magnetic, or grid north.

It is possible, on azimuthal maps, to accurately represent directions from the center of the map to all other points. Remember, however, that the azimuths of great circles that do not pass through the center of such projections are not shown correctly. It is also possible, using a gnomonic projection, to create a map of a limited area on which a straight line between any two points represents a great circle (see the section on the gnomonic projection, below). It is not possible, however, to create a map of the world on which all directions are correct.

MAP PROJECTIONS

A *map projection* is simply a systematic rendering on a flat sheet of paper of the geographic coordinates of the features found on the globe. The idea behind projections is most easily understood by considering actual geometric projections. The idea of a geometric projection is illustrated by using a transparent globe with the lines of latitude and longitude and the coastlines and other features drawn on it. When a light source is placed inside the globe, the various lines drawn on the globe cast shadows on any surface placed near it, and the outline of these shadows represents a map projection.

Many so-called map projections are actually arbitrarily arranged graticules designed to have particular characteristics; they could not be obtained by the use of the transparent globe and shadow approach. The idea is useful, nevertheless, as a means of demonstrating the basic concepts involved in map projections and is therefore taken as a starting point for this discussion.

Projection Surfaces

Three *physical surfaces* are commonly used for the construction of projections. These are the *plane,* the *cylinder,* and the *cone.*

Plane The simplest projection surface is a plane (flat) surface; projections onto such a surface are referred to as *azimuthal projections.* The most significant aspect of a plane surface is the fact that an outline projected onto it does not have to undergo further distortion or manipulation—it is already a flat map.

Developable surfaces The other projection surfaces are not flat at the time the projection is created, but they can be developed (flattened). Development is accomplished by making an appropriate cut in the form and unrolling it. In the case of a *developable surface* this is done without stretching or tearing and therefore without distortion of the surface or of the patterns drawn on it. The cone and the cylinder are the developable surfaces used for mapping purposes (Fig. 2.3). A cylinder is developed by cutting along its length and unrolling it. A cone is developed by making a cut from its base to its apex and unrolling it.

Light Source

For illustrative purposes, the discussion so far has assumed that the projection light source is located at the center of the globe. This is not required however; it is possible to locate the light source at any desired point. Although other locations are used, there are three common locations for the light source. These are (1) the *gno-*

Figure 2.3 A cone and a cylinder developed into flat surfaces.

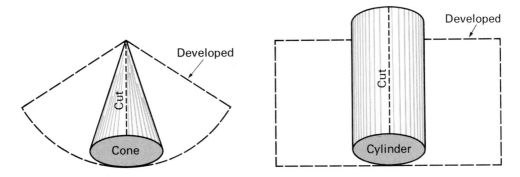

monic position, at the center of the globe; (2) the *stereographic* position, at the *antipode* (the point exactly opposite the point of tangency of the projection surface); and (3) the *orthographic* position, at infinity (Fig. 2.4). Changing the location of the light source, even though the projection surface and orientation are held constant, changes the characteristics of the resulting projection. The specific effects are discussed as the appropriate projections are described.

The idea of using different locations for the light source places some strain on the idea of shadows being cast. This is because the light may, in some positions, have to pass through two portions of the globe before reaching the projection surface. In some cases, such as the cylinder, the light source might also have to be moved in order to cast shadows everywhere. Finally, part of the projection surface may lie between the globe and the light source, so that it could not actually have a shadow cast on it. These examples illustrate some of the shortcomings of the transparent globe as the source for different map projections. The basic idea is clear enough, however, so there should be no confusion when situations arise in which allowances must be made for these difficulties.

Orientation

The orientation of the projection surface, and its tangency to the globe, is changed as desired. Tangent planes touch the globe at a single point. Cylinders and cones, when wrapped around a globe, are tangent along a line. Obviously, if the orientation of the projection surface is changed, the location of the point or line of tangency between that surface and the globe also changes. With different points of tangency the resulting projections have different-appearing graticules, but they usually have the same general characteristics.

Figure 2.4 Three common locations of the projection light source, showing the effect on the direction of the light rays passing through selected points.

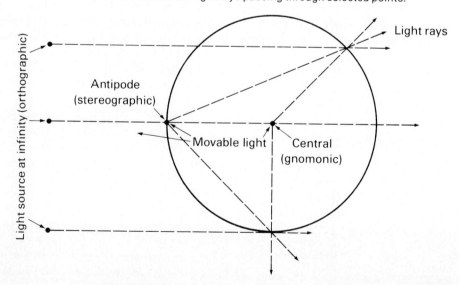

Certain locations of the tangency are "normal" for the various types of projections. In azimuthal projections, the normal position of the plane is tangent at the pole, which is then the center of the projection. In conic projections, the normal position of the cone is with the peak of the cone aligned with the axis of rotation of the earth. The result is that the pole is at the center of the projection and the cone is tangent along one of the lines of latitude. In cylindrical projections, the normal position of the cylinder is tangent at the equator.

The point (or line) of tangency of the projection surface may be shifted so that it is at a right angle to the normal. In azimuthal projections, this results in what is referred to as an *equatorial projection.* In cylindrical projections the right-angled orientation is called a *transverse projection.* Conic projections are seldom seen in this orientation, although it is perfectly feasible to use it.

When the tangency is not at the normal location, or at a right angle to it, the projection is called *oblique.* Oblique orientations are most commonly seen in azimuthal and cylindrical projections.

Scale Factor

Wherever the map projection surface contacts the model globe a one-to-one scale relationship is established between the two. Depending upon the particular projection surface being used, the contact is at a single point or along a line. A line of tangency is called the *standard line* of the projection.

As noted above, the scale of a map varies somewhat from one location to another. The scale at the point or line of contact is called the *nominal scale* of the map; the ratio between the nominal map scale (or globe scale) and the actual scale at a given point on the map is known as the *scale factor.*

Assume, for example, that the scale of a particular globe is 1:1,000,000. The scale of the map, at the point or line of tangency is also 1:1,000,000. At that point, the scale factor, which is the map scale divided by the globe scale, is 1.0. If the scale of a portion of the map is enlarged so that a particular line on the projection is twice as long as it is on the globe, the scale along that line becomes 1:500,000 and the scale factor is 2.0.[2] If the line is only half as long as it is on the globe, the scale becomes 1:2,000,000 and the scale factor is 0.5.

The scale factor may be determined for different areas on a given projection. This provides a useful means of evaluating the scale characteristics of the projection.

SPECIFIC PROJECTIONS

This portion of the chapter is devoted to illustrations and brief summary descriptions of some of the most common map projections. Within each general class, the geometrically constructed projections are presented first, followed by the nongeometric types that are similar to them. This is done in order to build on the concept

---

[2]It must be remembered that the map scale is a fraction. Therefore, $1/500,000 \div 1/1,000,000 = 1/500,000 \times 1,000,000 = 2.0$.

of geometric projection as the means of converting the graticule on the globe to a flat-map form. As will become apparent, however, nongeometric construction provides some of the most useful projections. All the descriptions are simplified and avoid mathematics—they concentrate on the arrangement of the graticule and the general characteristics of the projection. Once this preliminary material is absorbed, reference to the more specialized treatises listed in the Suggested Readings is recommended. In general, further study requires the utilization of some mathematics.

In many of the descriptions of specific projections, the measurements between meridians or parallels are referred to as being *truly spaced,* or at true spacing. This terminology indicates that the map distance between the two lines is the correct (scale) distance between the two lines as measured on the surface of the globe. It does not refer to a measurement obtained by measuring the *chord* distance between the two lines (Fig. 2.5). It is obvious that these two distances are quite different and must therefore be carefully distinguished.

Plots of Projections

The sample projections contained in this section were produced by the WORLD projection and mapping computer program.[3] A major advantage of using these computer-assisted plots is that the outlines of the landmasses and water bodies on each projection are based on the same data set. This consistency of data greatly enhances the ability to make visual comparisons between projections. Differences in the appearance of the outlines from map to map are due almost entirely to differences in the characteristics of the projections (although some effects due to in-

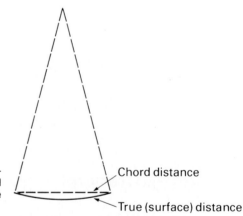

Figure 2.5 Difference in measurement of true distance and chord distance between two points on the earth's surface.

Chord distance

True (surface) distance

[3]Developed by Philip M. Voxland of the Social Science Research Facilities Center at the University of Minnesota. Information concerning its availability may be obtained from: Social Science Research Facilities Center, 25 Blegen Hall, University of Minnesota, 269 19th Avenue South, Minneapolis, Minn. 55455.

terpolation between data points remain). When conventional drafting or scribing techniques are used, on the other hand, drawing or plotting discrepancies inevitably occur. The result is that differences in the appearance of drafted or scribed maps are due to a mixture of unintended inconsistencies and actual differences between projections, which makes it difficult to make consistent comparisons. An additional major advantage of a computer program is that it can produce a wide variety of projections, far in excess of the selection presented here. In addition, these projections can be recentered and rescaled with complete flexibility and in a very short period of time (see Chapter 11).

Two concerns were taken into consideration in deciding to use computer-assisted techniques for the plotting of the sample projections (both of which are discussed in Chapter 11). One of these concerns is the slightly jagged appearance of some lines, especially regularly shaped curves and straight lines that run in diagonal directions. This jaggedness is the result of the resolution of the plotting system that was utilized. The second concern is that the outlines of the landmasses and water bodies are rather generalized. This is the result of using a readily available data set that is suitable for small-scale maps. These concerns were judged to be less significant than the advantages gained, especially considering the offsetting problems connected with conventional techniques.

Distortion diagram Many of the sample projections include graphic devices indicating the scale variations and shape distortions that occur in the particular projection.[4] The basis for preparing these diagrams is as follows.

A particular location on the earth's surface is first specified as the center of the diagram. A small circle is then defined around that location and the latitude and longitude of several points on the circle are calculated. Next, the coordinates of the points are transformed into locations on the particular projection involved. Finally, a line is drawn through the plotted points, producing a diagram of the original circle that reflects the distortion characteristics of the projection at that point.

If there is no distortion of shape or variation of scale at the chosen point, the plot of the diagram on the projection is a circle of unit size. Shape and scale do vary in differing proportions, however, depending on the particular projection involved and the location of the plot on that projection. These differences are reflected in the shape and size of the diagram.

The combinations of shape and size differences that can occur are essentially infinite, but several examples illustrate the general range of results. Scale variations change the size of the diagram. If the scale factor is the same in all directions at the selected point, the plot will simply produce a proportionately larger or smaller circle [Fig. 2.6(a)]. If the scale factor increases along a parallel or a meridian, however, east-west or north-south distances in the diagram are increased proportionately

---

[4]Although its appearance and application is similar, this diagram is not equivalent to Tissot's indicatrix, as described in Oscar S. Adams, *General Theory of Polyconic Projections,* Special Publication No. 57 (Washington, D.C.: U.S. Coast and Geodetic Survey, 1934), pp. 153–63.

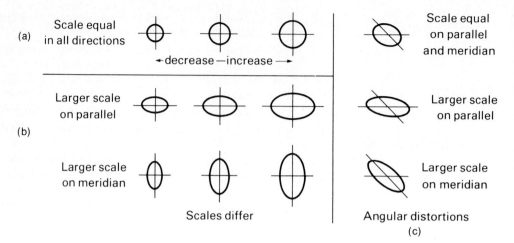

Figure 2.6 Typical variations in the shape of the distortion diagram: (a) Differences due to scale variation. (b) Differences due to scale variations on meridians and parallels. (c) Differences in the angle of crossing of the meridians and parallels, combined with scale variations.

and the diagram becomes elliptical [Fig. 2.6(b)]. Variations in shape result from the differing angles at which lines of latitude and longitude cross one another at different locations within the projection. These variations result in complementary changes in the shape of the diagram [Fig. 2.6(c)]. Thus, changes in both shape and scale result in a variety of shape and size variations in the diagrams.

Each diagram actually indicates the conditions that exist at a very small point on the projection. The plots are based on circles of measurable size, however, so that the shape and size variations are visible. For purposes of appreciating the general characteristics of the projection, each diagram is representative of the characteristics of the projection in the general area in which it is located.

Cylindrical Projections

This section discusses projections that are based on the idea of a cylinder that is wrapped around the globe. In the most common types the cylinder is tangent at the equator. This results in a basically rectangular graticule with straight-line meridians and parallels. In these cases the equator is of correct length and has a 1.0 scale factor.

On the globe the meridians converge toward the poles. On the normally oriented cylindrical projections, however, the meridians are parallel lines which do not converge. The spacing between meridians is based on an equal division of the equator. This means that a constant map distance, measured along the parallels, represents smaller and smaller actual earth distances as one moves away from the equator. As a result, the scale factor along the parallels increases toward the poles.

The spacing between the parallels varies for each projection, depending on the location of the light source or on the arbitrary pattern established for the particular projection. The emphasis in the descriptions that follow is on the differences in characteristics that result from different spacings of the parallels.

Central (perspective) cylindrical projection   In the *central cylindrical projection* the light source is located at the center of the globe (left portion, Fig. 2.7). This means the spacing between the parallels increases rapidly toward the poles, resulting in an increasing exaggeration in north-south scale away from the equator. This increase in north-south scale is accompanied by the increase in east-west scale, which is the common characteristic of the cylindrical projections. Because the scales in both directions are increasing simultaneously, there is a dramatic distortion of areas toward the poles.

This projection has no particularly useful characteristics, but it does provide a point of departure for discussing the very useful Mercator projection.

Figure 2.7   Comparison between the central cylindrical and Mercator projections.

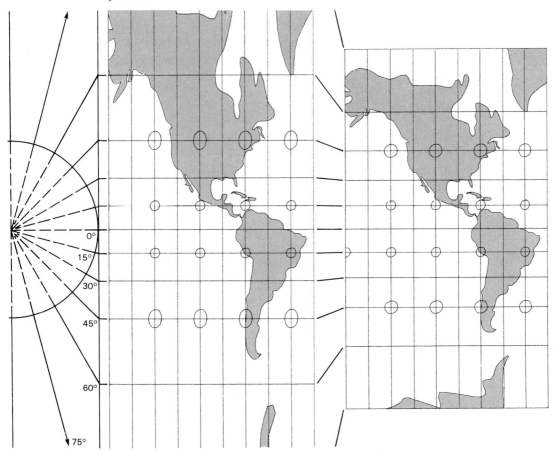

Mercator projection The *Mercator projection* is not obtained geometrically but it can be compared to the geometric central cylindrical projection. On the Mercator the spacing between the parallels does not increase as rapidly toward the poles as it does on the central cylindrical, and the north-south scale does not change as rapidly either (right portion, Fig. 2.7).

The Mercator is specifically designed so that the north-south scale increases at the same rate as the east-west scale. This means that the scale factor on the Mercator is the same in all directions at any given point on the map. This is not the same as saying that the scale is correct everywhere, however, because the scale factor is 1.0 only at the equator. For example, at 60° N or S, the distance between two meridians on the earth is half of the distance between the same two meridians at the equator. On the Mercator, however, the spacing between them is the same at 60° as it is at the equator. This means that the east-west scale factor along that parallel is 2.0. The projection is designed so the north-south scale factor at that point is also 2.0. At any point on the 60th parallel, then, the scale factor is the same in all directions, but is not the same as the scale factor at the equator or on any other parallel.

In addition to the equality of the scale factor at each point on the Mercator, the meridians and parallels of the projection all cross one another at right angles. These two factors, which are characteristics of the globe, mean that shapes on the Mercator are correct and it is classified as a conformal projection. It is reemphasized, however, that conformality does not mean that shapes are correct over large areas, such as continents. What it does mean is that the shapes of individual features are correct. (Technically, this statement is true with regard only to points but, for our purposes, it can safely be applied over small areas.) This is the most that can be expected of a conformal projection because only on a globe can the scale factor be the same everywhere.

Because the scale factor is the same in all directions at any given point, angles on the Mercator are also correct. A straight line, therefore, crosses any meridians in its path at a constant angle and represents a line of constant direction, or heading, on the earth. The fact that lines of *constant heading* appear as straight lines makes the Mercator particularly useful for navigational purposes. If a navigator using a Mercator chart joins any two points with a straight line the resulting plot indicates the heading which, if steered continuously, leads from the starting point to the destination (although suitable corrections for compass declination must be introduced). This line of constant heading is called a *loxodrome,* or *rhumb line.*

It is interesting to note the path of a loxodrome that is directed obliquely poleward. Because the meridians converge toward the pole, the loxodrome, which crosses each meridian at the same angle, traces out a spiral curve that converges closer and closer toward the pole, although it theoretically never reaches it (Fig. 2.8).

A loxodrome is useful for navigational purposes because it is the easiest course to steer. It has the disadvantage, however, that except for points that lie on the equator or on the same meridian, it does not represent the shortest distance between

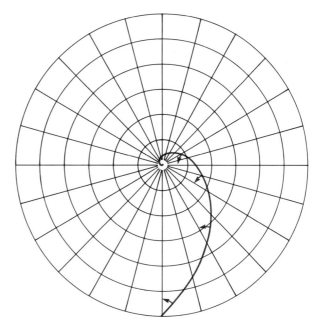

Figure 2.8 Path of an obliquely directed loxodrome. Note that the line crosses each meridian at a constant angle.

two points on the earth's surface. A loxodrome would not, therefore, be the most desirable course to follow if the points were anything but a short distance apart. This is because the most direct route between two points on a globe is the shortest arc of the great circle that intersects both points. Such a great-circle route is called an *orthodrome.*

Most great-circle routes have a constantly changing compass heading so they appear as curved lines on a Mercator projection (exceptions are the equator and the meridians) [Fig. 2.9(a)]. This problem is overcome by using the gnomonic projection in conjunction with the Mercator, because great circles appear as straight lines on the gnomonic projection (see the section on the gnomic projection, below). A straight line is drawn on the gnomonic projection to determine the desired orthodrome between two points [Fig. 2.9(b)]. Points from the gnomonic plot are transferred to the Mercator chart. The points on the Mercator chart are joined by straight-line segments that approximate the great-circle route. The azimuth for each of the line segments can then be determined and used for sailing each leg of the route.

Cylindrical equal-area projection   In the *cylindrical equal-area projection* the spacing between the parallels is determined by projection from a light source that is theoretically an infinite distance away from the globe (Fig. 2.10). This means that successive parallels are spaced progressively closer together toward the poles and therefore the scale along the meridians decreases toward the poles.

The decrease in the north-south scale offsets the poleward increase in the east-west scale that is common to the cylindrical projections. The offsetting scale differences give the projection its equal-area characteristic. The result is that the area

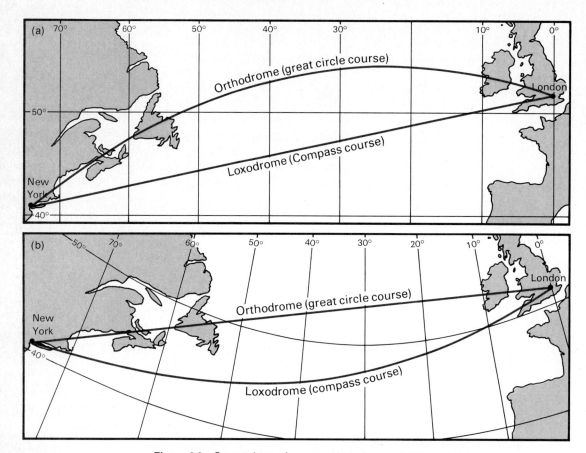

Figure 2.9 Comparison of a great-circle course (orthodrome) and a compass course (loxodrome) as plotted on Mercator and gnomonic projections: (a) Straight-line loxodrome and curved orthodrome on Mercator. [Based on Defense Mapping Agency map, "The World," (Series 1145, Edition 1-DMATC).] (b) Straight-line orthodrome and curved loxodrome on gnomonic. [Based on Plate IV, "Gnomonic projection of the North Atlantic Ocean," Charles H. Deetz and Oscar S. Adams, *Elements of Map Projection,* Special Publication No. 68, 5th ed. (Washington, D.C.: U.S. Department of Commerce, Coast and Geodetic Survey, 1944).]

bounded by any given pairs of meridians and parallels is in the correct proportion to the area enclosed within the same meridians and parallels on the globe.

Shapes on the cylindrical equal-area projection become very distorted toward the poles. This occurs because the parallels become progressively closer together than they are on the globe and the meridians become progressively too far apart. Shapes away from the equator are compressed north-south and stretched east-west. This is an illustration of the fact that an advantage in one characteristic of a projection (in this case, area) is inevitably accompanied by a disadvantage in another (shape).

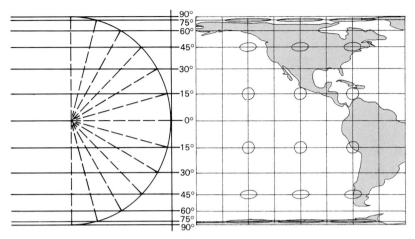

Figure 2.10   Cylindrical equal-area projection.

Equirectangular cylindrical projection   The graticule of the *equirectangular cylindrical projection* is constructed rather than actually projected. The equator, or a desired parallel, is first established as a standard line by drawing a straight line of true length. The meridians are then truly spaced on the standard line and are drawn as parallel straight lines at right angles to the standard line. Finally, the lines of latitude are drawn as truly spaced straight lines parallel to the standard line.

When the equator is chosen as the standard line, the spacing between each pair of meridians and parallels is the same everywhere. In this case, the equal-spaced projection is variously called the equal-spaced cylindrical, plane chart, square projection, or plate carrée (Fig. 2.11).

As with the geometrically projected cylindricals, the east-west scale of the equirectangular cylindrical increases toward the poles (and decreases toward the equator if the standard line is along a parallel). By construction, the north-south scale is correct throughout.

The projection has no particularly useful characteristics, other than ease and simplicity of construction, although its scale and shape characteristics are fairly good in a narrow band near the standard line. It is most useful to use a standard line other than the equator when a map of only a portion of the earth's surface is to be drawn. In this case, the standard parallel can be conveniently placed near the center of the area to be mapped; this will reduce the error in the east-west scale within the mapped area.

Gall's stereographic projection   In the *Gall's stereographic projection* the cylinder of projection is *secant* at 45° N and S. This means that the cylinder cuts through the globe rather than being tangent to it (Fig. 2.12). As indicated by the name of the projection, the light source is placed at the stereographic position. Because of this, scale exaggeration toward the poles is less severe than in the Mercator and the

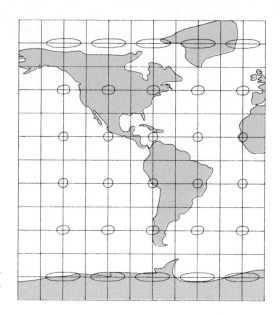

Figure 2.11 Equirectangular cylindrical projection, with the equator as the standard line.

Figure 2.12 Gall's stereographic projection.

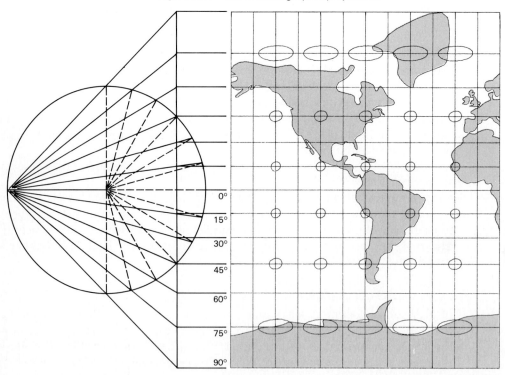

poles are shown as horizontal straight lines the same length as the equator. This projection is a compromise that has no specific useful qualities.

Miller's cylindrical projection   The *Miller's cylindrical projection* is similar to the Mercator except that the spacing between parallels does not increase as rapidly toward the poles (Fig. 2.13). The advantage of this is that the changes in the north-south scale, and the accompanying exaggeration of area, are less drastic. The poles are also shown as horizontal straight lines. The disadvantage, however, is that straight lines (other than meridians and the equator) do not represent constant headings, so the Miller cannot be used for navigation. No other significant qualities are gained—in short, it is a compromise projection.

Transverse Mercator projection   The *transverse Mercator* is a Mercator projection with the presumed cylinder of projection tangent along a meridian circle, instead of along the equator (Fig. 2.14). The central meridian is truly divided, just as the equator is on the standard Mercator. The other meridians intersect the equator at increasing spacing, which is the same as the spacing of the parallels on the standard Mercator. The shapes of the other parallels and meridians are determined by the

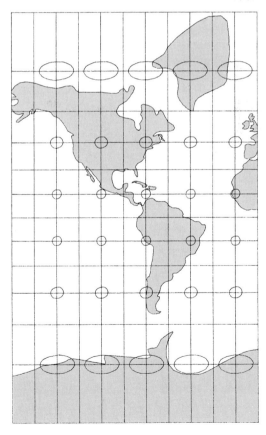

Figure 2.13 Miller's cylindrical projection.

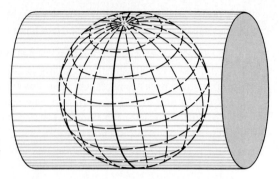

Figure 2.14   The transverse Mercator projection is projected onto a cylinder that is tangent along a meridian.

use of construction tables that provide the locations of their intersections. Most of the graticule consists of curved lines (Fig. 2.15); this contrasts with the standard Mercator on which all of the meridians and parallels are straight lines.

The transverse Mercator is conformal but, because lines of constant heading (loxodromes) are curved, it cannot be used for the same navigational purposes as the Mercator. One of the most important applications of the transverse Mercator is as the base for the Universal Transverse Mercator grid, which is described at the end of this chapter. This application uses only a narrow zone of the projection, parallel to the standard meridian, within which the amount of scale distortion is quite small.

Figure 2.15   Transverse Mercator projection of the Northern Hemisphere.

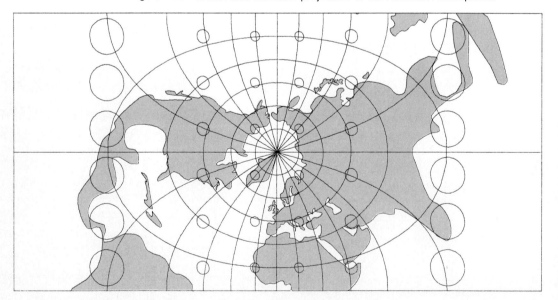

Conic Projections

In this group of projections, a cone is the standard projection surface. In the polar case, all of the conics have meridians that are evenly spaced straight lines radiating from the pole. The chief differences between these projections result from the choice of the *standard parallel* (or parallels) and from the variation in the spacing between the parallels which are, in each case, concentric circles centered on the pole. It is very unusual to encounter transverse or oblique conic projections; for this reason the descriptions here are confined to the polar case.

Constant of the cone   Regardless of their other characteristics, the polar cases of conical projections with single standard parallels have straight-line meridians that radiate from the pole. The angle occupied by these meridians varies depending upon the location of the standard parallel. For any given span of meridians, which may be as great as 360 degrees, all such conical projections with the same standard parallel have the same angle between their meridians. This relationship is known as the *constant of the cone.*

More formally, the constant of the cone is defined as the sine of the latitude at which the cone is tangent (usually designated as ϕ). When the standard parallel is close to the pole, the angle between the meridians on the resulting projection is relatively wide; when it is close to the equator, the angle is relatively narrow (Fig. 2.16). For example, on a projection tangent at 60°, the angle between meridians

Figure 2.16   Illustration of the constant of the cone, $r = R \cot \phi$, where R is the radius of the globe, ϕ is the latitude, and b is the arc of coverage.

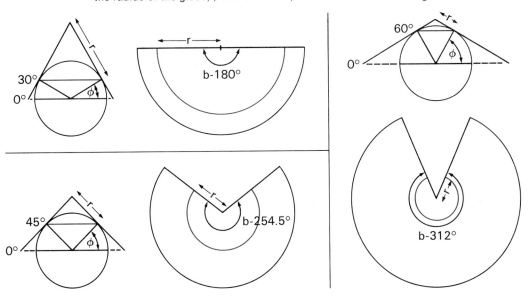

360 degrees apart is 360 degrees (sin ϕ) = 360 degrees (sin 60°) = 360 degrees (0.866) = 311.8 degrees. On the other hand, if the tangency is at 45°, the angle is 360 degrees (0.707) = 254.6 degrees; at 30° the angle is 360 degrees (0.5) = 180 degrees; and so on.

Although the examples given here are for projections with one standard parallel, the same general concept applies to projections with two standard parallels.[5]

It is interesting to note that the constant of the cone extends to projections onto a plane (azimuthal) or a cylinder. The plane is equivalent to a cone tangent at 90°. Because sin 90° is 1.0, the angle necessary to represent the full 360-degree sweep on the plane is 360 degrees (see Fig. 2.26, for example). Similarly, a cylinder is equivalent to a cone tangent at the equator; because sin 0° is 0.0, the angle between the meridians on the cylinder is 0 degrees—in other words, they are parallel (see Fig. 2.7, for example).

Central (perspective) conic projection   The cone of the *central conic projection* is tangent along one standard parallel, with the light source at the center of the globe (Fig. 2.17). The radius of the standard parallel is the distance between it and the peak of the cone. The other parallels are concentric circles, spaced according to the projected intersections on the cone. The spacing between the parallels increases rapidly in either direction away from the standard parallel.

The standard parallel is truly divided and scale is correct only along that parallel, with increasing scale away from it. The meridians are straight lines radiating from the pole, with the spacing between them determined by the true division of the standard parallel.

Because this projection has no particularly useful characteristics it is seldom

Figure 2.17   Central (perspective) projection, with 30° as the standard parallel.

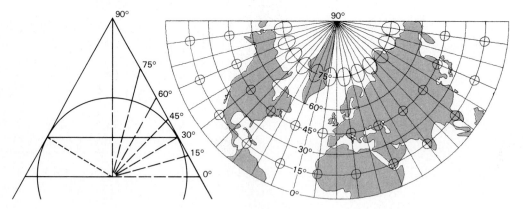

[5]Porter W. McDonnell, Jr., *Introduction to Map Projections* (New York: Marcel Dekker, Inc., 1979), provides examples of the determination of the constant of the cone in such cases.

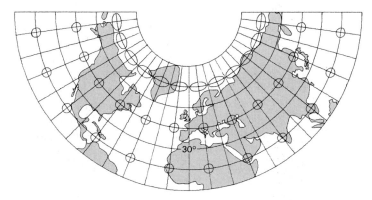

Figure 2.18   Simple conic projection, with 30° as the standard parallel.

used. It is included here because it is a basic example of the conic class of projections.

Simple conic projection   The *simple conic projection* is a modification of the central conic. There is one standard parallel, the radius of which is defined by the distance between it and the peak of the cone, just as in the central conic (Fig. 2.18). The meridians are truly spaced along the standard parallel and the parallels are concentric circles, truly spaced along the meridians. The pole, also, is a concentric arc at true scale distance from the standard parallel.

The scale is too large everywhere except on the standard parallel and along the meridians. The projection has no particularly useful characteristics but is simple to construct.

Conics with Two Standard Parallels

Instead of being in contact with the surface of the globe the projection cone may be made to cut through it. A cone that cuts through the globe in this manner is called a *secant cone*. Using a secant cone results in a projection with *two standard parallels* instead of one (Fig. 2.19). This arrangement has the advantage that scale is correct along both of the standard parallels and there is less scale distortion overall.[6]

Simple conic projection with two standard parallels   The construction of this projection begins with the selection of two standard parallels, spaced so that they are separated by about two-thirds of the north-south extent of the map. This placement serves to distribute the scale error across the map area. The line of tangency of the cone, called the tangent parallel, is then located midway between the standard par-

---

[6]The term *secant conic* is strictly applied only to a projection obtained by geometric methods. When the spacing between parallels is not the result of actual projection, but is determined in such a way that certain desired characteristics are obtained, the term *secant* does not properly apply. In common usage, however, any conic projection with two standard parallels is considered to be secant.

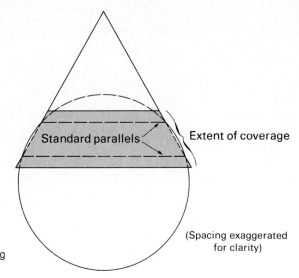

Figure 2.19 Secant cone, showing two standard parallels.

allels. The radius of this tangent parallel is defined by the distance between it and the peak of the cone, in the same manner as the standard parallel of the simple conic.

The other parallels are *concentric circles* drawn around the center established for the tangent parallel. The spacing between the parallels is based on the true distance over the surface of the globe, not on the distance along the secant cone (Fig. 2.20). Finally, the standard parallels are truly divided and the meridians are drawn joining the division points.

The east-west scale of the simple conic with two standard parallels is too small between the standard parallels and is too large outside them. Again, the projection has no particularly outstanding characteristics, but it is useful as a basis for comparison with the very useful Lambert conformal and Albers equal-area projections.

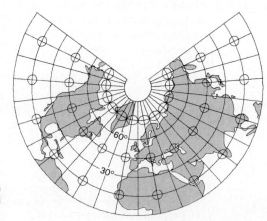

Figure 2.20 Simple conic projection with two standard parallels (30° and 60°).

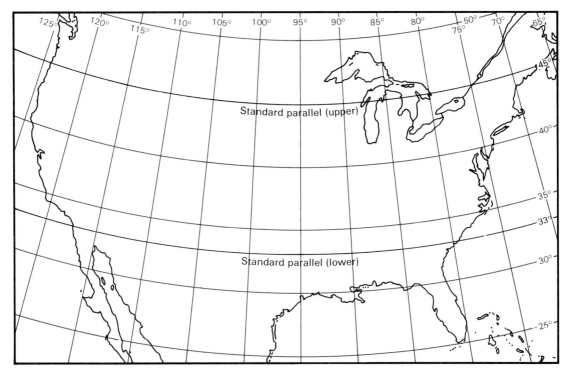

Figure 2.21 Lambert conformal projection.

Lambert conformal projection In the *Lambert conformal projection* (Fig. 2.21), the parallels are arcs of concentric circles. The meridians are straight lines that converge at a common point, which is the center from which the parallels are drawn. Using published tables, the spacing between the parallels along each meridian is adjusted so that the scale factor is equal to the east-west scale factor at that point. Between the standard parallels the scale is too small and outside the standard parallels it is too large. A variety of tables is available, with differing selections of standard parallels.

Despite the fact that scale varies from place to place, the construction of the Lambert conformal provides equal scale in all directions at each point, which is the first condition for conformality. The parallels and meridians also cross one another at right angles, which is the second condition for conformality.

Albers equal-area projection The parallels of the *Albers equal-area projection* are concentric arcs of circles and the meridians are straight lines drawn from the same center. Because of this construction, the parallels and meridians cross at right angles and the appearance is similar to the Lambert conformal.[7] In this projection, how-

---

[7]At the scale of Fig. 2.21, the differences between the Lambert conformal and Albers equal-area projections are too small to be shown.

ever, the tables provide a spacing between the parallels that is adjusted to offset the scale changes between the meridians. Between the standard parallels the east-west scale is too small, so the north-south scale is increased to offset it; outside the standard parallels the east-west scale is too great, so the opposite variation of north-south scale is used to offset it. Providing the proper scale relationships in this manner gives the projection its equal-area characteristics. This projection has a very small scale error when used for regions of greater east-west extent, provided the latitudinal span is not too great.

Modified Conics

The *modified conics* differ from the conics already discussed in that they have curved rather than straight-line meridians.

Polyconic projection The *polyconic projection* is based on the idea that a series of cones are tangent to the globe (Fig. 2.22). Therefore, every parallel is a standard line.

It is interesting to note that the "cone" tangent to the globe at the equator in the polyconic projection is, in actuality, a cylinder. This is an illustration of the fact that a cylinder is the *limiting case* in a series of successively more extended cones. The other limiting case is a perfectly flat cone, or a plane. In the polyconic, a plane is tangent at the pole.

To construct this projection, the equator is drawn as a straight line at right angles to a straight-line central meridian. The parallels intersect the central meridian at true spacing. Once the intersections are established, the parallels are drawn as nonconcentric arcs of circles. The radius of each parallel is equal to the distance between the line of tangency and the peak of the appropriate cone. Each of the

Figure 2.22 Polyconic projection of the Northern Hemisphere.

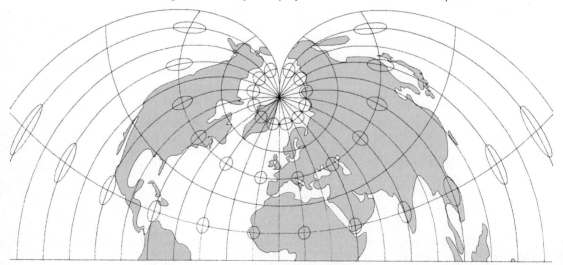

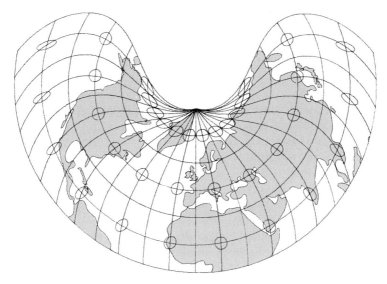

Figure 2.23   Bonne projection of the Northern Hemisphere.

parallels, including the equator, is truly divided and the curved meridians are drawn, connecting the intersection points and converging at the pole.

The polyconic is neither equal-area nor conformal. It is useful because it has small distortion near its central meridian, but scale error increases away from that meridian.

Bonne projection   The construction of the *Bonne projection* begins in the same manner as a simple conic projection, with a straight-line central meridian that is truly divided (Fig. 2.23). A standard parallel is then drawn with a radius equal to the distance between the line of tangency and the peak of the cone. The other parallels and the equator are concentric arcs of circles and are therefore centered on the same point as the standard parallel. The pole is not the center around which the parallels are drawn; instead, it is located at its true distance from the standard parallel. The difference between the Bonne and the simple conic is that all the parallels on the Bonne are truly divided and the meridians are therefore curved. The projection is equal-area and has small distortion near its central meridian.

In the extreme case, where the standard parallel is the equator, this projection is the same as the sinusoidal, discussed in the section on conventional projections.

Azimuthal Projections

Azimuthal projections are drawn on a plane surface[8] and are commonly presented in polar, equatorial, or oblique aspects. The location of the light source may be varied in each case, as well, so a great number of different graticules may be en-

---

[8]The term *zenithal* is sometimes used for projections on a plane, but *azimuthal* is generally preferred.

countered. The plane on which the projection is drawn need not be tangent to the globe, but variations in the distance of the plane from the globe result only in variations in scale, so the discussion here assumes that the plane is tangent.

All the azimuthal projections have several characteristics in common regardless of their orientation. All great circles passing through the point of tangency of the projection are straight lines radiating from that point. These lines also have the correct azimuth, which is why the term *azimuthal* is used to describe the projection. All points that are equally distant from the center of the projection on the globe are equally distant from the center of the map. (The plot of such points is called the *horizon circle*.) Places on the same horizon circle are subjected to equal distortion.

A set of azimuthal projections that are tangent at a common point but have the light source located differently, differ from one another only in terms of the radii of the horizon circles and the distance of each plotted point from the center of the projection. In the polar cases this means that the spacing of the parallels, which are all circles centered on the pole, is the only variable (Fig. 2.24).

Figure 2.24   Difference in the spacing of the parallels in the polar cases of five common azimuthal projections.

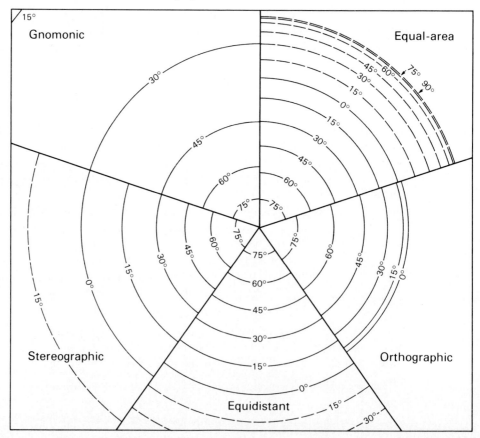

Because of the introductory nature of this discussion, only the polar cases are described here.

Orthographic projection   In the *orthographic projection,* the light source is assumed to be at *infinity,* which means that the projection rays are parallel lines (Fig. 2.25). The resulting projection is a pictorial view that is almost identical with the view that would be obtained from a distant observation point in space. The reason it is not identical to a view from space is that an observer in space would have a perspective view rather than an orthographic one. The observer would therefore see slightly less than a full hemisphere, whereas a full hemisphere may be shown on the projection.

The spacing between the parallels and meridians decreases rapidly toward the periphery of the projection. The scale also decreases in the periphery and shapes are greatly distorted. The great scale variation of this projection makes it unsuitable for most uses. The appearance of the earth as viewed from space is best illustrated by oblique views of the projection, such as the one shown in Fig. 2.26.

Stereographic projection   The location of the light source for the *stereographic projection* is the antipode of the center of the projection—that is, the point exactly opposite the point of tangency (Fig. 2.27).

A unique aspect of this projection is that, regardless of its orientation, any

Figure 2.25   Orthographic projection, polar case.

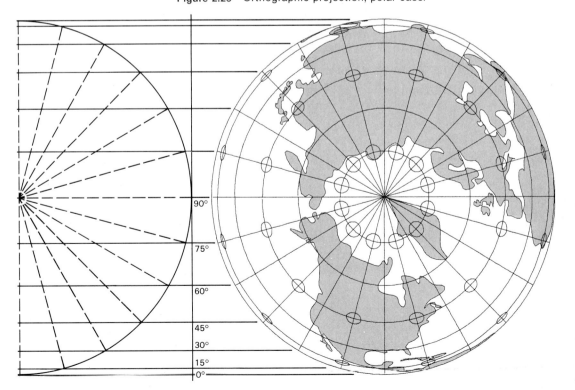

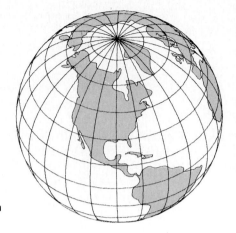

Figure 2.26 Orthographic projection
centered on Milwaukee, Wisconsin.

Figure 2.27 Stereographic projection, polar case.

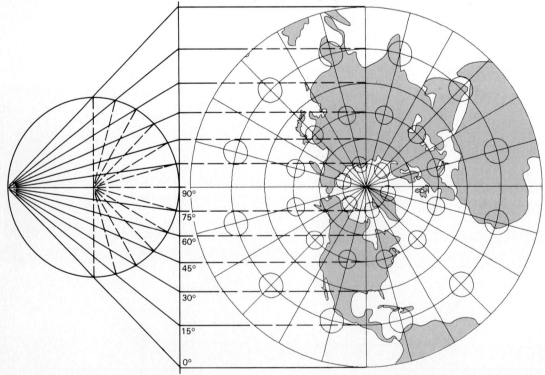

90°
75°
60°
45°
30°
15°
0°

circle drawn on the globe appears as a circle on the map; therefore, all the parallels and meridians are drawn as arcs of circles.[9] The spacing between the parallels is based on projection. The parallels and meridians intersect at right angles and, because the scale is the same in all directions at each point, the projection is conformal.

Gnomonic projection   In the *gnomonic projection,* the light source is at the center of the globe (Fig. 2.28). The spacing of the parallels therefore increases rapidly away from the center of the projection. Because the light source is at the center of the globe, it is not possible to show a full hemisphere on a gnomonic projection. The scale becomes increasingly exaggerated away from the center, so it is not practical to cover more than a portion of a hemisphere on a single projection.

The most important characteristic of this projection is that all straight lines drawn on it represent great circles. The reason for this can be visualized by remembering that any great circle is created by a plane that passes through the center of the earth and intersects the surface of the earth. If such a plane is continued out-

Figure 2.28   Gnomonic projection, polar case.

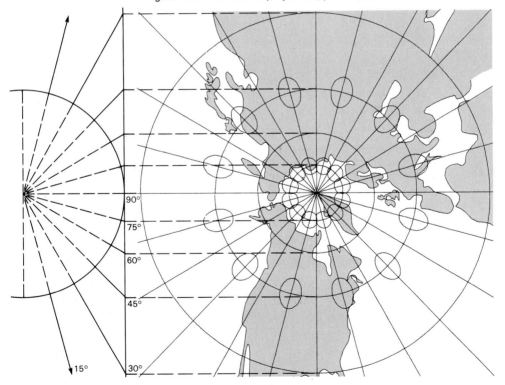

[9]An exception is the polar aspect, in which the meridians are straight lines. Here it may be argued that these lines are simply the arcs of circles of infinite radius.

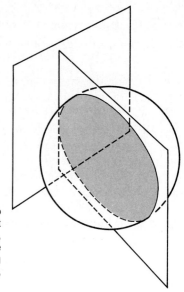

Figure 2.29   The intersection of two planes always occurs along a straight line. In the gnomonic projection, all projection planes pass through the center of the earth; the resulting great-circle plots are, therefore, straight lines on the map.

ward, it will intersect with the plane on which the projection is being made. Because the intersection of two planes always occurs along a straight line, the result is that all great-circle routes appear as straight lines on the map (Fig. 2.29).

The fact that great circles appear as straight lines on the gnomonic projection makes it very useful for navigation. It is only necessary to draw a straight line connecting any two points and that line will represent the great-circle route between them. Because almost all great-circle routes have constantly changing compass headings, they are not easy routes to steer. (The exceptions are routes that follow a meridian or a parallel, including the equator. The former are directly north or south routes; the latter are directly east or west.) The great-circle route is therefore plotted on the gnomonic projection and is transferred to the Mercator chart for navigational purposes, as described in the section on the Mercator, above.

Azimuthal equidistant projection   The *azimuthal equidistant projection* is not obtained geometrically; the radial scale is adjusted to provide correct scale. In the polar case, the parallels are concentric circles, truly spaced, centered on the pole (Fig. 2.30).

In all orientations, all points on the azimuthal equidistant are plotted at their true distance from the center of the projection and are in their true global direction from the center, hence the name. The antipodal point to the center of the projection becomes a circle with a diameter equal to the earth's circumference.

Distances and directions to and from points other than the center of the projection are not correct. Scales in directions other than along radials from the center, as well as shapes, become greatly exaggerated away from the center, especially if more than one hemisphere is shown.

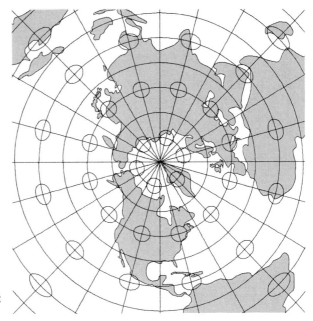

Figure 2.30 Azimuthal equidistant projection, polar case.

Lambert azimuthal equal-area projection   The radial scale of the *Lambert azimuthal equal-area projection* is adjusted to obtain the equal-area characteristic. In the polar aspect, this means that the chord distance of the parallel·from the pole is used to determine the spacing between the parallels (Fig. 2.31). The result is that the area of each zone between parallels is the same as the area of the same zone on a globe.

Tables are available to provide the necessary information so that the projection can be plotted in other aspects.

Conventional Projections

Many projections are arbitrary constructions that do not depend on "projection" in the geometric sense, and are not particularly similar to the geometric projections. In these so-called *conventional projections* the graticule is constructed on some logical or mathematical pattern. The conventional projections described here are designed to show the entire globe at once.

Sinusoidal projection   The equator of the *sinusoidal projection* is a straight line drawn to the correct length for the desired scale. The central meridian is drawn at right angles to the equator at the equator's midpoint. The central meridian is drawn half the length of the equator, which gives it the correct scale relationship (based on the assumption of a spherical shape). The central meridian is truly divided, and the parallels, which are straight lines, are drawn parallel with the equator. The equator and the parallels are truly divided, so that the meridians are truly spaced. The

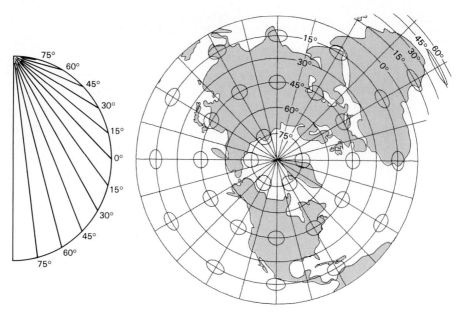

Figure 2.31   Azimuthal equal-area projection, polar case.

height of each grid square is therefore correct, as is the length of the top and bottom lines of each square. This gives the projection its equal-area characteristic.

The meridians have the shape of a sine curve, which gives the projection its name (Fig. 2.32). Because of the curve of the meridians, the angles at which they cross the parallels become increasingly acute toward the periphery of the projection. The result is an increasing distortion of shapes in those areas.

Homolographic (Mollweide) projection   Construction of the *homolographic projection* begins by drawing a circle that represents one hemisphere of the projection. A horizontal straight line is drawn through the center of the initial circle to represent the equator. The equator is continued on each side of the circle so that its total length is twice the diameter of the circle. A vertical central meridian is drawn through the same center; it is, of course, half the length of the equator. Both of these lines are of less than true length.[10]

The parallels are then drawn as horizontal straight lines parallel to the equator, at the spacing specified by a construction table. The spacings are wider than the true spacings near the equator and closer together toward the poles. The equator and the parallels are equally divided within the initial circle to establish the spacing of the meridians; this same spacing is continued along each parallel, for the required distance outside of the circle, in order to represent the other hemisphere.

[10]The radius (*r*) of a sphere, which has the same surface area as a circle, is obviously smaller than the radius (*R*) of the circle. The relationship is given by $R = r\sqrt{2}$.

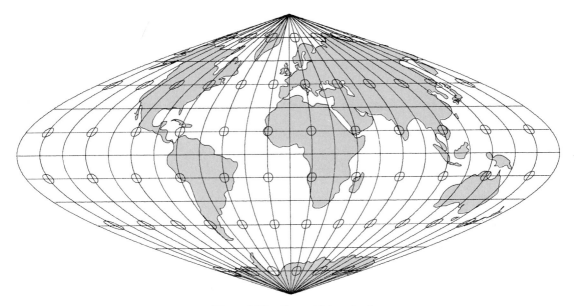

Figure 2.32 Sinusoidal projection.

The meridians that result from this construction are, in general, ellipses. The result is that the shapes in the polar areas of the homolographic are somewhat less cramped than on the sinusoidal (Fig. 2.33). The exceptions to the elliptical shape are the central meridian, which is a straight line, and the meridians 90° E and W of the central meridian, which together form a circle; both of these may be considered to be special cases of an ellipse.

The only parallels of true length on the homolographic are 40° 40′ N and S. The east-west scale along the equator and the parallels up to 40° 40′ N and S is too small; between 40° 40′ and the poles, the east-west scale is too long. These scale differences offset the progressively closer spacing of the parallels, resulting in the equal-area characteristic of the projection.

Homolosine (Goode's) projection   The *homolosine projection* is the result of a merger of the homolographic and sinusoidal projections. Because the scale along the parallels of the homolographic is true at 40° 40′, and the scale along all parallels is true on the sinusoidal, the two projections are identical at that latitude. In order to take advantage of the best-shaped areas of each, the equatorial portion of the sinusoidal and the polar portions of the homolographic are joined along the line of true scale (Fig. 2.34).

The homolosine projection is interrupted so that the major continental areas are each approximately centered on their own central meridian. This interruption reduces the amount of skewing and the related shape distortion in the higher latitudes.

Alternatively, the interruptions are placed on the continental areas and the

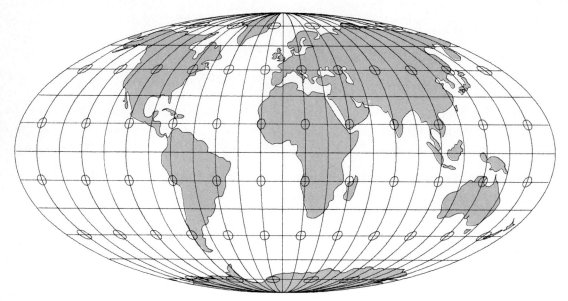

Figure 2.33   Homolographic (Mollweide) projection.

major oceanic areas are centered on their own central meridians. The result is an equal-area map of the oceans.

Hammer projection   The *Hammer projection*[11] is very similar in form to the homolographic except that its parallels are curved rather than straight (Fig. 2.35). This provides somewhat better shapes in the peripheral areas of the projection because the crossings of the meridians and parallels are closer to the correct right angle. The major characteristic of the projection is that it is equal-area.

Eckert IV projection   All of the projections in the *Eckert family* represent the poles as a line one-half the length of the equator. Differences in the shapes of the meridians and in the spacings between the parallels result in several different projections, each of which is called a "case." The most commonly used projection from this group is known as the Eckert IV.

In the Eckert IV, the equator is a line of correct length and the central meridian is a line one-half the length of the equator, drawn at right angles to it (Fig. 2.36). The pole is a line that is also one-half the length of the equator. The meridians are ellipses and the parallels are horizontal lines, spaced so that projection is equal-area. A tangent circle is drawn on either side of the central meridian to form the outer meridians. The parallels are equally divided.

The angles of intersection of the meridians and parallels are not as extreme

---

[11]The name Hammer is used here, rather than Aitoff-Hammer, which is sometimes used. See John B. Leighly, "Aitoff and Hammer," *Geographical Review,* 45 (1955), 246–49.

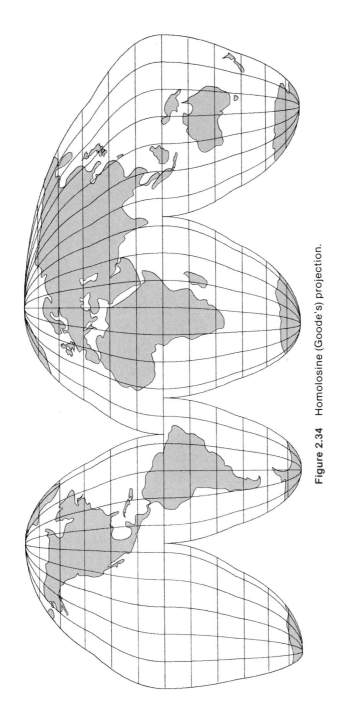

Figure 2.34 Homolosine (Goode's) projection.

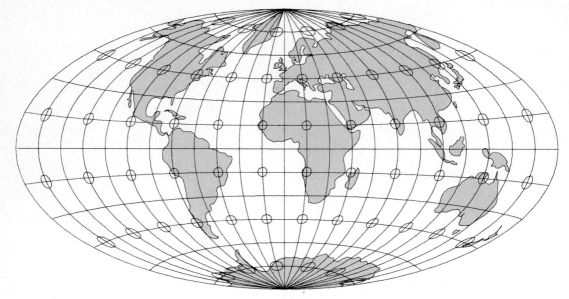

Figure 2.35   Hammer projection.

toward the periphery as in the homolographic. For that reason, the Eckert IV provides better shapes in the polar regions.

Selection of Projections

The characteristics of the available map projections are taken into consideration when a selection is made for a particular application.[12] The first decision is to select the major characteristic—shape, equivalence, direction, or distance—that is the most important consideration in relation to the purpose of the map. Once this choice is made, the class of projections from which the final choice will be made is determined. Obtaining the most important characteristic results in the distortion of other, potentially important characteristics, so the choice inevitably involves some compromise with the ideal result. The cartographer, therefore, must finally select the projection that best meets the specific needs and, at the same time, does the least damage to the other desirable characteristics. In fact, if none of the listed characteristics is of outstanding importance, the use of a compromise projection may be preferred.

The following discussion centers on the selection of projections for medium- to small-scale maps. The choices for large-scale maps, such as topographic sheets and navigation charts, have already been made by the appropriate agencies. The Mercator and gnomonic projections are utilized for navigation charts, for example,

[12]Chapters 9–11 of D. H. Maling, *Coordinate Systems and Map Projections* (London: George Philip and Son Limited, 1973), are especially recommended for a detailed discussion of this topic.

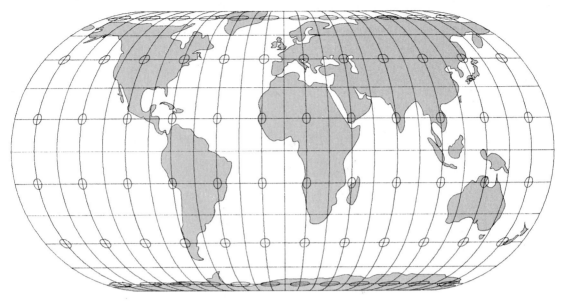

Figure 2.36 Eckert IV projection.

because of the characteristics discussed earlier. Similarly, the Lambert conformal conic projection is frequently used for mid-latitude air charts because straight lines drawn on it very closely approximate great-circle routes. Also, in recent years conformal projections, such as the transverse Mercator, have been increasingly utilized for topographical maps.

Basic considerations   The size of the area being mapped has an influence on the selection of a projection. If a relatively small area is involved, such as one of the European countries, or one of the states in the United States, there is no real difficulty. The amount of distortion on virtually any projection would be difficult to detect at the usual map scale, provided it is centered in the vicinity of the center of the area which is to be mapped. In this case, the choice will likely be determined by the projection on which available base maps are drawn. When an area the size of a continent is involved, however, the amount of distortion can become extreme, so the selection is much more difficult and important.

The latitude of the area to be mapped is important as well, because the location of the areas of zero distortion varies among the different classes of projection. In the areas near the equator, for example, cylindrical projections tend to be favored because the cylinder, in the normal orientation, is tangent along the equator, which is the standard line. The standard line, or lines, of the conical projections are along the parallels, which makes them a likely choice for an area in the middle latitudes. Pole-centered azimuthal projections are suitable for areas near the poles because the amount of distortion is at a minimum at the pole and increases toward the lower latitudes. Different versions of this class of projection have special characteristics, including correct distances from the center or equivalence.

The shape of the area to be mapped also influences the choice of projection, because of the different direction of the lines of zero distortion of each particular projection. When the area is long in one direction and narrow in the other, the line of zero distortion should be aligned along its long axis. The polyconic, Bonne, sinusoidal, and transverse Mercator projections, for example, are useful for mapping areas that are long in the north-south direction but have little east-west extent. This is because their area of least distortion lies along their central meridian. The central meridian is aligned through the approximate center of the area to be mapped, in order to utilize the zone of least distortion. One of these projections would be useful in the case of Chile, for example.

Conic projections are particularly good for maps of areas in the middle latitudes, as already suggested, especially for areas with considerable east-west extent and relatively less north-south extent. The Lambert conformal and Albers equal-area projections, for example, are useful for such areas, because of their excellent characteristics. In the case of the United States, the long dimension of the country runs from east to west; maps of this country on either the Lambert or Albers projection are very common.

Because of the introductory nature of this chapter, the suggestions above do not include any consideration of "unorthodox" centering or orientation to take further advantage of the characteristics of particular projections. In the past, the cost in time and effort of preparing such especially designed graticules was often prohibitive. It seems likely, however, that special selections will be more feasible in the future because of the flexibility introduced by computer-assisted methods. When the appropriate geographic data base is available, the computation of any desired projection, centered at a preferred location and with a particular orientation, is now a relatively simple, not overly expensive, option (see Chapter 11).

Other examples   The following examples illustrate some additional, typical uses that take into account the specific attributes of particular projections.

The mapping of areal distributions is best done on equal-area projections. This is because it is important to be able to compare the area occupied by a particular phenomenon in one part of the world with the areas occupied in other parts of the world. The equal-area projections, by definition, allow such comparisons to be made. Conformal projections, on the other hand, are useful when compass directions between locations are important. The Mercator, for example, is used when it is important to record direction accurately, as in plotting winds and ocean currents.

Four azimuthal projections have particular applications. The azimuthal equidistant, for example, is useful when it is centered on points of origin other than the pole. It is then used for determining airline distances and directions from the origin to any other place in the world. The oblique aspects of the orthographic projection, on the other hand, are used to represent views of the earth from space. The difference between the projection and the actual perspective of an observer in space is so slight it is unnoticeable to most users. The third type, the stereographic projection, is often used for plotting purposes when radiating patterns are involved. Any circle plotted from the globe will appear as a circle on the stereographic. Finally, the gnomonic projection is useful for radio or seismic work because the waves involved in such studies travel in approximately great-circle directions and are therefore plotted as straight lines on the gnomonic.

Map Grids

Grid references are often added to maps for the sake of convenience. This involves preparing a map, using a projection with the desired characteristics, and plotting the earth's features in terms of their latitudinal and longitudinal positions. A square pattern of arbitrary grid lines is then superimposed on the map (Fig. 2.37). This grid is used as a system for referring to desired points, instead of using latitude and longitude.

Typically, the grid is based on a starting point that is located to the south and west of the mapped area, so that the coordinates used for location purposes are always positive numbers, reading to the east (right) and north (up) from the origin. When the origin is outside the area plotted on the projection it is referred to as a false origin.

The grid system may be a simple, square locational grid, such as is frequently

Figure 2.37 UTM and state plane coordinate grid lines superimposed on a portion of the earth's graticule. (Based on a portion of USGS Pleasant Prairie quadrangle, Wisconsin, 1971.)

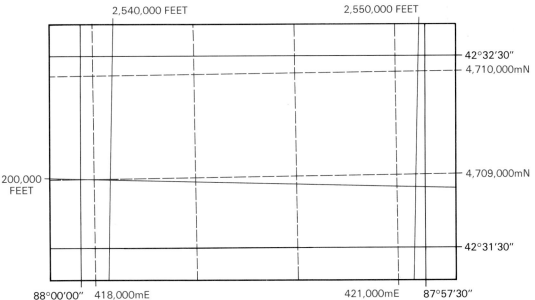

2,540,000 FEET   2,550,000 FEET

42°32′30″
4,710,000mN

4,709,000mN

200,000
FEET

42°31′30″

88°00′00″   418,000mE   421,000mE   87°57′30″

encountered on street or highway maps, which requires little explanation. Two important grid systems that have broader applications are in use—these are the *state plane coordinate* system and the *Universal Transverse Mercator* system. The importance of these systems warrants describing them in some detail.

State plane coordinates   In the United States, the state plane coordinate system provides, for each state, a framework of rectangular coordinates that are used for identifying locations within the state. This is particularly useful as a reference system for local surveys. In this application the state plane coordinate system allows surveying and mapping computations to be done as though the earth were a plane, thus eliminating the need to consider spherical trigonometry. At the same time, however, the surveys are incorporated into the national geodetic horizontal network with an error of less than 1 part in 10,000 (see Chapter 3).

The system is based on the use of conformal map projections. The Lambert conformal conic is used for states having large extent east-west and the transverse Mercator for states having large extent north-south. Each state is divided into zones as necessary, so that each zone is approximately 150 mi wide. A separate projection surface is established for each zone. In the case of Lambert conformal projections the zones extend east-west, whereas the zones for the transverse Mercator extend north-south.

A *false origin* is assigned to each zone. It is usually a point 2,000,000 ft west of the central meridian and somewhat south of the south edge of the zone. A square grid is based on this origin and measurements are made, in feet, from the origin, with grid lines established at 1000 ft intervals. The location of any required point is stated in terms of its distance east and north of the particular false origin. The state and zone in which the feature is located is also identified. As an aid to surveyors, the location of every triangulated or leveled point in the state is determined and listed in terms of the state grid coordinates.

An example of the use of state plane coordinates is shown in Fig. 2.38. The location of the northernmost tip of the runway of the Kenosha Airport is marked on a portion of the United States Geological Survey (USGS) 1:24,000 Pleasant Prairie quadrangle. The original map, which is shown here in color, includes only short marginal tick marks to identify the grid locations. In this figure, for purposes of clarity, the full grid is added in black. The designations of the grid lines are also added in black. On the actual map only some of the lines are identified, as indicated by the colored numbers at the upper right. In addition, a considerable amount of marginal information is deleted from the map so that the use of the grid will be clear. Based on this grid, the runway corner lies in the grid square between 2,550,000 ft E and 2,560,000 ft E and between 220,000 ft N and 230,000 ft N. Estimated to the nearest 10 ft, the exact location is 2,557,910 ft E; 225,360 ft N; Wisconsin; S (for South zone).

Beginning in 1983, the state plane coordinate system is being revised and tied in with the North American Datum of 1983 (see Chapter 3). The basic approach is the same as in the earlier system. The main difference is that it is based on the

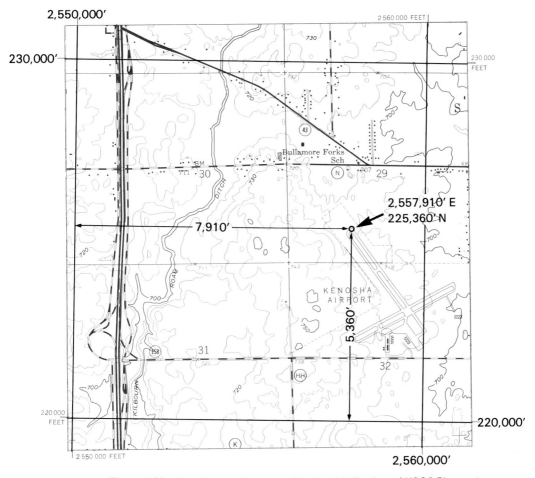

Figure 2.38 Use of state plane coordinate grid. (Portion of USGS Pleasant Prairie quadrangle, Wisconsin, 1971. Original scale 1:24,000—illustration reduced.)

Universal Transverse Mercator projection throughout (although the Lambert projection is retained in Michigan). The plane coordinates are in meters in the new system, instead of in feet. This is in line with the trend toward the use of metric units throughout the mapping professions.

Universal Transverse Mercator system   This system is based on the Universal Transverse Mercator (UTM) projection with two standard lines, between 80° S and 84° N. It is used in conjunction with the Universal Polar Stereographic (UPS) projection that covers the polar caps.

The UTM system involves establishing 60 north-south zones, each 6 degrees of longitude wide [Fig. 2.39(a)]. Some overlap is provided into the adjoining zones.

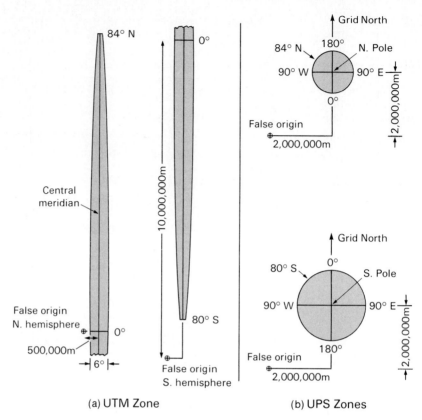

(a) UTM Zone   (b) UPS Zones

Figure 2.39 Universal Transverse Mercator and Universal Polar Stereographic zones. (a) UTM Zone; (b) UPS Zone.

This allows easy reference to points near a zone boundary regardless of which zone is in use for a particular project.

A transverse Mercator projection is centered on each zone, with the cylinder of projection secant with the globe. The two standard lines for each zone, which are not meridians, are located 180,000 m each side of the central meridian. The scale on the central meridian is therefore slightly too small (its scale factor is 0.9996), whereas at the edge of the zone the scale is slightly too great (a scale factor of 1.00155 would be reached on the grid lines located 400,000 m each side of the central meridian).

In the UPS system, two polar zones are established, using the polar stereographic projection [Fig. 2.39(b)]. The northern zone extends from the 84th parallel to the pole and the southern zone is from the 80th parallel to the pole, each with a slight overlap into the UTM zones. The projection plane is secant at 81° 06′ so that the scale between that parallel and the pole is too small and the scale outside it is too large.

Two methods are used to identity locations using the UTM and UPS systems. The first is intended for civilian use and the second for military use. The basic framework is the same for both schemes but, because the civilian system is most commonly encountered, it is described here.

Civilian system   First, false origins are established 500,000 m west of the central meridian of each UTM zone. In the Northern Hemisphere these origins are on the equator and in the Southern Hemisphere they are 10,000,000 m south of the equator. A square grid, with the lines spaced 100,000 m apart, is extended north and east from each origin to provide a basic locational framework. Within this framework any point on the earth's surface within each zone has a unique coordinate.

A locational grid system is imposed on the two polar (UPS) projections, as well. Grid north is arbitrarily established so that the prime meridian is at the top-center of the south zone and the 180th meridian is at the top-center of the north zone. These grids have an origin that is located at the lower left corner of each grid, 200,000 m to the left and 200,000 m down from the pole.

The first step in locating a feature is to identify the zone and hemisphere within which it lies. Assume, for example that the location of the Kenosha Airport is to

Figure 2.40   Use of UTM coordinate grid. (Portion of USGS Pleasant Prairie quadrangle, Wisconsin, 1971. Original scale 1:24,000—illustration reduced.)

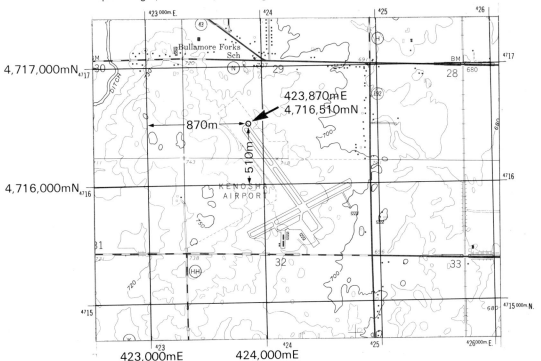

be specified. Kenosha is located in zone 16 in the Northern Hemisphere, so this is the first portion of the locational description. The specific location in relation to the origin is then determined. This location is specified in terms of eastings (distances measured from west to east) and northings (distances measured from south to north).

The UTM coordinates are shown on the edges of many topographic maps. A portion of the USGS 1:24,000 Pleasant Prairie quadrangle is shown in color in Fig. 2.40. A considerable amount of extraneous marginal information is deleted so that the UTM system is more clearly shown. Note that the UTM grid designations are abbreviated in most locations—this involves omitting the last three zeroes and showing designations of 100,000 or more in smaller type. In this figure, for purposes of clarity, the full identification numbers for a portion of the grid are overlaid in black. The grid itself is also shown in black, although it is indicated only by short blue tick marks in the margins of the original.

As an example of the use of the UTM grid system, the northernmost tip of the runway of the Kenosha Airport is again identified in the figure. It is located in the UTM grid square that lies between 423,000 m E and 424,000 m E and between 4,716,000 m N and 4,717,000 m N. Within the neareast 10 m, the exact location is 870 m east and 510 m north of the southwest corner of the grid square. The full citation for the location, is therefore given as UTM Northern Hemisphere, zone 16; 423870-4716510.

Because the location reference uses only numbers, it is easily handled by computer systems, which is an advantage in many applications.

Suggested Readings

DEETZ, C. H., and O. S. ADAMS, *Elements of Map Projection with Applications to Map and Chart Construction,* Special Publication No. 68 (5th rev. ed.). Washington, D.C.: U.S. Department of Commerce, Coast and Geodetic Survey (now National Geodetic Survey), 1944. A standard source regarding many aspects of map projections.

DEPARTMENT OF ENERGY, MINES AND RESOURCES, *The Universal Transverse Mercator Grid: As Applied to National Topographic System Maps of Canada.* Ottawa: Department of Energy, Mines and Resources, 1969.

DEPARTMENT OF THE ARMY, *Universal Transverse Mercator Grid,* TM5-241-8. Headquarters, Department of the Army, Washington, D.C., April 1973.

FISHER, IRVING, and O. M. MILLER, *World Maps and Globes.* New York: Essential Books, 1944. Nonmathematical approach to the concept of map projections and to the description of several of the more common projections.

GRIME, A. R., *The Earth Grid.* Scarborough, Ont.: Bellhaven House Limited, 1970.

HOFFMEISTER, H. A., *Construction of Map Projections.* Bloomington, Ill.: McKnight & McKnight, 1946. Simplified, mostly geometrical, methods of construction for 21 common projections.

KELLAWAY, GEORGE P., *Map Projections.* London: Methuen and Co. Ltd., 1949 (reprinted 1970).

MALING, D. H., *Coordinate Systems and Map Projections.* London: George Philip and Son Limited, 1973. Highly recommended, modern quantitative treatment. Requires knowledge of plane geometry and spherical trigonometry and some calculus.

MCDONNELL, PORTER W., JR., *Introduction to Map Projections.* New York: Marcel Dekker, Inc., 1979.

MITCHELL, H. C., and L. G. SIMMONS, *The State Coordinate Systems: A Manual for Surveyors,* Special Publication No. 235. Washington, D.C.: Department of Commerce, Coast and Geodetic Survey (now National Geodetic Survey), 1945.

RICHARDUS, PETER, and RON K. ADLER, *Map Projections for Geodesists, Cartographers and Geographers.* Amsterdam: North-Holland Publishing Company, 1972.

STEERS, J. A., An Introduction to the Study of Map Projections (14th ed.). London: University of London Press, Ltd., 1965. Uses simple trigonometry to explain the process of projection, as well as many commonly used projections.

3

Large-Scale Mapping: Filling in the Graticule

The physical and cultural features shown on a map are first located in relation to the worldwide system of latitude and longitude. They are then plotted on the graticule of the particular map projection that is being used. Their elevation is also related to a *vertical datum,* or starting level. Unless these ties are provided, each map remains an individual entity that cannot be directly related to other maps or to the rest of the world.

The reference framework for horizontal locations is a *geodetic control network.* This network consists of a set of points whose latitudinal and longitudinal location and elevation are precisely determined and recorded and that are identified on the ground by permanent *monuments.* When these control points are established, additional measurements are taken, using the monuments as starting points, to determine the relative horizontal positions of other points.

Separate networks of control points are established through leveling surveys in order to provide a vertical reference framework. This vertical control network is identified on the ground by permanent *benchmarks* and the elevation of the benchmarks above a common datum is recorded.

HORIZONTAL CONTROL

Establishing the primary, horizontal control network requires determining the latitudinal and longitudinal positions of the control points through a process known as *triangulation.* This involves defining a starting line, called a *baseline,* and finding the latitude and longitude of its end points. From this baseline a network of straight lines is extended to the desired control points. The angles formed at the corners of the network are measured and the techniques of trigonometry are used to determine distances and locations within the network. In doing this work, allowance is made for the detailed shape of the earth through the use of *spherical trigonometry.*

The portion of the horizontal framework that is measured to the highest level of accuracy is called the *first-order* (primary) network. Once the first-order network is established, *second-* and *third-order* networks can be set up within it. These networks provide the denser array of control points that is needed as a base for local surveys; starting local surveys from geodetic control points ensures that any survey errors that are introduced will not be cumulative and also ties separate surveys together.

The difference between the three orders of triangulation networks is simply that the accuracy requirements are less exacting as one moves down the hierarchy. In the lower orders of survey, the types of instruments used are less precise, the time spent is less extensive, and the expense involved is decreased. First-order network measurements must be accurate within 1 part in 25,000; second-order measurements, within 1 part in 10,000; and third-order measurements, within 1 part in 5000. Measurements that are less accurate, but still accurate enough to result in "no appreciable map error," are referred to as *fourth-order* measurements.

Baseline Determination

The first step in setting up a triangulation network is establishing the baseline on which the rest of the network is built. In the United States today, baselines are usually about 8 to 15 mi in length, although longer lines were common in the past. After the locations of the end points of the baseline are selected, their latitudes and longitudes are determined, using the astronomical observation methods described in Chapter 1.

High elevations that are visible from one another are favored locations for survey end points. In the absence of suitable natural elevations, special towers are erected to lift the observer and the instruments above the surrounding terrain. Towers may be necessary even in flat terrain because the curvature of the earth limits the distance that can be observed from ground level (Fig. 3.1). At times, relatively permanent structures are built, although it is sometimes possible to use a more easily erected and dismantled prefabricated steel tower for the purpose. Whichever type is used, the structure usually consists of two separate elements; one of these is an inner tripod that supports the instruments and the other is an outer platform on which the observer stands. The physical separation of the two elements prevents the instrument from shifting as the observer changes position on the platform.

If the line is to be measured using tapes, it is located so that the measurements can be conducted along as clear and level a route as possible. These considerations are not a factor if electronic measuring devices are used because such instruments only require an unbroken line of sight.

Before measurements are taken, the instruments are precisely aligned over the monuments that mark the exact location of the control points. When the instru-

Figure 3.1 Elevation increases observation distance.

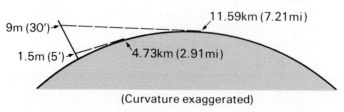

9m (30')
11.59km (7.21mi)
1.5m (5')
4.73km (2.91mi)

(Curvature exaggerated)

ments are placed on the ground the alignment is accomplished by the use of an *optical plummet*. This device is built into the instrument that will be used to take the angular or distance observations and takes the place of the more traditional plumb bob. The plummet allows the operator to sight through the center of the instrument in an exact vertical direction as determined by the pull of gravity. The position of the instrument is adjusted so that the control mark is exactly centered in the viewfinder of the plummet. When the instruments are placed in a tower, a similar alignment process is carried out using slightly different instruments that are usually located on the ground under the tower.

Nighttime observations are frequently used for geodetic surveys so that *light signals* can be utilized. These signals are clearly visible for much longer distances than are regular visual targets in the daytime. Observations taken after dark also generally encounter less of the distortion that results from heat radiation from the earth's surface.

Deflection of the vertical Locations obtained by the use of astronomical observations are established with reference to the geoid. This is because the instruments are aligned by the use of plumb bobs, optical plummets, or levels that respond to the pull of gravity. If the earth were a regular figure of uniform mass, determining the direction of vertical would not be complicated—a plumb bob held anywhere above its surface would point to its center. Because the earth is not a regular figure of uniform mass, however, the direction in which gravity pulls varies from place to place. A plumb bob, therefore, will not necessarily point toward the center of the earth, but may instead be deflected away from the true vertical direction. The difference between the actual vertical and the observed vertical is called the *deflection of the vertical* (Fig. 3.2).

Because the amount of the deflection of the vertical varies from place to place, the error in the latitude and longitude observations made at different locations also

Figure 3.2 Deflection of the vertical.

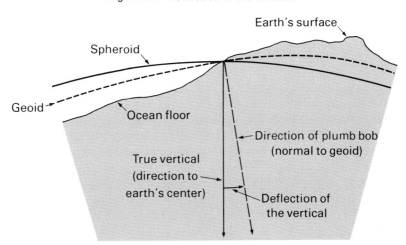

varies. The existence of this variation means that the relationship between the latitude and longitude observations made at different points is not absolutely consistent. It is necessary, therefore, to take steps to compensate for the variation introduced by the deflection of the vertical. One means of doing this is to determine, by observation, the latitude and longitude of several locations connected by the same triangulation network. The observed locations are then compared with the expected locations, based on measurements from a single starting point. The differences are then averaged out over the stations and adjusted coordinates are used in place of the observed locations. This method involves compromise and judgment, but it does allow consistency within the network. Another method of compensating for the deflection of the vertical involves detailed gravimetric surveying to determine the undulation of the geoid. Once the detailed form of the geoid is known, it is possible to modify individual astronomical observations on the basis of the expected deflection of the vertical at the point of observation.

In the United States, the location of the origin of the nationwide triangulation network has been determined on the basis of an analysis of many individual geographical locations in the major control network, as established by individual astronomical observations. This datum is centered on a monument located at Meade's Ranch, Kansas. This is the origin point for the control network called the North American Datum of 1927, which is used for the national mapping systems of Canada and Mexico as well as the United States. The network is based on Clarke's 1866 spheroid. Positions in the network have been recalculated for use in connection with the North American Datum of 1983, which is based on a different ellipsoid (see Table 1.1).

Measurement techniques   The length of the baseline itself must be measured with the greatest possible accuracy. One method of doing this involves the use of special tapes. These tapes, which are typically 50 m long, are made of *invar*. Invar is a nickel and steel alloy that is very stable in relation to temperature change; it has a *coefficient of expansion* that averages only about one-tenth that of steel. Prior to use, the exact length of each tape is determined by careful testing in the certification laboratory of the National Bureau of Standards. This testing is carried out by comparing the tape against a standard measure under strictly controlled conditions of temperature, tension, and support.

In use, the invar tape is supported on a flat surface, or is suspended on several tripods, in order to reduce measurement errors due to *sag*. A *standard tension* is also established in the direction of the line by suspending weights from the ends of the tape or by using a spring balance to measure the pull on the tape. One end of the tape is lined up over the starting mark and a temporary mark is made at the other end of the tape. The tape is then moved and the process is repeated until the mark at the other end of the line is reached. The reading at the end of the run, of course, is usually a fraction of the full length of the tape. The number of full lengths, plus the fraction at the end, is recorded and is used to compute the nominal distance between the end points. The direction of measurement is maintained by observation from the end of the line, using a theodolite. As part of the procedure, each measurement is carried out several times and the results of the several sets of observations are averaged together; this ensures that the effect of any error that may occur in an individual observation will be greatly reduced.

When the nominal measurement of the baseline has been taken, certain corrections are introduced to obtain the refined measurement. The first of these takes into account the actual length of the tape as determined by the standards test. Other corrections may be necessary to compensate for any differences from standard conditions that occurred during the measurement process. These include corrections for ground slope, differences in temperature at the time of measurement as compared to the temperature at the time of standardization, differences in the number and placement of supports, and variations in tension. Finally, the length is mathematically adjusted to the datum level—that is, to what it would be if it were measured at sea level. This adjustment is required because the distance measured on the topographic surface is longer than the measurement on the geoidal surface would be, even though the angular distance (latitudinal and/or longitudinal distance) between the points is the same. This is because the two surfaces are at different distances from the center of the earth (Fig. 3.3). (At certain locations, such as Death Valley, the topographic surface lies below the geoidal surface and the opposite correction is needed.)

Recently, *electronic distance measuring* devices have come into use. These utilize, for example, infrared light waves, microwaves, laser light beams, or radio waves. The use of these devices involves centering a *transmitter-receiver* unit [Fig. 3.4(a)] over the mark established at one end of the line that is to be measured. A *retransmitter* is placed over the mark at the other end. A beam of the required type is then sent from the transmitter to the retransmitter and is returned to the receiver; the length of time required for the signal to make the round trip is accurately re-

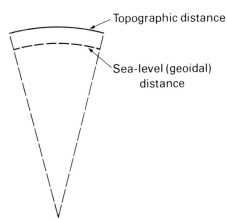

Topographic distance

Sea-level (geoidal) distance

Figure 3.3 Difference between topographic and geoidal distances between points located equal angular distance apart.

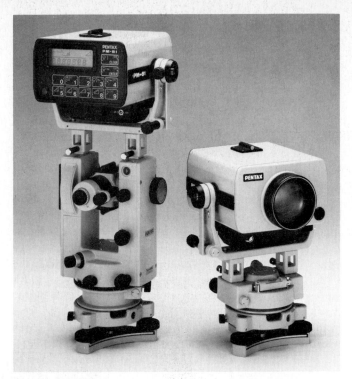

(a)

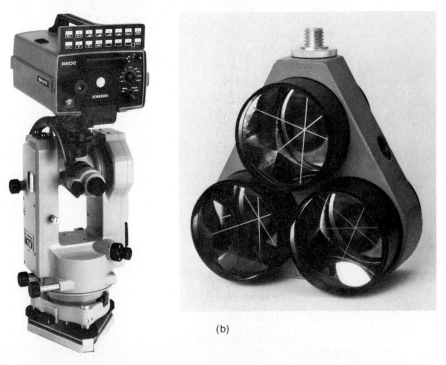

(b)

Figure 3.4 Electronic distance measuring equipment. (a) Transmitter-receiver unit with retransmitter. (Courtesy of Topcon Instrument Corp. of America.) (b) Transmitter-receiver unit and reflector. (Courtesy of The Lietz Co.)

corded. Alternatively, a transmitter-receiver unit is placed at one mark and a set of *reflective prisms* is placed over the other [Fig. 3.4(b)]. Because the waves travel at a known speed, the recorded time measurement can be converted to a measurement of the total distance the beam traveled; this distance, divided in half, is the distance between the two end points. The temperature and other atmospheric conditions at the time of the transmission are also noted and their effect on the speed at which the wave traveled is taken into account when the distance calculation is performed. Some instruments automatically introduce the necessary corrections for atmospheric conditions and give a direct, digital readout of the distance between points.

Electronic distance measuring devices have variable ranges, but one type can be used for first-order measurements of up to 50 km in length, with an average error of ±3 ppm. Distances of up to 100 km can be measured with almost equal accuracy by some of the devices. One model has an accuracy of ±1-2 cm, at a range of 1 km. Because of the effect of atmospheric conditions on these instruments, observations are improved by working at night when conditions tend to be more stable.

Whatever techniques are used to carry out the baseline measurement, its accuracy is critical. This is because the baseline is the only distance in the triangulation network that is actually measured; the lengths of the sides in the rest of the survey are determined solely by triangulation. This means that the computations by which the lengths are determined are based on the angular measurements in the system in relation to the length of the baseline. To the extent that any errors in a geodetic survey are left unresolved, the additional surveys that are based on it will be equally inaccurate. The techniques used in the geodetic survey are selected carefully, and are executed as accurately as possible, so that the high accuracy standards are met.

Primary Triangulation Network

Upon completion of the baseline measurement, three things are known about the line: the coordinates of its starting and ending points; its direction, or azimuth; and its length. The baseline is then used as the reference line for the rest of the primary triangulation network (Fig. 3.5). The locations of the trigonometric stations that make up this network are selected so that there is an unbroken line of sight between the stations to be observed from one another. As with the end points of the baseline, hill tops, tall buildings, and other high points are favored and, if necessary, towers are erected.

From the stations at each end of the baseline the angles between the other visible stations in the network are measured, again using a theodolite. To accomplish this, the theodolite is first sighted from one base station to the other and its angular reading is determined. It is then sighted on a station in the network and a second angular reading is taken. The difference between the two measurements is the angle between the two stations, as viewed from the base station. This process

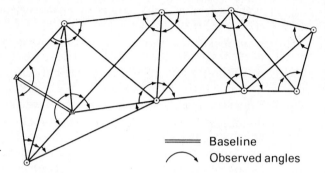

Figure 3.5 Typical primary triangulation network.

Baseline
Observed angles

is repeated, with the instruments turned in a prescribed sequence in order to minimize the chance of mechanical error, until angles for all of the desired stations are determined. The entire set of measurements is also repeated a number of times in order to average out any possible errors. The instruments are then moved to the second base station, sightings are taken from it to the same stations that were observed from the first base station, and the relevant angles are again recorded.

Because the baseline makes up one side of a triangle, and its length and the angles at each end are known, it is possible to calculate the lengths of the other sides of the triangles as well as the coordinates of the observed stations [Fig. 3.6(a)]. The network is extended by moving from station to station and measuring the angles to the other stations. At times, not all the lines can be observed from both ends. The steeple of a church, for example, may be observable from a number of locations but it may be impossible to use it as an observation station. When this type of situation occurs it is taken into consideration in determining whether or not the network meets the accuracy requirements for the survey.

Strength of net A minimal triangulation network consists of a series of interconnected triangles called a *weak net* [Fig. 3.6(b)]. In order to provide a higher level of accuracy, however, additional angles must be measured. This allows cross-checking and the adjustment of any inconsistencies that may occur in an individual measurement. Some strengthening of the network results from using a pattern called a *completed quadrilateral*. This consists of a relatively rectangular pattern, with the interior angles of both diagonals measured at the corners [Fig. 3.6(c)]. An even stronger net is the *polygon with central station,* which involves placing an additional station near the center of the quadrilateral (or any other polygon) and measuring the additional angles that are created [Fig. 3.6(d)].

Calculation of the strength of net that is needed to meet the requirements of a particular survey is based on a preliminary reconnaissance to establish the probable arrangement of the stations and the approximate distances and angles between them. This calculation takes into account such factors as the sizes of the angles that will be observed; the number of lines that will be observed, and whether they will be observed from both ends or from one end only; and the number of stations

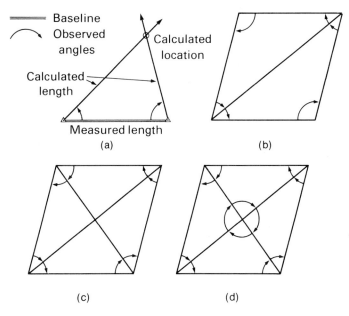

Figure 3.6 (a) Measurements obtained by triangulation. Triangulation networks of increasing strength: (b) Weak net. (c) Completed quadrilateral. (d) Polygon with central station.

involved, including stations from which observations may be taken as well as stations that can only be observed.

Spherical excess In plane geometry the interior angles of a triangle always add up to exactly 180 degrees. In spherical geometry, however, the sum of the angles in a triangle exceeds 180 degrees. This is a phenomenon called the *spherical excess,* and it occurs because the measurements are being taken on a three-dimensional, almost spherical object.

The reason for the existence of the spherical excess can be appreciated by considering a very large triangle on the earth's surface. Assume that one corner of this triangle is at the intersection of the prime meridian and the equator; by definition, this is a 90-degree angle [Fig. 3.7(a)]. Next, assume that the second corner is at the intersection of the meridian at 90° W longitude and the equator; again, this is a 90-degree angle. Finally, note that the two meridians involved, which form the two long sides of a triangle, converge at the pole, in this case at an angle of 90 degrees. The sum of the three angles in this triangle, then, is 270 degrees. This outcome is impossible in a triangle drawn on a plane surface because it is impossible to have more than one 90-degree angle; if there are two 90-degree angles, the sides adjacent to those right angles are parallel and can never converge to form a triangle [Fig. 3.7(b)].

Although no triangle in a survey network covers the large area described here, some spherical excess is encountered in the smaller triangles that are actually in-

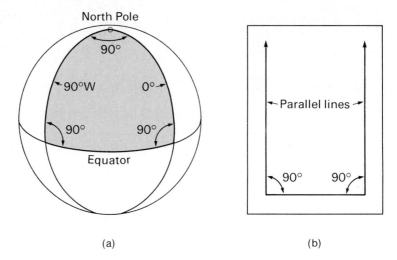

Figure 3.7 (a) Extremely large spherical triangle; corner angles total to more than 180 degrees. (b) Ninety-degree angles drawn on a plane result in parallel lines that never meet.

volved. The amount of the spherical excess is proportional to the area of the triangle and, because of the slight flattening of the earth, is also affected by the average latitude of its vertices. For our purposes, it is sufficient to realize that the spherical excess exists and that geodetic surveying involves the use of mathematical procedures to eliminate its effect when the lengths of the sides of the network are calculated.

Adjustments   If the stations in the network are not at the same elevation, the vertical angles of elevation or depression between them are also measured. This is necessary because any vertical difference increases the length of the measured distance, compared to the true horizontal distance between the two points, and appropriate adjustments must be made (Fig. 3.8).

As the extension of the triangulation network continues, additional measurements are taken in order to check the accuracy of the overall process and to make needed adjustments. One means of checking is to establish supplementary baselines and to compare their length, as measured on the ground, with their theoretical

Figure 3.8   Difference between observed distance and horizontal distance resulting from altitude difference.

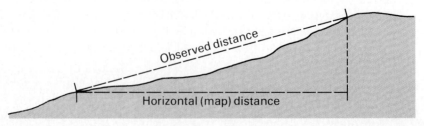

length, as calculated on the basis of the triangulation. Supplementary baselines are now much easier to establish because the use of electronic devices greatly speeds up the process of taking the measurements. Another check is to determine the azimuth of a side of the network by astronomical observation and to compare it with the calculated azimuth. Check angles may also be measured between pairs of stations that were not included in the network itself to see if they match the calculated values. Finally, the astronomical coordinates of a station may be determined and compared with the calculated coordinates, provided the magnitude of the deflection from the vertical is known.

Trilateration

Electronic distance measuring equipment has greatly decreased the difficulties inherent in distance measurement. Very long lines, as much as 500 mi in length, can be measured, using radar-based systems such as Shoran or Hiran. It has therefore become feasible to develop geodetic control networks through the process of *trilateration,* which involves measuring distances instead of angles.

Using trilateration, it is relatively simple to cross significant water bodies in order to tie islands into a mainland control network or to forge an interconnection between control networks in adjacent areas. One Hiran network has been established to tie North America to Europe, for example, and another connects some of the islands of the Caribbean to continental South America.

A trilateration network starts from a measured baseline whose azimuth is known, as are the latitude and longitude of its end points. The network is extended by measuring the lengths of the sides of triangles, which are arranged in the same manner as the sides of a triangulation network (Fig. 3.9). The calculation of the latitudes and longitudes of the other control points is based on the lengths of the sides instead of the sizes of the angles between the sides as is the case with triangulation.

Satellite Observations

As technology improves, observations of earth satellites are increasingly used to determine the relationship between ground positions. The techniques used are based, for example, on the observation of light waves or radio waves transmitted from a

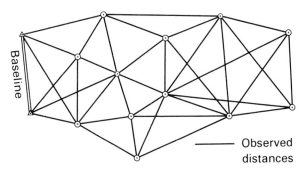

Figure 3.9 Typical trilateration network.

———— Observed
distances

satellite. It is well beyond the scope of this book to describe in detail the methods involved in such observations. It is possible, however, to provide a brief description of the basic ideas so that the general approach can be appreciated.

One method, which is called the *simultaneous method,* involves the use of a satellite that emits a precisely timed, intermittently flashing light. Simultaneous photographs are taken of these flashes from the earth's surface. The photographs are taken from several observation points, two or more of which are part of the same geodetic network. Using the background of stars that appears in each photograph, along with the knowledge of when the photograph was taken, the position of the satellite can be determined relative to the stars. Using this information as a base, it is then possible to calculate the location of the unknown observation locations relative to the known points. Photographs taken during more than one orbit are used to decrease the effect of measurement errors.

A second method involves an application of the *Doppler effect.* The usual illustration of this effect is the change in sound frequency heard by a stationary observer when a train whistle first approaches, then passes, and finally moves away from the observer's position. Even though the sound emitted by the whistle is of a constant frequency, the observer first hears a sound with a higher pitch. This effect occurs as the train is approaching because each wave that is emitted has a shorter distance to travel than the previous wave. The result is an increase in the frequency of the sound at the observer's position and a corresponding increase in pitch. When the train passes the observer and is moving away, the frequency of the sound waves is decreased and the pitch drops. This change in frequency, due to the movement of the sound source relative to the observer, is what is known as the Doppler effect.

The Doppler effect is used to determine the position of an unknown location on the earth's surface, relative to known locations such as geodetic control points. Doppler satellites transmit continuous signals on fixed shortwave radio frequencies. These signals are monitored by stations on the ground and their frequency is compared with the known frequency of the transmitted signals. The received frequency is higher than the transmitted frequency when the satellite is approaching the receiving station and lower when it is moving away. Measuring the amount of shift in frequency even allows the calculation of the angle between the satellite's orbit and the receiving station's location. This information is used to determine the location of the satellite relative to the network of receiving stations. The position of the unknown station is then determined from a study of its relationship to the satellite's position.

VERTICAL CONTROL

The topographic surface of the earth is the surface that cartographers most often wish to represent on maps. It is, simply, the irregular, observable, physical surface that immediately comes to mind when the words, ''the earth's surface,'' are mentioned. In comparative terms, the irregularity of the topographic surface is not very great. On a globe 1 m (3.28 ft) in diameter, for example, the relief features of the ocean basins and the continents would be contained within a layer 1.8 mm (0.07 in.) thick. These dimensions are vital to mapping, despite their small relative size, and what is needed is a framework, called a *vertical control network,* on which to record the variations in the topographic surface so that they are properly related to one another.

Datum

The first step in setting up a vertical control network is the determination of a starting level, or *datum.* As was explained, the most desirable level for this purpose is the surface of the geoid and, if there were no tides, the surface of the ocean would provide part of the required surface. For this reason, measurements that eliminate the variation due to tidal action are used to establish the sea-level datum. This requires the recording of the tidal levels at a given point at hourly intervals over a 19-year period.[1] These readings are then averaged to establish what is called a *mean datum.* The standard datum of the North American Datum, which is used in the United States and the rest of North America, was adjusted in 1929 and again in 1983 (NAD83). Other levels, such as the mean low tide or mean high tide, may be calculated for special purposes, like plotting navigational charts and determining boundaries.

Measurement of Altitude

Once a datum is established, the determination of the elevation differences between it and the desired control points allows absolute elevations to be calculated. Elevation differences are established by *barometric, trigonometric,* or *leveling* techniques.

Barometric methods   The fact that *barometric pressure* decreases in a regular manner as altitude increases is used in the determination of elevation differences. The basic approach involves taking simultaneous barometric pressure readings at two or more points, one of which has a known elevation (the datum). The *pressure differential* between these readings allows the altitude difference between the observation points to be calculated. It is then very simple to determine the elevation of the unknown point by adding the elevation difference between the points to the elevation of the starting point, or subtracting it, as appropriate.

   Correction factors are introduced into the calculation when barometric pressure is being used. These corrections take into account the air temperature and humidity at the time the readings are taken because both of these factors affect the specific pressure variation per unit of altitude. The readings are also taken simultaneously, or at least as close together in time as possible, because changing weather

---

[1]The pattern of movement of the moon corresponds to the metonic cycle, which consists of 235 lunar months—very nearly equal to 19 years. The variations in the moon's influence on the tides are averaged out over the 19-year period.

patterns could cause independent changes in the pressure readings and thus affect the accuracy of the elevation calculations.

A variation of the barometric method involves the use of altimeters rather than barometers. An *altimeter* is essentially the same as a barometer except that it is calibrated to indicate elevations directly instead of indicating only pressure. The altimeter must be set to the current local sea-level pressure reading before it is used.

Barometric methods are relatively quick and easy to use, but are not as accurate as the other methods that will be described. They are most useful, therefore, for work in rough country or in reconnaissance surveys.

Trigonometric method   A more accurate method of establishing altitude differences involves measuring the *vertical angle* between a point of known elevation and the point whose elevation is to be determined. A theodolite or similar instrument is used for this purpose. The slope distance between the two points must also be known or measured. The availability of these two pieces of information makes it a matter of simple trigonometry to determine the altitude differential between the two points (Fig. 3.10). The height of the instrument and the height of the target are taken into account when the measurement of the angle is taken. Because atmospheric conditions may affect the accuracy of the angular reading, it is preferable also to take a reading from the point whose elevation is to be determined, back to the point of known elevation, in order to verify the angle.

Differential leveling method   The most accurate method of measuring altitude differences between points is to use differential leveling. This method utilizes *vertical rods* [Fig. 3.11(a)] that have movable targets attached to them; the targets move over the scale to indicate distance above the ground. One rod is placed at a point of known elevation and a second rod is placed at a point of unknown elevation. A *level* [Fig. 3.11(b)], which is a telescope that can be set to a perfectly horizontal alignment, is placed on a tripod at the point midway between the two rods. The operator first sights through the level at the rod located at the starting elevation and signals the rod holder who raises or lowers the target on the rod. When the center of the target is aligned with the level, the rod holder records the reading. The align-

Figure 3.10   Determination of elevation difference by triangulation.

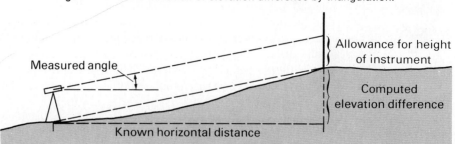

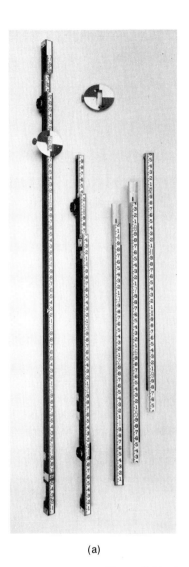

(a)

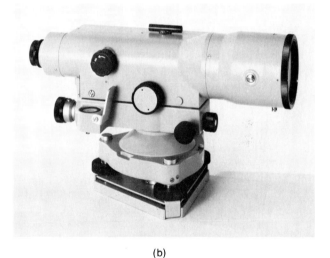

(b)

Figure 3.11 Instruments used in leveling surveys: (a) Philadelphia-type leveling rod, with target. (b) Precise level. (Courtesy of The Lietz Co.)

ment process is repeated with the second rod and the difference between the two readings is the difference in elevation between the two points (Fig. 3.12).

The rod that was on the known point is then advanced to a new point, the level is again positioned, readings are taken, and the new elevation differences are determined. This process of taking forward and backward readings can be continued along a given route for considerable distances, with benchmarks established at desired points along the route. The rods are standardized in order to verify their

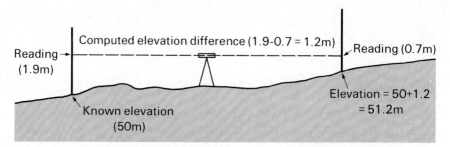

Figure 3.12   Determination of elevation difference by differential leveling.

accuracy. Temperature differences that occur at the time of observation require the correction of the readings taken.

As mentioned, the level is placed equidistant between the two rods on which the readings are being taken. This reduces the effect of refraction, which occurs due to atmospheric conditions, and also eliminates the effect of the earth's curvature on the measurements (Fig. 3.13).

Inertial Positioning

The typical instrumentation used for *inertial positioning* consists of three *gyroscopes* and three *accelerometers,* linked by a *computer.* The devices are usually mounted in either a truck or a helicopter to allow rapid movement over relatively long distances.

An inertial survey begins at a ground control point whose position is known. At the starting point, the three gyroscopes are aligned in relation to known orientations (horizontal, vertical, and azimuth). The instrument package is then moved from the initial point to each survey point in turn, in the same manner as a traverse (described in the next section of this chapter). As the move proceeds, the gyroscopes and accelerometers respond to changes in direction and speed and feed information regarding these movements into the computer. Based on this information, the computer keeps track of changes of position, elevation, and direction in relation to the location and elevation of the starting point and the initial azimuth. The process

Figure 3.13   Equal-sight distances between *a* and *b* eliminate the effect of the earth's curvature on the measurement of elevation differences that would be present with unequal sight distances (between *a* and *c*, for example). Notice that a horizontal line is perpendicular to the direction of gravity at the observation point. A level line, on the other hand, is perpendicular to the direction of gravity at every point.

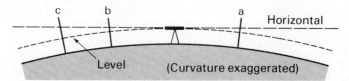

continues until, usually, the traverse is closed by returning to the starting point or to another point whose position is known. A survey that does not close on a known point, which is the equivalent of an open traverse, is also possible, but it suffers from the fact that no check is available to allow the survey to be adjusted. The horizontal position and elevation of each control point visited during the traverse is determined on the basis of the information received from the gyroscopes and accelerometers and is used in the same manner as location and elevation information obtained from other types of surveys.

The differential leveling and inertial positioning methods are the most satisfactory means of determining accurate levels for geodetic control networks. Three levels of accuracy are recognized in connection with leveling surveys. The amount of error allowed, in relation to the distance covered by the survey, determines the level, with the accuracy required increasing from first to third.

PLANE SURVEYING

Plane surveys are carried out for any number of purposes, such as establishing property lines within a property subdivison, aligning a power line, or setting out a road alignment. They are also conducted to add detail within the geodetic control networks that have already been described, or to establish control points for aerial photography, and it is these aspects that are most important for our purposes. The difference between a plane survey and a geodetic survey is that the plane survey, because it is limited to a relatively small area, does not take the curvature of the earth into account. A plane survey does not require as high a degree of accuracy as a geodetic survey.

In order to be useful for anything other than a strictly local purpose, a plane survey must be started from a known point. It is preferable to use a geodetic survey monument for this purpose because its exact location is accurately established and recorded, as discussed above. From the starting point, measurements are taken to determine the locations of other significant points within the area to be surveyed and these points are then incorporated into the map.

The most common approach to plane surveying is described here to illustrate how such surveys are tied in with the development of a map.

Traverse

A *traverse* is a survey in which the sides are not the sides of triangles. Instead, it involves the direct measurement of the lengths of the sides and the observation of their relative directions by the measurement of the angles between them. The lengths are measured using tapes or electronic measuring devices and the angles are measured with a telescopic observing instrument called a *transit* (Fig. 3.14).

The traverse method may be adapted to involve the use of triangulation techniques, if desired. In this approach the *survey route* is laid out so that the corners,

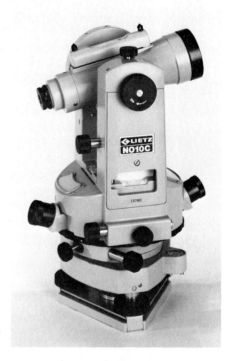

Figure 3.14   Surveyor's transit. (Courtesy of The Lietz Co.)

or *stations,* are intervisible and the area being surveyed is divided into a pattern of triangles. The stations are established at significant locations, such as property corners, road intersections, and stream crossings.

In either approach, the route of the survey is laid out first. The selected stations are marked by placing slim red-and-white-striped poles, called *ranging poles,* vertically in the ground at the selected locations. Once the ranging poles are set out, the distances and directions between them are measured. In the past, distance measurements were taken using linked chains. Today, however, surveyor's tapes, electronic measuring devices, or *tacheometry* are much more common (the latter method is described in the section on plane table mapping, which follows). The measurements taken along the routes between stations are recorded in a *field book* and these field observations are later converted into map form. Important points that do not fall on the sides of the triangles are located by using *offsets.* These are short, right-angle distances measured from points established along the line of survey (Fig. 3.15).

After the route is selected and marked, the survey party occupies the starting position. Preferably, this is a monumented control point that is part of a triangulation network. A sighting is taken on a second control point in the triangulation network; because the azimuth of this leg is known from the triangulation survey, it provides a reference direction for the traverse. A sighting is then taken on the second point in the traverse and the angle between this sighting and the reference

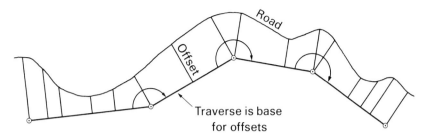

Figure 3.15 Use of offsets to locate points off-line of traverse.

sighting provides the means of determining the azimuth of the first leg of the traverse. If a tie with a triangulation network is not available, the azimuth of the first leg of the traverse is determined by means of a compass. Correction for compass declination is taken into account when this procedure is used (see Chapter 1).

When the direction of the first leg of the traverse has been recorded, the party moves to the second station. The length of the leg between the two stations is measured as the move is made, using one of the methods already mentioned, and the results are recorded in the field book. At the second station, the change in azimuth between the original direction and the direction to the third station is determined and recorded. This process continues until the route is completed.

Ground slopes are taken into account when the measurements of the sides of the traverse are being taken. This is because the distances that are recorded must be horizontal or map distances, not the distances along the surface of the ground; the measurements taken along a sloping surface are longer than the horizontal distance between the end points.

Upon completion of the field work, the information is taken to the survey office. The angles and distances recorded in the field book are used to compute the proper locations of the critical points, which are then plotted on the map. These computations are now frequently carried out by computers, which can also be tied to plotters that draw the map of the survey. Indeed, the angles and distances that are observed may be recorded directly onto magnetic tapes that are then read into the computer. Such techniques greatly increase the speed and accuracy of surveying.

If the traverse returns to its starting point or to another point whose location has previously been accurately established, it is called a *closed traverse;* if not, it is called an *open traverse* (Fig. 3.16). The advantage of a closed traverse is that it allows the *error of closure* of the survey to be accurately determined. The error of closure is the difference between the correct location of the end point of the survey and the location that results from the calculations based on the survey itself. If the plot of the final point in a closed traverse does not coincide with its expected location, *compensations* must be introduced to bring the two points together, thus improving the overall accuracy of the traverse. If the survey does not end at a known point there is no way to determine whether any error exists. This means that com-

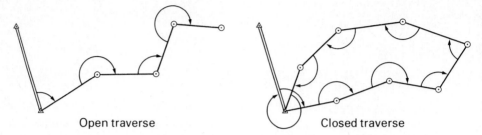

Open traverse   Closed traverse

Figure 3.16 Comparison between a closed traverse, which returns to its starting point, and an open traverse, which does not.

pensations cannot be introduced and the overall accuracy of the survey suffers as a result.

Plane Table Mapping

A description of *plane table mapping* is included here because it is a useful field technique that can be undertaken with relatively simple equipment. Experience with plane table mapping provides valuable insights into the more complex techniques that have been described.

Plane table mapping involves actually drawing a map in the field, rather than acquiring observations that will later be converted into map form. The method is usually used for quick reconnaissance mapping.

The *plane table,* which gives this technique its name, is a flat board mounted on a tripod in such a way that it can be leveled. Once leveled, it can also be swiveled horizontally without disturbing the tripod. The paper on which the map is drawn is mounted on this board.

Three additional instruments are typically used in conjunction with the plane table. One of these instruments is a *level,* which is used to be certain that the table is horizontal. A second instrument is a *trough compass,* which is simply a compass mounted in a box. When the compass is aligned with the north arrow, the side of the box provides a straightedge that is used for drawing a north-south orientation line on the map. The remaining instrument is an *alidade,* which is used to take directional sightings (Fig. 3.17). The most useful type of alidade is a telescope mounted so that its axis is parallel to a straightedge that is fastened to the base of the instrument. When the alidade is aimed at a target, the straightedge is used to transfer the line of sight to the paper.

The alidade may be of a type that allows the use of *tacheometry,* which is a method of rapidly measuring distances by observation. This technique involves the use of special marks, called *stadia lines,* which are visible in the telescope. To use this technique, the surveyor takes a sighting through the alidade onto a *stadia rod,* which has vertical measurements marked on its face. The stadia lines in the telescope intersect two points on the scale on the stadia rod and the surveyor reads the values

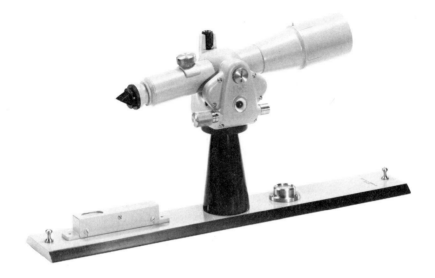

Figure 3.17   Plane-table alidade with level and trough compass. (Courtesy of Kratos/Keuffel & Esser.)

of the points of intersection (Fig. 3.18). The distance between the stadia lines is set so that the distance between the two points that are read on the staff is a fixed proportion of the distance between the stations. The ratio between the stadia measurements and the distance between the stations is usually 1:100, so that the ground distance is determined by multiplying the stadia rod scale measurement by 100. The distance obtained by use of a stadia rod requires correction if the reading is not taken horizontally. The expected accuracy of this technique is approximately 1 part

Figure 3.18   Stadia lines as seen through a horizontal telescope. In this example, the upper wire reads 6′ and the lower wire 5′, a difference of 1′. Because the stadia ratio is 1:100, the distance from the instrument to the rod is 100 × 1′ = 100′. (Courtesy of David White Instruments, Division of Realist)

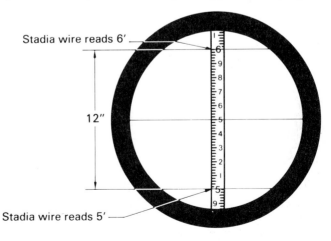

Stadia wire reads 6′

12″

Stadia wire reads 5′

in 500, so it is only used in circumstances where this relatively low level of accuracy is acceptable.

A variation of the tacheometry technique involves the use of a *subtense bar*. This is a special horizontally mounted bar made of invar. The bar has precisely scaled markings, usually spaced 2 m apart. The subtense bar is placed over one end of the line to be measured. A theodolite is placed over the other end of the line and is used to determine the horizontal angle between the markings on the bar, and the angle is then used to calculate the distance between the two locations (Fig. 3.19). This technique also requires correction for any elevation differences, which are determined by recording the difference between the angle of view and the horizontal.

The use of the plane table for plotting involves one of four different approaches, or a combination of approaches.

Intersection method   The method of *intersection* is the equivalent of the triangulation techniques used for geodetic surveying. In this case, a short baseline is measured and the plane table is set up at one end of it. At the starting point, the board is leveled and orientation is provided by drawing a line to magnetic north, using the trough compass. A point is then marked on the plane table to indicate the location of the base starting point. From the starting point, the alidade is aimed at the other end of the baseline and the sight line is drawn, passing through the marked starting point. Sightings are also taken on the features to be mapped, and *radiating lines* are drawn in each of these directions through the same starting point mark.

The plane table is then moved to the opposite end of the baseline and is set up and leveled. It is oriented by lining up the straightedge on the alidade with the drawn baseline and then taking a *backsight* on the first base station, turning the table to bring the point into alignment. The distance between the two base stations is plotted on the map, using the desired scale, and the location of the second base point is marked on the sheet. Sightings are then taken on each of the same features that were observed from the starting point, and rays are drawn from those features, through the second base point on the map. The points of *intersection* of the two sets of rays are the proper map locations of the features [Fig. 3.20(a)].

This process can be continued to points not visible from the original base points by extending a triangulation network from the points established by the initial sightings. Three or more sightings are usually used to verify the extended points with sufficient accuracy. This method has the advantage that it is not necessary to visit all of the stations in order to complete the map.

Figure 3.19   Determination of distance by tacheometry.

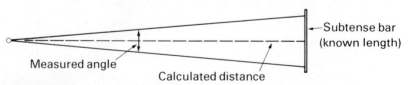

Measured angle

Calculated distance

Subtense bar
(known length)

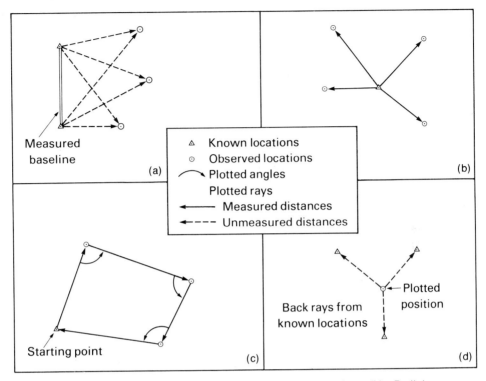

Figure 3.20 Plane-table techniques: (a) Intersection. (b) Radials.
(c) Traverse. (d) Location of unknown point by resection.

Radial method   In a second method, called the *radial method,* the plane table is set up at a central point within the area to be surveyed. After the plane table is leveled, a point is marked near the center of the table to represent the position of the table. Sight lines are then drawn from that point by successively aligning the alidade on the points to be mapped and drawing lines along the straightedge. The distance to each feature is also measured and is plotted to the desired scale along the appropriate *ray* [Fig. 3.20(b)]. Like the intersection method, the radial method has the potential to be done without visiting all of the stations. This allows the mapping process to proceed rapidly, so long as all of the points involved are intervisible. The exception is the case in which the distances are being taped.

Traverse method   The *method of traverse* is the equivalent of the plane survey traverse. In this case, the plane table is moved sequentially from point to point along the route to be surveyed. The sight lines between the points are drawn and the distances between them, as well as the angles of directional change, are measured and plotted as the survey progresses [Fig. 3.20(c)].

Resection method A feature that is to be mapped is not always visible from the observation points used for the mapping, or it may be necessary to add an additional point to the map. In either case, it is possible to determine the location of the feature on the map by the method known as *resection.*

Resection is begun by placing the plane table at the point whose location is to be determined. After the table is correctly oriented, the alidade is sighted on at least three known points and the directions thus determined are used to draw backrays through the mapped locations of each of those points. The plotted intersection of the backrays then establishes the location of the point that is to be added [Fig. 3.20(d)]. If all three backrays do not intersect at one point, the orientation of the table must be adjusted until they coincide.

Map Accuracy Standards

All maps must be drawn accurately, but large-scale maps, such as topographic maps, must be particularly so. This is because they are used for many purposes including, for example, engineering analyses, boundary determinations, the planning of routes, and the delimitation of conservation zones. It is appropriate, therefore, to provide some method of specifying the degree of accuracy of a particular map, so that potential users will know whether or not it meets their accuracy needs.

Accuracy standards of the type discussed here are not used for the testing of small-scale maps such as those typically found in books and atlases. This is because such maps are necessarily very generalized, and the uses to which they are put are of a less exacting nature. This does not mean that accuracy is not a concern in small-scale mapping; it is simply not amenable to the same type of testing as is used in large-scale mapping.

The U.S. government has developed a set of *national map accuracy standards* for large-scale maps that are typical of the testing approach currently in use.[2] These standards are based on tests of the final mapped location of well-defined test points. These are points that are readily identifiable on the map and on the ground, and whose positions have been determined by a higher-order survey. The actual surveyed locations of test points, such as benchmarks, survey control points, property corners, road intersections, building corners, and so on, are first determined. These locations are then matched against the mapped locations of the same features to determine how much map error exists. On a map that is published at a scale of 1:20,000 or larger, no more than 10 percent of the tested points can be located more than 1/30 in. from their correct location. This level of accuracy is not sufficient, however, for very large-scale engineering surveys that might be at a scale of 1 in. to 200 ft or more, because the level of accuracy achieved on such surveys is much greater. Maps published at a scale of less than 1:20,000 are tested in the same manner, except that 1/50 in. is used as the error limit.

---

[2]See Chester C. Slama, ed., *Manual of Photogrammetry,* 4th ed. (Falls Church, Va.: American Society of Photogrammetry, 1980), pp. 372–73, for a formal quotation of the government standards and a similar set of standards published by the Photogrammetry for Highways Committee.

The accuracy of the elevation information provided by contour maps is tested in a similar manner. On these maps, the elevations of selected points are determined and compared against the plotted elevation of the same location. No more than 10 percent of the elevations of the tested points are allowed to deviate from their actual elevations by more than one-half the contour interval used on the map. The elevation accuracy of a point may be improved by moving it slightly from its plotted location. This is permitted, provided the deviation from the proper location is no more than the permissible horizontal error.

Government map-publishing agencies test their own maps against these standards. They are allowed to determine which maps will be tested, and the extent of the testing (the number of points selected, for example). Maps that meet the standards are allowed to include a statement in their legend that "This map complies with national map accuracy standards."

A *statistical approach* to testing map accuracy is also possible and has been considered for adoption. This approach would involve establishing an allowable standard or average error for maps of given scales. A *standard error* is computed by testing a series of map points to determine how far each point is located from its correct location, based on a suitable survey. The proposed test establishes the standard error as an average of the errors that actually exist, whether small or large. This would be an improvement on the present approach, which simply says that only a limited number of points are in error by as much as the established test amount, but does not reflect the amount by which the limit is exceeded. Neither does the present system reflect the error in the location of the remaining points; as long as they do not deviate by more than the limit they are assumed to be correct.

The proposed average for testing is the mean square root of the sum of the squared individual errors (see the discussion of the mean in Chapter 9). The formula for this computation is

$$d = \sqrt{\frac{\Sigma e^2}{n}}$$

in which *d* is the standard error, *e* represents each individual error, and *n* is the number of points tested (Σ indicates that the squared individual errors are added together before the square root is taken). The acceptable standard could then be varied, according to the scale of the tested map.

Suggested Readings

BOUCHARD, H., and FRANCIS H. MOFFITT, *Surveying* (5th ed.). Scranton, Pa.: International Textbook Co., 1967.

BRINKER, R. C. and W. C., TAYLOR, *Elementary Surveying* (4th ed.). Scranton, Pa: International Textbook Co., 1967.

CLENDINNING, J., and J. G. OLLIVER, *Principles and Use of Surveying Instruments* (3rd ed.). London: Blackie and Son Limited, 1969.

GOODE, C. D., *Fundamentals of Plane Surveying*. London: Butterworths, 1971.

KISSAM, PHILIP, *Surveying Practice: The Fundamentals of Surveying* (3rd ed.). New York: McGraw-Hill Book Co., Gregg Division, 1978.

WHITMORE, GEORGE D., *Advanced Surveying and Mapping*. Scranton, Pa.: International Textbook Co., 1949. The descriptions of basic surveying instruments and operations are very clear and do not require a knowledge of mathematics. Mathematics is required for the more advanced portions of the text.

4

Selected Aspects
of Remote Sensing:
Aerial Photography
and Other Techniques

INTRODUCTION

Remote sensing is not a new concept—human beings have always utilized the natural remote sensing capabilities associated with eyesight and hearing. The natural forms of remote sensing, however, have definite limitations: (1) they detect only a small portion of the variety of signals that are potentially available, and (2) the information that is received is not recorded in a form that is easily and accurately measured, stored, or analyzed. In order to overcome these shortcomings, special equipment is used for remote sensing applications in fields such as mapping.

The essence of remote sensing is that it involves a detector located some distance away from the object that is being detected. The natural forms of remote sensing are greatly extended by the use of devices that are capable of measuring and recording a variety of forms of energy, many of which are beyond the realm of the human senses. Special detectors provide information, for example, about acoustic waves, gravitational or magnetic fields, or a range of different wavelengths of electromagnetic radiation.

Remote Sensing Imagery

Much of the information that is needed for mapping purposes is obtained by direct measurement, using the surveying instruments and techniques described in the preceding chapter. Increasingly, however, information about the earth, the moon, and even other planets is also obtained from remote sensing instruments mounted in aircraft or spacecraft.

The types of remotely sensed information that are used for mapping purposes involve measurements of the amount and type of energy emitted, radiated, or reflected from the objects being mapped. In each case, the equipment used to gather the information is designed to record the intensity and location of the particular energy form that is of interest. For this reason, *remote sensors* include such diverse instruments as cameras, lasers, radio receivers, radar systems, sonar, seismographs, gravimeters, magnetometers, and scintillation counters.

Not all remote sensing information is obtained in a form that is directly useful for mapping. Maps are, however, one of the more popular products of many remote sensing programs. These maps may show information of a qualitative nature, such as the areas affected by a particular plant disease, or they may show quantitative information, such as surface temperatures.

The discussion in this chapter is limited to some of the remote sensing techniques used for significant mapping purposes. *Aerial photography* is and has been of major importance in the historical development of these techniques. In recent years, however, a variety of nonphotographic methods, as well as special photographic techniques, have supplemented or replaced traditional aerial photography as a means of gathering mapping information. These techniques range from using special film emulsions in aircraft-mounted cameras to obtaining scans of ultraviolet, infrared, or microwave radiation, using instrumentation sent aloft in aircraft or in satellites.

The broad topic of remote sensing is of great importance to cartographers because the use of such methods greatly expands the variety, accuracy, and currency of the information that is available to be mapped. For two reasons, however, the emphasis in this book is on the conventional aerial photographic aspects of remote sensing. First, the complex set of topics related to remote sensing deserves extensive, separate coverage that is impossible to develop within the framework of a general treatment of the whole field of cartography. Second, although the information gathered through other remote sensing techniques is of great significance, the more traditional aerial photographic methods continue to be of primary importance in the compilation and production of maps. In addition to the relatively detailed treatment of aerial photography, descriptions of some of the other remote sensing techniques are provided in order to indicate the various approaches that are increasingly coming into use.

Types of Energy

Several types of energy are exploited to provide remotely sensed data for mapping applications. Echo sounding, for example, involves the emission of *sound energy* and the collection of reflected signals. This technique is used for the delineation of geological information, such as subsurface structure, ocean depth, and sea-floor characteristics. It is also used to record certain atmospheric characteristics, such as wind patterns and thermal structures. Similarly, information about *gravitational force* is used to obtain clues regarding variations in the nature of the earth's crust from place to place. This approach involves the use of information obtained from gravimeters mounted in aircraft. Airborne magnetometers also provide mappable information, in this case regarding variations in the earth's magnetic field that are used to determine the location of certain types of mineral deposits.

Despite the use of acoustical and force-field techniques such as those just described, there is no doubt that the *electromagnetic spectrum* is the most important remote sensing medium for mapping applications. For this reason, the balance of this discussion will deal with methods for utilizing information derived from the electromagnetic spectrum (Fig. 4.1).

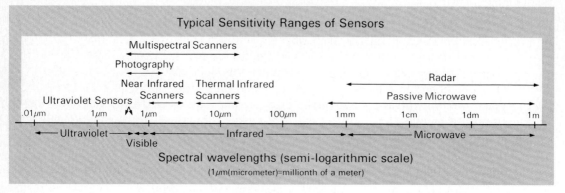

Figure 4.1   The portion of the electromagnetic spectrum commonly used for remote sensing applications.

Spectral Types

Everything in nature, whether it is naturally illuminated by sunlight or is subjected to artificial sources of energy, has its own unique distribution of reflected, emitted, and absorbed radiation. The variations in the wavelengths and intensity of this distribution provide a pattern called a *characteristic curve* or *signature.* The distinctive signature of an object is used to distinguish it from other objects or to obtain information about its properties. Absorption spectrometry, which is based on analyzing the intensity of emitted radiation in different wavelengths of the electromagnetic spectrum, is used, for example, to remotely sense gas emissions. These include man-made pollution sources and earth resources information, such as the location of volcanic activity.

Devices used for the remote sensing of the electromagnetic spectrum are classified into *broad, narrow, bispectral,* and *multispectral* types. Broad waveband devices use a nonspecific sensor that receives energy from many wavelengths and integrates it into a composite image. A simple example of a broad waveband approach is the use of *panchromatic film* in an aerial camera. This film creates an image that is a composite response to the entire range of wavelengths of light within the visible spectrum (Fig. 4.2). Narrow waveband devices, on the other hand, use a single, selected waveband of the electromagnetic spectrum. *Radar,* for example, transmits and receives a narrow range of electromagnetic energy.

Bispectral and multispectral instruments simultaneously record radiation in two or more wavebands. For example, two cameras may be used to take simultaneous photos on different film emulsions, each of which is sensitive to different electromagnetic wavelengths. Alternatively, a multispectral scanner may be fitted with special filters to simultaneously record separate information about several different wavelengths. The detection of more than one waveband allows comparisons of the data received in each waveband. Such comparisons frequently provide more information than does analysis of a single waveband. The comparison of the varying patterns of emissions from different objects permits the recognition of the spectral

Figure 4.2 Sample oblique aerial photograph taken on panchromatic film. Mt. St. Helens during eruption. (USGS photo.)

signatures of different materials. Various rocks, for example, have differing patterns of emission or reflection within the overall range of the spectrum. Cross-checking of the images obtained on various wavebands, then, will often allow several types of rock to be distinguished from one another, or from other materials.

Multispectral systems using as many as 24 wavebands are available. It has been found that as few as 4 well-selected wavebands often provide sufficient information; the use of a large number of bands greatly increases the complexity of the analysis without necessarily improving the quality of the results proportionately. The number of wavebands needed must be determined for the particular purpose of each project. As a practical matter, the choice will be from the standard sets of wavebands used in programs like the series of Landsat satellites, which is described toward the end of this chapter. These standard wavebands are selected in an attempt to meet the needs of a wide variety of users.

Active and Passive Techniques

Both *active* and *passive* types of remote sensing equipment are used for mapping purposes. Active sensors rely on the transmission of controlled signals that are emitted by special equipment and are then reflected back to the sensing device from the object being detected. For example, radar involves the transmission of electromagnetic signals. When the transmitted signal strikes the surfaces of objects, a portion of the energy is reflected back to the receiving station where it is detected and analyzed.

Passive sensors, on the other hand, rely on the detection of natural energy sources. One category of passive sensor detects energy that is reflected from an object and another type detects energy that is naturally emitted. Normal aerial photography, for example, uses portions of the sun's electromagnetic energy that are reflected from objects on the earth's surface. On the other hand, all matter that has a temperature above absolute zero radiates electromagnetic energy and sometimes other forms of energy as well. This fact allows the use of passive sensors, such as infrared scanners, that detect the relative amount of heat emitted by sources of different temperatures, or microwave radiometers, which are used for temperature monitoring and for determining soil moisture content.

AERIAL PHOTOGRAPHY

Experimental aerial photographs were first taken in France in the 1850s. These early photos were taken by suspending cameras from high-flying kites and balloons. Later, during the American Civil War, aerial photographs taken from balloons anchored near the front lines provided information about the disposition of military positions. After a long period of relatively slow development of instruments and techniques, more extensive use of photos taken from aircraft came about during World War I. Soon after that war, aerial photography began to play an increasingly important role in map production. Developments since that time have moved aerial photography into a primary position as a source of detailed information regarding the physical and cultural landscape. The characteristic that led to this application of aerial photography is that the image captured on the photographic emulsion can later be subjected to detailed interpretation and analysis. The information obtained is then used, in conjunction with ground surveys, to produce detailed maps.

Photo Interpretation and Photogrammetry

Two related fields of study, *photo interpretation* and *photogrammetry,* are based on the analysis of aerial photography. The background and skills required for detailed work in either of these fields is rather distinct, although there is inevitably some overlap.

Photo interpretation involves the recognition and identification of the great variety of natural and man-made features on the earth's surface. The identification of features is achieved by considering the size, shape, color, tone, texture, and shadow of objects and surfaces. It involves, as examples from a seemingly endless list of applications, the identification, counting, and measurement of building types; the recognition of crop and soil types; the delineation of various urban land-use areas; the preparation of timber type and volume inventories; the preliminary reconnaissance of transportation routes; the detection of water pollution sources; the development of animal censuses; the selection of military targets; and the discovery of potential archeological sites. In addition, photographs taken from the same location, but at different times, are often used for comparative purposes. By comparing the images on two such photographs, it is possible to determine the nature and extent of any changes that have occurred in either the natural or man-made environment.

Applications such as those described above, as well as similar information obtained from sources such as satellite imagery, must usually be verified by *ground truth* checks. This process involves the random selection of a sample of sites within the area being analyzed. The characteristics of the sites are then predicted through the interpretation of the remote sensing information. The sites are next visited on the ground and the same characteristics are measured by direct observation. The comparison of the expected and the actual site characteristics allows an evaluation of the statistical accuracy of the interpretation process, as well as providing data for the improvement of that process.

Ordinary aerial photographs are used for many interpretation purposes, but other techniques are used as well. Depending upon the applications, different types of film are sometimes used in the aerial camera, including ultraviolet, infrared black-and-white, color, and infrared color. In addition, images obtained from thermal infrared scanners, radar imagery, or microwave detection devices, which are described later in this chapter, may also be used.

Special films assist photo interpretation because they are sensitive to different portions of the electromagnetic spectrum. *Black-and-white infrared film,* for example, is more sensitive to the near-infrared wavelengths, which are slightly beyond the visible range. One application of infrared film is based on the fact that broadleaf vegetation is highly reflective in the infrared range; the result is that such vegetation is recorded in light tones on photos produced using infrared film. Coniferous vegetation, on the other hand, is less reflective and appears to be much darker on the same photos. These characteristics assist in mapping areas of different vegetation types. Similarly, bodies of water are usually quite dark on black-and-white infrared photos. This assists in the determination of the shorelines of lakes and canals, and the edges of swamps and marshy areas, which may be very indistinct on other types of film. Black-and-white infrared film also has some haze-penetrating ability that improves the quality of results obtained when conditions are not ideal for regular panchromatic film.

Color film is very useful for interpretation purposes because features that have distinctive colors may appear in similar shades of gray on black-and-white film, so that their identity is lost. Color film, therefore, is particularly useful for identifying soil types, rock outcroppings, and shorelines, among other features. Many aerial mapping firms today use color film almost exclusively because of the greater ease of identifying features through their color characteristics; this quality often makes it easier to accomplish photogrammetric tasks as well.

Infrared color film produces a false color image; that is, various materials are recorded in colors that are not the same as the colors they exhibit when they are viewed by the human eye or are photographed on ordinary color film. This characteristic of infrared color film was initially used to assist in camouflage detection. Imitation foliage, painted or dyed to represent real foliage, or natural foliage that has been cut, is recorded on infrared color film as purple or blue, whereas normal deciduous foliage is recorded as magenta or red. This same characteristic of infrared color film makes it useful for detecting plant diseases and insect infestations. This is because leaves or needles of plants that are dead or dying turn up as bright green, compared to the red to bluish purple of normal deciduous leaves or evergreen needles. The sensitivity of the film to this color change often allows the detection of crop or natural vegetation problems before they are visible to the eye.

The information obtained by photo interpretation techniques is often converted into map form. The extent of areas of diseased vegetation, for example, can be mapped very quickly and effectively by transferring their outlines from photos to base maps, using a projector or a sketchmaster. Indeed, the photos themselves may serve as very effective map substitutes. Photogrammetry, however, is concerned more specifically with the measurement of distances, the determination of locations of features, the alignment of boundary lines, and similar information involved in map compilation. The following discussion emphasizes the photogrammetric approach to the study of air photos, because of its importance in relation to map measurement.

Types of Aerial Photos

The two major types of aerial photographs are *verticals* and *obliques*. Vertical photos are taken with the camera lens as nearly perpendicular to the earth's surface as possible. Oblique photos, on the other hand, are taken with the camera deliberately tilted away from the vertical axis. *High oblique* photos are taken at such a high angle that the horizon appears within the photo, whereas *low obliques* are taken at an angle that is closer to the vertical, so that the horizon does not appear within the photo (Fig. 4.3).

In addition to vertical and oblique photographs, special cameras are available that take *composite* photos. These consist of two or more oblique photos combined with a vertical photo. Composites are particularly useful for rapid reconnaissance purposes because they cover a large portion of the earth's surface at one time.

Oblique or composite photographs are sometimes preferred for illustrations and publicity purposes and for situations in which it is important to show the re-

Figure 4.3   Relative angles of view of vertical, low-, and high-oblique aerial photographs.

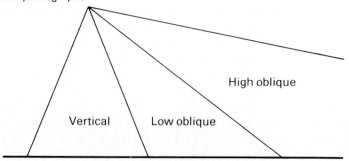

lationship of one feature or location to another, more distant feature or location. The relatively difficult geometry involved in measuring oblique and composite photos means that vertical aerial photographs are the predominant type used in mapping, although the other types are sometimes used when speedy mapping of large areas is required. Overlapping vertical photos are most suitable for the three-dimensional viewing that is needed for many mapping purposes. Because of the primary importance of vertical photos in mapping, the discussion here is limited to the uses of single, or overlapping, vertical photo coverage.

Taking Vertical Photographs

Vertical photographs are taken by an *aerial survey camera* that is positioned over an opening in the floor of an airplane (Fig. 4.4). A typical camera has a lens with a focal length of from 88 to 300 mm (3.5 to 12 in.) and produces a negative 23 cm (9 in.) square, although negative sizes as small as 12.7 cm × 17.8 cm (5 in. × 7 in.) and as large as 20.3 cm × 25.4 cm (8 in. × 10 in.) are common.

Ideally, vertical photographs are taken from an airplane in smooth, level flight. Because there is always vibration in an airplane, as well as some turning and movement involved in keeping it level and on course, the camera requires a *special suspension*. The suspension sometimes includes a system of pivots called a *gimbal,* which allows the camera to pivot so that it will stay as vertical as possible despite movement of the airplane. In addition, it is sometimes *gyroscopically stabilized* (Fig. 4.5). This type of suspension usually results in very close to vertical photographs but some tilt may still occur because no system yet developed can completely eliminate movement of the camera.

The film is rolled on a spool that contains enough material for a large number of exposures—as many as 490 in one type of camera. Typically, the film is auto-

Figure 4.4 Aircraft camera, with accessories. (Courtesy of Carl Zeiss, Inc., Thornwood, N.Y.)

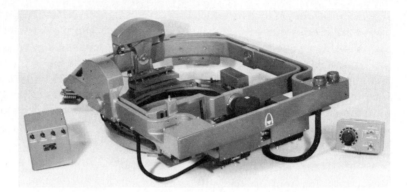

Figure 4.5 Gyro-stabilized camera mount. (Courtesy of Aeroflex Laboratories Inc.)

matically advanced as each exposure is made. Provision is also made to flatten the film at the time of exposure so that the photo is not distorted by waviness in the film. This is done with a pressure plate or with a vacuum back that holds the film in place by air pressure.

Because many of the uses of aerial photographs require *overlapping photo coverage,* flight plans are laid out with these requirements in mind. It is usual to take succeeding photographs in the same *flight line* so that they *overlap* by about 60 percent (Fig. 4.6). As the airplane flies each flight line, the time between photo

Figure 4.6 Flight-line plan, with provision for overlap.

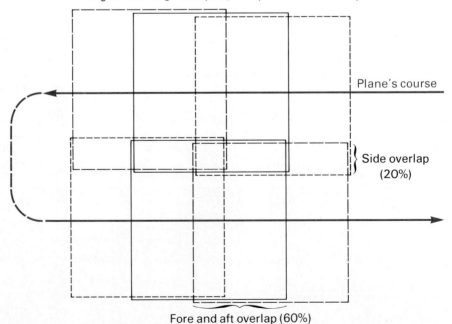

Plane's course

Side overlap (20%)

Fore and aft overlap (60%)

exposures is controlled to provide this fore and aft overlap. Adjoining flight lines are flown close enough together so that the photos overlap on the sides by about 20 to 30 percent. The use of modern navigational aids, such as the radar-based Decca navigator system, allows accurate control of the flight lines. Under ideal conditions the Decca system can determine the position of an aircraft within ±25 m. This type of control ensures that the flight lines, and even the individual photos within the flight lines, are correctly located. In the absence of such navigational aids, visual clues such as road intersections, railroad lines, hilltops, rivers, and fence lines must be relied on for aligning the flight lines.

The influence of crosswinds sometimes forces an airplane to fly at an angle in order to follow its desired flight path. Too great an amount of *crabbing,* as this is called, results in the reduction of the desired coverage and overlap in a set of photos (Fig. 4.7). The amount of crab must be controlled or it can render a set of photos useless. This is accomplished, in some camera systems, by rotating the camera on its vertical axis.

Characteristics of Vertical Photographs

Some of the basic characteristics of vertical aerial photographs will now be explained so that the manner in which the photos are put to use can be appreciated.

Initially, the assumption is made that a single photograph is taken while the plane is in smooth, horizontal flight over an area of the earth's surface that has no hills, valleys, or other terrain features. When the camera's shutter opens, light from the ground features passes through the camera lens and is focused on the film in the focal plane of the camera. This creates a *latent photographic image* (see Chapter 7) that, when developed, produces a *photographic negative.* Aerial photos are usually taken on continuous tone film, on which the images are shown as varying shades of gray. As already mentioned, however, special emulsions are sometimes used, depending upon the purposes and needs of each survey. The assumption is made throughout this discussion that normal, black-and-white, continuous tone, panchromatic film, which is sensitive to all of the visible frequencies, is being used.

Figure 4.7 Effect of crab on photo coverage.

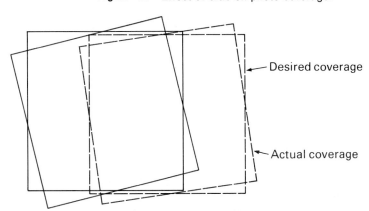

Desired coverage

Actual coverage

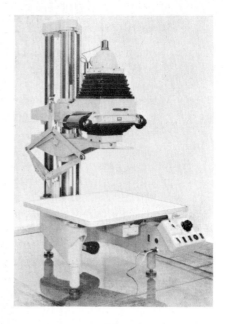

(a)   (b)

Figure 4.8 (a) Contact printer. (Courtesy of Alan Gordon Enterprises, Inc., North Hollywood, Calif.) (b) Enlarger. (Courtesy of Wild Heerbrugg Instruments, Inc.)

The negative of the aerial photo can be used to produce a *positive print* for interpretation and measurement purposes. The negative is placed directly in contact with the photographic paper in a *contact printer* [Fig. 4.8(a)], an exposure made, and the print developed. This print, which is the same size as the negative, is called a contact print. If an enlarged or reduced print is needed, the negative is placed in a photographic *enlarger* [Fig. 4.8(b)]. In the enlarger, light shines through the negative and is focused on photographic paper that is placed under the lens to receive the exposure. Depending on the distance between the lens and the printing surface, the resulting print can be the same size as the negative or larger or smaller. The relationship between the earth's surface, the photographic negative, and different sizes of photographic positives is shown in Fig. 4.9. Three positives are shown to illustrate how scale is changed. Positive B is the same size as the negative, whereas positive A is at a smaller scale and positive C is at a larger scale. As indicated in the diagram, the distance between the lens and the printing surface is increased to increase scale or decreased to decrease scale. Unless otherwise stated, the following discussion refers to contact prints.

Scale   The most useful aspect of the positive print is that the geometry involved in its creation provides information about the size of features on the ground. Con-

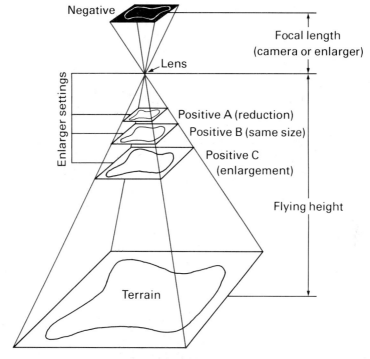

Figure 4.9 Relationship between terrain, photo negative, and various size positives.

sider two features that are located on the ground at points *A* and *B* [Fig. 4.10(a)]. The light rays from point *A,* which is directly below the lens, are focused at point *A'* on the film. This point, which is at the center of the print, is called the *principal point* of the photograph. The light rays from point *B* are focused at point *B'*. In this situation, three crucial factors are fixed at the time the photograph is taken: the focal length of the lens, the altitude of the camera above the earth's surface, and the vertical direction of the camera. These factors are sufficient to determine the scale of the photograph (complex factors, such as lens distortion, which must be taken into account in actual practice, are ignored here).

The reason these factors are sufficient to determine the scale on the photograph is as follows:

1. The focal plane of the camera is horizontal, as is the surface of the earth. (Because of the small area involved, the curvature of the earth can usually be ignored.) The lines representing these features are therefore parallel to one another.
2. The angles *a* and *a'*, in Fig. 4.10(a), are right angles, because the photograph was taken vertically.
3. Based on 1 and 2, angles *b* and *b'* are equivalent angles.

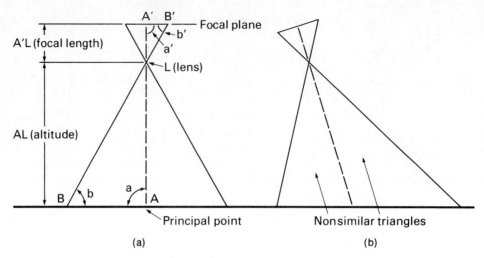

Figure 4.10 (a) Simplified geometry of a vertical aerial photograph. (b) Effect of tilt on relationships between camera and terrain.

4. Based on 1, 2, and 3, triangles *ABL* and *A'B'L* are *similar triangles.*
5. Because of their location in the similar triangles, the ratio between the lengths of sides *AL* and *A'L* is the same as the ratio between the lengths of sides *AB* and *A'B'*. This is the equivalent of saying that the scale of the photo is given by the ratio between the altitude and the focal length of the lens (*AL:A'L*).

$$\text{Scale} = \frac{f \text{ (focal length of lens)}}{A \text{ (altitude above ground)}}$$

The result is that measuring the distance from *A'* to *B'* on the film, and applying the scale ratio, will tell us the distance from *A* to *B* on the ground. It also means that the scale of the aerial photo can be determined by taking the ratio between a known distance between two objects, either from a direct measurement or from a map, and the distance between the same features on the aerial photo.

In a more normal situation, scale varies throughout the photograph for reasons that are discussed in the next section. It is usual, therefore, to measure several known lines and to average the scales that are obtained. This average scale is then used as a representative scale for the photo.

Scale variation *Scale differences* will often occur from one photograph to the next even if the terrain is perfectly level. This happens if the altitude of the airplane, and hence of the camera, varies from one photograph to the next. The change in altitude obviously affects one portion of the scale formula and the final scale is changed accordingly.

The scale within a single aerial photograph may vary from place to place because of two factors. First, the photograph may not be truly vertical. This happens if the airplane is *tilted* at the moment the photograph is taken; even with an automatic leveling mechanism there may be a lag in the correction. The triangles described in Fig. 4.10(a) are then no longer similar triangles. The ratio between the distance from the ground to the lens and the focal length of the lens differs from one point to the next [Fig. 4.10(b)]. The variation in scale due to tilt changes continuously from one side of the photo to the other, and is a function of the varying distance from the camera to the surface of the ground.

Second, if there are variations in elevation within the area that is photographed, the scale of the photo differs from place to place. This scale variation is directly tied in with *planimetric displacement* and is therefore discussed in the next section.

Planimetric displacement   A feature plotted on a map is placed in its planimetrically correct position. This means that its position in relation to latitude and longitude is projected vertically (orthographically) onto the assumed surface of the ellipsoid. When a print is made of an aerial photograph, however, there may be a shift in the planimetric location of certain points. This is because an aerial photograph is a perspective projection and not an orthographic one (Fig. 4.11).

As is shown in Fig. 4.12, the amount of planimetric shift of a feature in a photograph is related to its height above the datum that has been adopted (usually sea level) and to its distance from the principal point. In the first drawing [Fig. 4.12(a)], the apparent location of the top of the tower (T) appears at a location on the negative (T') which is shifted away from the location of the bottom of the tower (B), which appears at (B'). On a map, the locations of both the top and the bottom of the tower are located at B. The farther the feature is from the principal point the greater the amount of shift [Fig. 4.12(a) and (b)]. Also, the greater the height of the feature above the datum, the greater the amount of shift that will occur [Fig. 4.12(b) and (c)]. The amount of planimetric displacement from either source is decreased, however, as the altitude of the camera is increased [Fig. 4.12(a) and (d)].

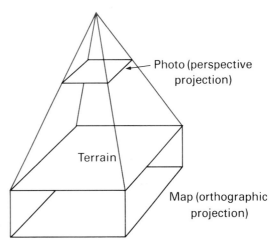

Photo (perspective projection)

Terrain

Map (orthographic projection)

Figure 4.11   Relationship between the terrain, an orthographic map projection, and the perspective projection of an aerial photograph.

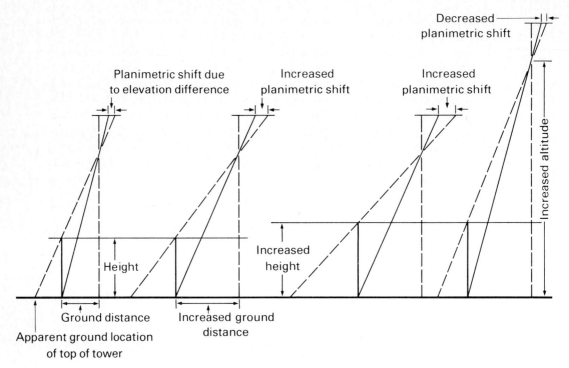

Decreased planimetric shift

Planimetric shift due to elevation difference

Increased planimetric shift

Increased planimetric shift

Increased altitude

Height

Increased height

Ground distance

Increased ground distance

Apparent ground location of top of tower

Figure 4.12 Variations in planimetric shift due to changes in the distance of the image from the principal point, height of an object, and the altitude of the aircraft.

It is also apparent that planimetric displacement, because it is a function of the distance of the feature from the principal point, is distributed in a *radial pattern*. Furthermore, the principal point is at the center of the pattern, as is shown in Fig. 4.13. This diagram shows the direction and amount of displacement of the images

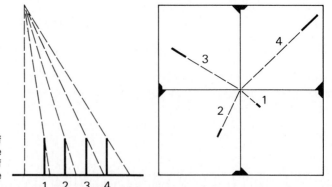

Figure 4.13 Radial arrangement of displacement of image around the principal point and amount of displacement relative to distance from principal point.

of several objects of the same height that are located at varying distances and directions from the principal point.

Rectification

The introduction of the corrections required to offset overall scale errors and errors due to tilt is called *rectification*. Rectification is accomplished by making corrected prints in a special printer, called a rectifier, which is a photographic enlarger with a tilting surface on which the prints are made (Fig. 4.14). The rectifier is adjusted to correct for scale errors due to tilt or to altitude differences. Rectified prints still contain planimetric displacements that are due to terrain elevation variations within the area of the print.

If the tilt in a given photo amounts to more than 2 or 3 degrees, significant

Figure 4.14 Autofocus rectifier, with tilting easel. (Courtesy of Kratos/Keuffel & Esser.)

distortions will be present in the print and the assumptions involved in the use of vertical photos will be violated. If this condition exists, it is necessary for many purposes to make a rectified print to correct the tilt.

Tilt is removed by placing the negative in the rectifier and slanting the projection board so that the original tilt of the camera is counteracted by the tilt of the board. The correct setting is determined by matching the image against plotted ground control points. An interlocking device on the rectifier changes the plane of the negative to keep it in the correct relationship to the printing surface.

It is also virtually certain that some of the photos in a series will be taken from an altitude that differs from the standard. This is due to vertical movements of the airplane as it encounters updrafts and downdrafts, as well as to differences in the average elevation of the terrain. If there is altitude variation, the scale of the affected photo is increased if the plane is closer to the ground and is decreased if the plane is higher.

The rectifier is used to make altitude corrections by increasing or decreasing the distance between the lens of the projector and the projection table, thus changing the scale of the print. The lens-to-image distance is increased to counteract a smaller scale and is decreased to offset a larger scale, as was previously explained. The amount of scale correction is also verified by matching the image against plotted ground control points.

It is likely that a given photo will contain both types of scale variations: those due to tilt and those due to altitude differences. It is feasible, by using proper ground control checks, to correct for both problems at the same time. In this case, the spacing between the lens and the projection table is changed to adjust for the altitude variations and the projection table is tilted to adjust for the camera tilt.

Mosaics

A single aerial photograph covers only a limited portion of the earth's surface. The size of the area covered is dependent upon the altitude from which the photo is taken and the focal length of the lens, which affects the angle of coverage of the camera. When a photo of a larger area is desired, a number of photographs may be joined together to form an *aerial mosaic*.

Uncontrolled mosaic An *uncontrolled mosaic* simply requires a sufficient number of individual photographs so that all the area to be shown is covered by at least one photo, with some overlap between photos. The photos are usually unrectified prints and the overlap is required because it is preferable to use only the central portion of each photo, thus minimizing the effect of the scale and locational errors they contain.

Assembly of a mosaic begins with the photo that is at the center of the area to be covered. This photo is fastened to the center of a flat board. One of the adjoining photos is then overlapped with the first photo so that features shown on both photos are aligned over one another as closely as possible. The excess portion of the overlapping photo is then trimmed away and the remaining portion is temporarily fastened in place. The same process is followed with the other photos, with each additional photo being matched as closely as possible with those previously put in place. Aligning the additional photos usually requires some adjustment in the locations of the photos already positioned, which is why they are not secured in place immediately. When all the adjustments are made, the final gluing and trimming is done. The result is, in effect, a large aerial photograph of the area (Fig. 4.15).

Anyone attempting to join a series of aerial photos in the manner just described rapidly encounters difficulties due to the scale variations caused by tilt, terrain variation, and altitude variation. Assume, for example, that a road intersection that shows in the first two photos is selected as one matching point. The scale variations within the two photos may make it impossible to line up the images of other features when the road intersections are aligned. It may be possible to match one

Figure 4.15 Mosaic of aerial photographs, without tone matching. Lines between prints are easily seen in this example. (USGS photos.)

such feature without losing the alignment of the road intersection, but a third feature may then be out of alignment. When this occurs, it is necessary to compromise, selecting an arrangement that comes the closest to aligning all the desired points but that, in the end, may not precisely match any of them.

Alignment problems are usually more and more difficult to resolve as additional photos are matched to one another, progressing farther and farther from the starting point. Uncontrolled mosaics, then, quickly become filled with an increasing range of errors—errors that are inherent in the original aerial photos and that accumulate as photos are added. It is desirable, therefore, to introduce some means of structuring the assembly of the mosaic.

Controlled mosaic   Structure can be provided for a mosaic by using an outline map drawn at the average scale of the aerial photos. This need only be a simple, skeletal map, either an existing map or one especially drawn for the purpose. The major requirement is that it show the correct planimetric location of major features that are recognizable on the aerial photographs. These include, for example, road and railroad alignments and intersections, fence lines, property corners, and major buildings.

Special *control points,* such as survey monuments, may be marked on the ground in advance of taking the aerial photos. An example of such special control points is provided by the white X's that one frequently encounters painted on the surface of a highway. The center of the X, which shows up very clearly in an aerial photo, is the precise location of a surveyed control point. Wooden, plastic, or cloth targets are used in areas where it is not possible to provide a painted target. Points marked in this way are easily identified on the photos.

If control points are not established in the field prior to taking the photographs, they are obtained later. This requires identifying the desired points on the aerial photographs themselves, and sending a survey crew into the field to locate the points on the ground. A suitable survey is then carried out so that the locations of the control points can be mapped (see Chapter 3).

Providing external controls has the advantage that errors no longer accumulate from photo to photo as they do in an uncontrolled mosaic. The photographs used in a controlled mosaic are usually rectified before they are used. The use of rectified prints ensures that, when the mosaic is assembled, photo error is minimized because the errors due to tilt and altitude variations are eliminated, although planimetric displacements remain.

It is also possible to use *orthophoto* prints for a mosaic. These are prints in which the planimetric displacements are also removed. The production of orthophotos is discussed at the end of the section on aerial photography.

Assembly of a *controlled mosaic* is carried out by securing the base map to the mounting board and fastening the individual photos over it, as with an uncontrolled mosaic. The difference here is that the features on the photos are matched to their plotted locations as closely as possible before they are fastened in place. Overlapping areas are removed so that adjoining photos blend together as well as possible, and the photos are glued down. In many cases even the tone of the photos is matched, and the edges of the photos are feathered so that the cut lines are difficult to detect.

Completed photomosaics are frequently photographed and reproduced. Additional information such as place names, boundary lines, and a locational grid is sometimes added to the mosaic, producing a photomap.

Maps from Prints

In addition to being used for the assembly of mosaics, aerial photographic prints are used as a source for map detail. The use of triangulation methods, which are based on the geometry of aerial photography, provides a means of extending map control and for plotting information from the photographs onto the map. Before these plotting methods are described, however, it is necessary to explain how aerial photographs are viewed stereoscopically and how certain points on the photos are located and identified.

Three-dimensional viewing   A person viewing an ordinary scene sees it in three dimensions. Because the eyes are slightly separated from one another, each eye receives an image that is slightly different from the image received by the other. This fact can be tested by picking out an object across the room and alternately opening one eye and closing the other; the object will appear to shift its position depending on which eye is open. This difference in apparent position, which is due to the changing point of view, is called *parallax.* The brain integrates the slightly different information obtained from each eye, along with other clues, and produces the perception of three-dimensional objects.

Because aerial photographs are two-dimensional, a special viewing technique, called *stereoscopic viewing,* is necessary to obtain the three-dimensional view that is needed for many mapping applications. The basic requirement for stereoscopic viewing is that the aerial photographic coverage must provide pairs of photos that overlap one another. The coverage given by these photos, each taken from a slightly different point of view, provides the needed parallax effect (Fig. 4.16). When the differing photos are viewed simultaneously, the brain integrates the views, just as it does in ordinary direct viewing. In this way, a three-dimensional effect, called a *stereoscopic model,* is achieved.

A special instrument called a *stereoscope* permits the simultaneous viewing of two photographs that is required to achieve the desired stereoscopic effect. A simple *pocket stereoscope* consists of a pair of lenses arranged so that one eye sees one of the photos and the other eye sees the second photo. It has a framework that holds the lenses at the correct height above the photographs, so that the image is in focus

Figure 4.16 Effect of planimetric displacement due to difference in point of view in two successive aerial photographs. (USGS photos.)

[Fig. 4.17(a)]. The distance between the lenses, which is called the *interpupillary distance,* provides the needed separation of the images. The interpupillary distance may be fixed at about 65 mm (2.55 in.) so that it is suitable for most users, or it may be adjustable to the actual interpupillary distance of the user, typically from 55 to 72 mm (2.17 to 2.83 in.).

Because the photographs must be aligned under the closely spaced lenses, only a portion of the area of overlap may be viewed at one time when a pocket stereoscope is used. A *mirror stereoscope* is often preferred, therefore, because it has a system of mirrors, or prisms, that allows the prints being viewed to be physically separated from one another [Fig. 4.17(b)]. The entire area of overlap contained in the two photos can be viewed at one time under a mirror stereoscope, which allows for more convenient working conditions.

Preparing Photos

Certain points must be identified on the photographic prints in order to prepare them for stereoscopic viewing.

In a vertical photograph, the optical center of the photograph, which is called the *principal point,* is the point directly in line with the central axis of the lens of

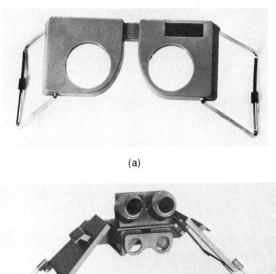

(a)

(b)

Figure 4.17 (a) Pocket stereoscope. (b) Folding-mirror stereoscope with photos and parallax bar in place. (Courtesy of The Lietz Co.)

the camera. Special marks, called *fiducial marks,* are recorded on the edge of each photo at the time it is taken (Fig. 4.18). The principal point is located on the photo at the point of intersection of lines that are drawn joining these fiducial marks. To identify this point on a photo, a hole is pricked through the print, using a steel needle. A small circle, about 5 mm (0.2 in.) in diameter, is then drawn around the point to make it easier to locate. This circle is drawn in ink, using a drop-bow pen (see Chapter 6).

Because we are assuming that the photos that are being used are truly vertical, the principal point of the photo is also what is called the *nadir,* which is the point on the ground that is directly below the camera. This assumption simplifies the discussion.

If the coverage overlaps sufficiently, the principal point of one photo can also be seen on the adjoining photos in the same flight line. From the standpoint of a given photo, the principal points of the adjoining photos are referred to as *conjugate principal points.* The conjugate principal points must also be located and marked on the photo. This is facilitated by preliminary stereoscopic viewing of the photos.

Stereoscopic viewing is achieved by carrying out the following steps. After the principal points of both photos are located and marked, the photograph on which

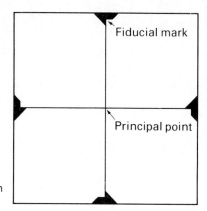

Figure 4.18 Relationship between fiducial marks and principal point.

the conjugate principal point is to be marked is fastened to the table surface. The adjoining print is placed next to it, so that identifiable features that appear on both prints are the correct distance apart—about 6.0 cm (2.36 in.) for pocket stereoscopes or 25.4 cm (10 in.) or more for mirror stereoscopes. The stereoscope is then placed over the prints so that the left-hand lens is over a feature on the left-hand print, and the right-hand lens is aligned over the same feature on the right-hand print. Looking through the lenses of the stereoscope will then produce a three-dimensional view of the terrain in the area of overlapping coverage. If a pocket stereoscope is being used it will usually be necessary to lift the edge of one photo in order to view the area under it.

The position of the stereoscope is then adjusted so that the location of the conjugate principal point is within the area of stereoscopic viewing. The point of a needle is aligned on the first print so that it appears to match exactly the location of the principal point of the second print. The location of the conjugate principal point is then pricked with the needle and a small circle is inked around it. This process is repeated for the principal point of the adjacent photo on the opposite side. All prints will have a principal point and two conjugate principal points, unless they are the end photo in a flight line.

A straightedge is then aligned between the pricked principal point and each of the conjugate principal points, and a fine ink line is drawn, joining the circles that have been drawn around each point. This line is called the *flight line* because it shows the presumed path that the airplane followed between the times the first and second photos were taken. The flight lines between the two conjugate principal points and the principal point of the photo do not usually lie in a single straight line because of variations in the flight path of the airplane.

Radial line plotting As has already been noted, the images of objects in aerial photos are displaced from their correct planimetric positions because of the elevation variation of the terrain. Points higher than the datum are displaced outward from the principal point and those lower than the datum are displaced inward. The principal point itself is not displaced regardless of its elevation. The pattern of these displacements is radial, with the principal point at the center. The result is that the actual location of each point on the photo is somewhere along a line drawn through that point and the principal point of the photo. The problem is to determine where on that line the feature is actually located. The answer to this problem is provided by *radial line plotting*.

This method requires adequate photo coverage, with fore and aft overlap, so that each point in a flight line appears in at least two photos. There must be adequate side lap between flight lines so that some points can be identified on the photos from adjoining flight lines. A base map at average photo scale, with ground control points plotted, is also required. If these materials are available it is possible to use the information contained in the air photos to construct a triangulation network. This network gives the correct map locations of additional control points so that features on the photos can be plotted onto the base.

Three methods are used for the radial line plotting of a triangulation network. The paper template method, which is the least expensive of the three methods, is described first and the other two methods are then compared to it.

Base map   The first step in plotting the triangulation pattern onto the base map is to mark the locations of the principal points, conjugate principal points, and flight lines on all of the photos that will be used. The procedures for doing this have already been described.

Other points are also identified and marked. The ground control points that will be used to relate the aerial photographs to the ground survey are located first, on each print. Control points are selected so that they are easily located on the ground as well as on the photos. They are marked on the prints with colored ink circles in order to make them readily identifiable. *Wing points* are then established on each print. These are features that are readily identifiable on the photos and that are selected so that they can be used later to relate the air photos to the base. Six wing points are established on each photo (except that only four may be needed on the end photos of each flight line). The wing points are located so that they are near the edge of the photo, opposite the principal point and the conjugate principal points (Fig. 4.19). They are marked on the print in the same manner as the principal points.

The second step is to prepare the *paper templates*. These are squares of tracing paper, or drafting plastic, the same size as the individual aerial photographs. Each photograph is placed on a light table and a blank template is placed over it. The light table has a translucent top with a light source underneath it, so that the light will shine through the pricked points in the print, making them readily visible. All the marked points and the flight lines are drawn on the template with a sharp, hard pencil. Straight lines are then drawn from the principal point through each of the wing points and control points, and the template is numbered with the proper print number. When a template is completed for each photo, assembly onto the base map begins.

The base map is placed on the light table and one of the paper templates is selected. Preferably, this is a template that shows the location of three control points,

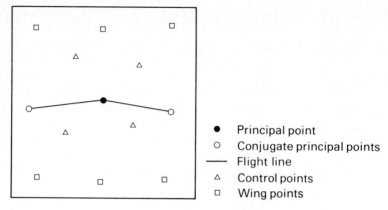

Figure 4.19 Typical relationship between principal point, conjugate principal points, flight line, control points, and wing points.

so that the correct scale will be established. The template is positioned so that the correct *radial lines* pass through their respective control points and is taped in place on the base. An adjoining template from the same flight line is then positioned so that the flight line drawn on it is superimposed on the flight line of the first template. The second template is moved, with the flight lines still coinciding, so that the correct radial lines from its principal point pass through the same control points. This places the second template in its correct position and it is taped in place. The radial lines on the two templates, which pass through the common wing points, will now intersect at the correct locations of those points.

The remaining templates in the first flight line are added, following the same general procedure, using the plotted control points as a check on the process. After the first flight line is completed, the adjoining flight line is added and the process is continued until all of the templates are in place. The locations of all of the principal points, conjugate principal points, and wing points are transferred to the base by pricking their locations through the templates and into the base with a needle. The templates are then removed and, as this is done, an identification number for each point is noted on the base. These numbers usually specify the type of point and the print on which it is identified. They are selected so that each point has a unique number, which assists in matching the photos to their correct location on the completed base when the transfer of photo detail is being done.

A second method of radial line plotting uses *slotted plastic templates* in place of the paper templates. In this method a hole is cut at the location of the principal point. Slots are then cut along the same alignments where the radial lines would be drawn on the paper templates. The slotted templates are then assembled over the base map by sliding them into position so that alignment studs can be passed through the principal points, as well as through the intersections of the slots (Fig. 4.20). The studs representing the control points are centered over the correct points on the base and govern the positioning of the entire network of templates. When the complete set of templates is assembled, prick marks are made on the base map by pressing a steel needle through the hole that is provided in the center of each stud. These

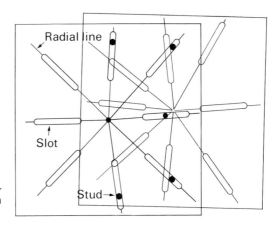

Figure 4.20 Radial line plotting using slotted templates assembled on studs that represent control points.

prick marks establish the locations of the principal points, conjugate principal points, and wing points on the base.

Finally, in the *radial arm template* method, a post is used to represent the principal point of each photo. Adjustable radial arms are used to establish the flight line as well as the radial lines to the wing points and control points (Fig. 4.21). The

Figure 4.21 Radial arm template assembled on pins placed at control points. (Courtesy of Alan Gordon Enterprises, Inc., North Hollywood, Calif.)

assembly of the templates and the transfer of the points is done in essentially the same way as with slotted templates. The advantage of radial arm templates is that they are adjusted by swinging the arms and can therefore be reused.

Transfer of detail   When the base map is completed, information from the aerial photos is plotted onto it. This is done by using a *reflecting projector* or some type of *camera lucida.*

If a reflecting projector is used, the required aerial photograph is placed in position in the projector and its image is reflected onto the base map. The scale of the projected image is adjusted by moving the head of the projector up or down. Tilt corrections are made by tilting the board on which the base map is placed.

Various types of camera lucida are available, including *sketchmasters* (Fig. 4.22). In general, these are used by placing the base map on a table top with the sketchmaster aligned over it and with the photograph fastened in place. The optical system of the device is designed so that the viewer sees the image of the photograph superimposed on the image of the base map. Tilt corrections are made by differentially raising or lowering the legs of the device, or by tilting the components of the optical system. Scale adjustments are made by raising or lowering the device or, in some cases, by changing the lens in the eyepiece.

The general procedure for plotting is the same regardless of the type of device which is used. An initial triangular set of points is selected on the base map; these can be principal points, wing points, or control points. The correct photo is then located and projected onto the base map. The necessary scale and tilt adjustments are made so that the selected points match the same points on the base map. The desired details within the triangle of selected points are then traced onto the base map, using the projected photo image as a guide. When the desired detail within the first set of points has been transferred, the photo image is matched to the next set of points and the tracing process is repeated. This process is continued until the entire area is mapped.

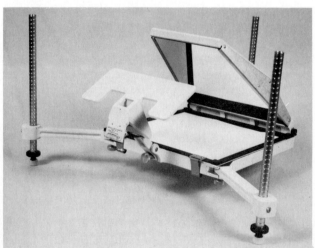

Figure 4.22 Vertical sketchmaster. (Courtesy of Alan Gordon Enterprises, Inc., North Hollywood, Calif.)

Other types of plotters allow the transfer of information to the base map using stereo pairs of photographs (Fig. 4.23).

Stereoscopic Techniques

Some stereoscopic viewing is involved in the use of aerial photo prints for the plotting of map information, as was just explained. The utility of aerial photographs in map production is greatly increased by the use of techniques that are more completely based on stereoscopic viewing. These techniques allow the vertical as well as the horizontal dimension of features to be examined and measured. This means that topographic information can be obtained in addition to planimetric information. Stereoscopic techniques use overlapping photographic coverage and, for maximum utility, require a base map on which the horizontal and vertical control points that have been established by ground survey are plotted.

Height determination   How can information regarding the height of objects be obtained from viewing two-dimensional photographs? The key to this is the fact pointed out earlier, that height differences within an aerial photograph result in a radial shift in the apparent planimetric location of the features. This shift is one of the differences between an aerial photograph and a map, and it must be eliminated if the best use is to be made of single, vertical photos. What is a problem in the use of single photos, however, is an asset in stereoscopic viewing. This is because the shifts that occur can be measured and compared, and the results can be used to obtain information regarding elevations.

The manner in which three-dimensional information is extracted will be ex-

Figure 4.23   Zoom transferscope. (Courtesy of Bausch & Lomb.)

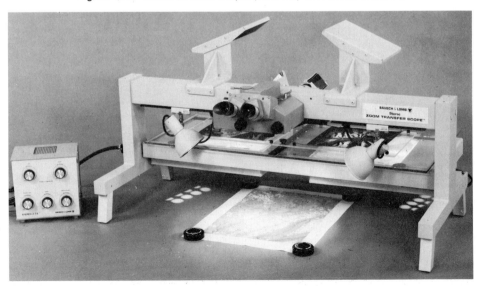

plained, using a simplified example. Assume that we have a pair of overlapping aerial photographs suitable for stereoscopic viewing. Both photos were taken at the same elevation, the terrain is perfectly flat, and a tall chimney is the only feature on the landscape. The datum is sea level and both principal points are at that level. More complex situations involving tilt, terrain variations, different altitudes, or a different datum will not be treated. This is because the goal here is simply to point out that the relationship between parallax difference and height differential allows photo measurements to be used to determine elevation differences.

The two overlapping aerial photographs are prepared for stereoscopic viewing by positioning them with their flight lines in alignment. They are spaced the correct distance apart so that the matching features on the two photos are properly lined up for comfortable viewing. The exact spacing is a function of the particular stereoscope that is being used and of the visual characteristics of the person doing the viewing.

When the required spacing has been established, the distances between matching points on the two photographs are measured. The distance between the principal point of one photograph and its conjugate principal point on the adjoining photograph is what is usually measured. This distance is called *absolute parallax* (Fig. 4.24).

Figure 4.24 Measurement of parallax difference. (See text for explanation.)

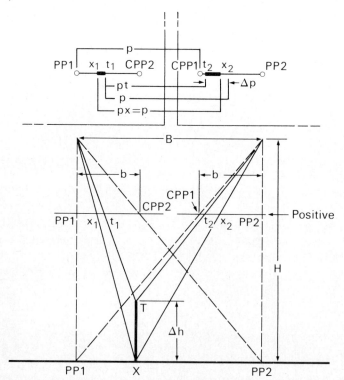

In this example, all the ground area in the photographs is at the same elevation. The absolute parallax measurement, therefore, is the same no matter which points on the ground are considered. In the case of the chimney, however, there is a difference in the parallax measurements taken at the top and the bottom of the chimney, as shown in Fig. 4.24. The base of the chimney is located at X and its top is located at T, which is directly above X. On a map, the points T and X would be placed at the same horizontal location; the chimney would be represented by a dot. On the aerial photographs, however, the top of the chimney is farther away from the principal point of each photo than is its base. The separation between the top and the bottom of the chimney is greater in photo 2 than in photo 1. This is because the chimney is located farther from the principal point of photo 2.

The *photo base* is measured next, using a millimeter scale. The photo base is the distance, at the photo scale, between the location of the airplane at the time one photo was taken and its location at the time the second photo was taken. On the photo this is the distance between the principal point and the conjugate principal point. In this example, either $b1$ or $b2$ may be used because there is no tilt in either photo. This measurement establishes the scale relationship between the photo and the actual terrain.

The following description of the technique for measuring parallax is based on the use of a parallax bar and stereoscopic viewing. If the points are clearly identifiable, the measurement can be done, with somewhat less reliability, by using dividers (see Chapter 5) and without a stereoscope.

The *parallax bar* is a rodlike device with a transparent plate attached to each end (Fig. 4.25). One plate is fixed and the other is moved in the direction parallel to the bar by turning an adjusting knob. Each plate has on it a *half-mark,* which is a small circle, cross, or dot. Changes in the distance between the half-marks are indicated on a scale attached to the adjusting knob. When the half-marks are matched to a feature in the photo and are properly adjusted, they merge with one another and appear as a floating mark. Moving the marks farther apart makes them appear to fall away from the surface of the stereomodel; moving them closer together creates the opposite effect.

The stereoscope is placed over the photos and the parallax bar is placed on the surface of the photos, parallel to the flight line. The bar must be kept parallel to the flight line in order to avoid errors in measurement. The floating mark is first placed and adjusted so that it appears to be just touching the ground surface adjacent to the base of the chimney. The absolute parallax for that elevation is then determined by reading the indicator dial, which is calibrated in fractions of millimeters. In this example, as already suggested, the absolute parallax of X is the same as the absolute parallax of the principal points of both photos, because all three points are at the same elevation.

Figure 4.25 Parallax bar. (Courtesy of The Lietz Co.)

The *parallax difference* between X and T is then determined by moving the parallax bar and adjusting the location and spacing of the half-marks so that the floating mark appears to just touch the top of the chimney. This requires moving the right-hand half-mark the distance Δp closer to the fixed mark.

The relationship between parallax difference and elevation difference is given by the equation: $\Delta h = (H/b)\Delta p$. This equation shows the positive relationship between the two measurements, which means that as the elevation difference (Δh) increases, the parallax difference (Δp) increases proportionately. The reason for this relationship can be appreciated by noting that the apparent location of the top of an object (T') depends upon its elevation above the datum (Fig. 4.26); for example, if T were twice as high (above the datum), T' would be located twice as far from the principal point (Fig. 14.12). This displacement, in turn, is represented by the parallax difference (Δp) between the bottom and the top of the object, as can be noted by observing the similar triangles LXT' and Lxt.

Assuming that the parallex difference in this example is 1.37 mm, the photo base is 92.3 mm, and the altitude of the airplane when the photos were taken was 3,658 m (12,000 ft), the height of the chimney is found to be 54.3 m (178 ft).

Stereoscopic plotters   *Stereoscopic plotters* use a projected, three-dimensional image as the basis for plotting map information from aerial photographs. This image is tied to surveyed control points and the information it contains is then plotted onto a manuscript map.

Corrections must be made in the three-dimensional model because of variations in the tilt of individual photographs and the altitude differences between photographs. The locations of surveyed control points are used as guides in this process. Because of the three-dimensional nature of the image, the problem of lateral displacement is not encountered when a stereoscopic plotter is used. The map location of points plotted from the image is therefore correct.

Many varieties of stereoscopic plotting instruments are in use, but the following description is based on a typical, fairly simple type called a *multiplex* (Fig. 4.27).

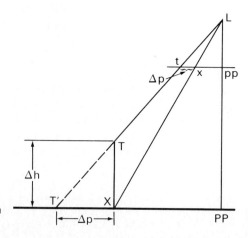

Figure 4.26 Relationship between parallax and elevation.

Many aspects of the complex processes involved in setting up and using the multiplex are left out of this description and those that remain are simplified. This is because the goal is to emphasize how the technique is used and not to provide a guide for the actual operation of the instrument.

The three-dimensional image that is the basis of stereoscopic plotting is obtained by viewing two images simultaneously, as was described when the use of the stereoscope was explained above. In a multiplex plotter, however, the manner in which the image is obtained and the viewing accomplished is somewhat different.

The first step is the creation of a *diapositive plate.* This is a photographic positive that is made on a glass plate instead of on paper. The resulting image is much like a photographic slide. Depending on the type of plotter being used, the diapositive may be reduced in size from the original aerial photo negative or it may be the same size as the original.

The plotter has two or more projectors. These are much like photographic

Figure 4.27   Relationship between projectors, stereomodel, tracing table, and the manuscript map in a multiplex type plotter. (Courtesy of TBR Associates Inc.)

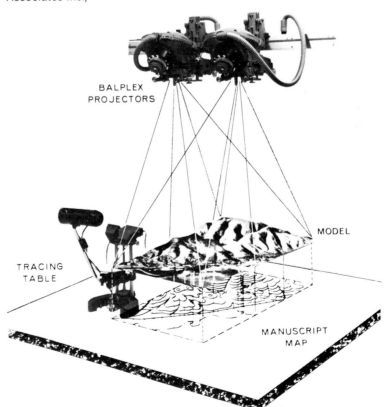

enlargers in that they contain a light source that shines through the diapositive and a lens that is used to focus the image. One diapositive is placed in each projector and the projectors are arranged in essentially the same relationship to the table surface as the airplane was to the ground when the photographs were taken. The horizontal distance between the projectors represents the horizontal distance between the points from which the photos were taken. The vertical distance from the projector to the plotting table represents the altitude of the camera above the terrain. As part of the adjustment process, the projectors are tilted to offset any tilt in the original photographs. If one photograph was taken at a different elevation from the other, the projectors are also set at the proper heights so that the scale differences are offset. When they are properly oriented and viewed, the projected images provide the basis for a visual, *three-dimensional model* of the original terrain.

The visual model is obtained because of the parallax difference between the photos, in the same manner as when prints are viewed through a stereoscope. In this case, however, the separation of the images is obtained by the use of filters. A red filter is placed in front of one projector and a cyan (greenish blue) filter is placed in front of the other. The operator wears a pair of glasses with one red and one cyan-colored lens. The filtering effect of these lenses allows the operator to see one image with one eye and the other image with the other eye. When the separate images are thus viewed simultaneously, the result is a mental fusion of the images; the operator sees the apparently three-dimensional view of the terrain which is called a *stereomodel* (Fig. 4.27). This method of creating the image is referred to as an *anaglyph system.*

Other systems, which involve the use of polarized light or of alternating shutters, can provide for the simultaneous viewing of the two images. Whatever the system, however, the end result is the same—a three-dimensional model of the terrain is obtained.

A movable *tracing table* is located on the table surface of the plotter (Fig. 4.27). This tracing table consists of a framework on which is mounted a circular white viewing screen called a *platen*. The platen is adjusted vertically by turning a calibrated dial; a scale indicates its height. In the center of the platen is a pinpoint light source, called the *floating mark*. The stereomodel is seen against the reflective background of the platen. The platen essentially disappears from view but the floating mark remains visible and appears to be suspended in space. A *plotting pencil* is located directly under the floating mark. This pencil can be raised and thus can be moved without making a mark. When it is lowered so that it touches the base map that is fastened to the plotting table, it traces on the base the exact path followed by the floating mark as it is moved over the surface of the table.

The line image drawn by the plotting pencil is called a *manuscript map.* Some plotters have a mechanical linkage, or an electronically controlled tracing device, so that the manuscript map is traced on a table located outside the image area. This is done for convenience and does not alter the principle involved.

Before plotting begins, the two projectors are adjusted so that the stereomodel is seen. The location of the stereomodel on the plotting table is adjusted so that the control points in the model are correctly positioned in relation to their plotted locations on the base map. This is accomplished by locating the floating mark so that it just touches the image of the control point. The relationship between the base map and the stereomodel is then adjusted so that the plotting pencil is located at the plotted location of the control point. This process is continued until all the control points within the area of the model are correctly located. At this time, final corrections for tilt are accomplished, because the three-dimensional location of the control points in the stereomodel will not match the plotted control points if any tilt remains.

Vertical data, such as the location of a contour line, are obtained from the stereomodel by locking the floating mark at the desired altitude. The determination of the correct height of the floating mark is obtained by bringing the floating mark to the apparent height of each of the vertical control points within the image, in turn, and reading the height scale. The relationship between the scale reading and the actual elevations of the control points is then calculated. This ratio is used to establish the scale setting necessary to represent any desired height.

When the floating mark is set at the correct height, it is moved until it just touches the apparent surface of the stereomodel. The plotting pencil is then lowered and the floating mark is moved so it remains in contact with the surface of the model—that is, so that it follows a contour line. As it is moved, a planimetric line image of the contour is traced on the map by the plotting pencil. Additional contours are drawn by raising or lowering the floating mark to the correct height to represent the desired elevations and then tracing the line of contact at each elevation.

Horizontal data, such as the route alignment of a road, are obtained by moving the floating mark until it is at one end of the feature and is just touching the apparent surface of the feature in the stereomodel. The mark is then moved so that it follows the center line of the feature. Because the feature moves up and down over the surface of the terrain, the mark is moved up and down to keep it in contact with the feature's surface. The plotting pencil traces the horizontal path followed by the floating mark and thereby records the planimetric location of the feature that is being traced.

When all of the desired data have been traced from a particular stereomodel, one of the diapositives is removed from its projector and the other diapositive is put in its place. (In the case of a plotter with multiple heads, the next projector is turned on and the first projector is turned off. The filters must also be placed in the correct projector.) The diapositive of the next photo in the flight line sequence is then placed in the empty projector. The images of these two diapositives are then viewed and a new stereomodel is obtained. This model, which will partially overlap with the original model, is matched against the appropriate control points and the existing map manuscript, and the plotting continues. Minor adjustments in the plot are made as needed, so that details obtained from this second model match those obtained from the first model. For example, contour lines, road alignments, and other plotted features may need slight adjustments in order to continue across the image area as continuous lines. The process of extending the plot to adjacent areas and to adjacent flight lines is continued until coverage of the total area is completed.

After the manuscript map is completed it provides the basis for the production of a final map, using the techniques described in Chapter 5. *Field checking,* which involves actually comparing the manuscript with the mapped features, is usually a necessary part of the map production process. This is because it is not always possible to be absolutely certain about the identity of certain features in the photograph—only a visual check on the ground will ensure against misinterpretations of the photo image.

Two other types of plotters are illustrated in addition to the multiplex in order to give an indication of the range of available equipment. In the first type, there is a mechanical linkage that joins the platen and the light source (Fig. 4.28). This arrangement has the advantage of focusing the light on the portion of the diapositive that is being used at a given time, thus creating a brighter image. In the second type, the diapositives are viewed through a system of prisms and lenses rather than

Figure 4.28 Multiplex type plotter with mechanical linkage. (Courtesy of The Kelsh Instrument Div., Danko Arlington Inc.)

Figure 4.29   Stereoplotter. (Courtesy of Kern & Co.)

being projected, so there is no anaglyph-type image on the plotting table (Fig. 4.29). The movement of the floating dot that appears in the image area of this plotter is controlled by a *scanning carriage* located in a position similar to that of the platen in the multiplex. The scanning carriage possesses mechanical linkages that control the movement of the autopositives in relation to the light source in order to keep the correct area of the stereomodel in view. In addition, a pantograph moves in conjunction with the movement of the floating dot and traces the path of the dot on the manuscript plot; this plotting is done on a table that stands conveniently to one side of the viewing system.

Analytical Plotter

Since the 1960s, an advanced form of device for the extraction of information from stereopairs has been developed. The plotters described in the section above are called *analog plotters*—that is, they produce a manuscript map that is a physical analogy to the stereo-image. The newer form of plotter is called an *analytical plotter,* because it produces a digital record of the stereo-image rather than a visible plot.

An analytical stereoplotter (Fig. 4.30) consists of a stereoviewing device, a computer, and, frequently, a *coordinatograph* (often called a flatbed plotter—see Chapter 11). Using this type of device brings about a great improvement in the accuracy and speed with which measurements can be extracted from the aerial photographs and, later, corrected and otherwise manipulated. This is because the phys-

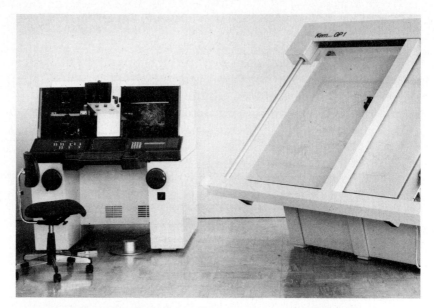

Figure 4.30 Analytical stereoplotter. (Courtesy of Kern & Co.)

ical limitations of the mechanics and optics of analog plotters are eliminated. In addition, the digital form of the information allows the introduction of automatic corrections of known errors, such as the focal length and distortion characteristics of the camera, the curvature of the earth, and so on, by mathematical manipulation.

The stereoviewer portion of an analytical plotter consists of two illuminated stages that support a stereoscopic pair of diapositives (either black-and-white or color photographs may be used). A system of prisms and lenses allows the operator to view one of the diapositives with one eye and the other diapositive with the other eye, thus creating a stereoscopic image. There is a floating mark that moves over the surface of the stereomodel under the control either of the operator or of the computer.

The operator controls the extraction of information from the stereomodel by moving the floating mark horizontally, vertically, or both. For example, information regarding control points is obtained by moving the floating mark to each point and activating the system which reads, records, and stores the horizontal and vertical coordinates of the point in the desired coordinate system. Similarly, the path of contour lines is recorded as a series of horizontal coordinates at the same elevation. Planimetric features, such as road alignments, are located by recording the horizontal and vertical coordinates of points along their path.

The basic idea of analytic plotting is to determine the relationships between the photographic image coordinates and the ground coordinates of the same objects in the real world. For example, when the floating mark is placed on identified control points in the model, the model coordinates are compared with the actual ground coordinates of the same points obtained from survey data and previously stored in the computer. The relationships between the measured model coordinates and the known surveyed coordinates are solved and stored by the computer, thus providing the basis for adjusting the model and, eventually, the plotted map to fit the control network.

When the desired information from the stereomodel is stored, a number of different applications can be carried out. For example, the area or volume of a given zone can be computed by simply moving the floating point to a sequence of locations that outline the desired area. After the points are identified, the appropriate computer program is called upon to carry out the desired computation, using the data stored in the system. This procedure does not require any additional measurement of the model. Another application is to use the relationships between control points to mathematically solve their planimetric shifts. This approach can be extended to determine the correct locations and elevations of other points within the model. An example of a particularly useful application of information obtained from an analytical plotter is the creation of a digital terrain model.

Digital terrain model   A *digital terrain model* (DTM) is a set of regularly organized, three-dimensional coordinates that represent the visual stereomodel and, by analogy, the actual terrain. To create a DTM, the floating mark in the analytical plotter is moved over the model in a prearranged pattern, under computer control. While the floating mark is moving, the operator of the analytical plotter is required to keep it continuously on the surface of the stereomodel. The horizontal and vertical coordinates generated during this scanning are stored in the computer as a sequenced digital representation of the terrain—the DTM.

Digital terrain models can be created from existing maps or from other sources—all that is required is that the horizontal and vertical locations of an organized sequence of terrain points be converted into digital form. The U.S. Geological Survey (USGS), for example, has created digital terrain tapes for the entire United States, extracted from existing 1:250,000-scale maps, as well as data for some areas at a scale of 1:24,000. These magnetic tapes, as well as tapes containing selected planimetric information based on the 1:2,000,000 National Atlas sectional maps, are available for purchase.

One use of a DTM is the creation of a plot of a series of *terrain profiles* consisting of cross sections through the model. Such plots present a graphic representation of slope direction and steepness and an apparent bird's-eye view of the terrain (Fig. 4.31). Another application has been in the area of forest-fire control planning, and other uses are certain to evolve. A DTM can also be used to control the movement of the scanning point in an orthoprojector, thus speeding up the process of completing an orthophotograph, which is described in the next section.

Orthophotographs   A device called an *orthoprojector* (or orthophotoscope) is used to change the perspective image of an aerial photo to an orthogonal image. This

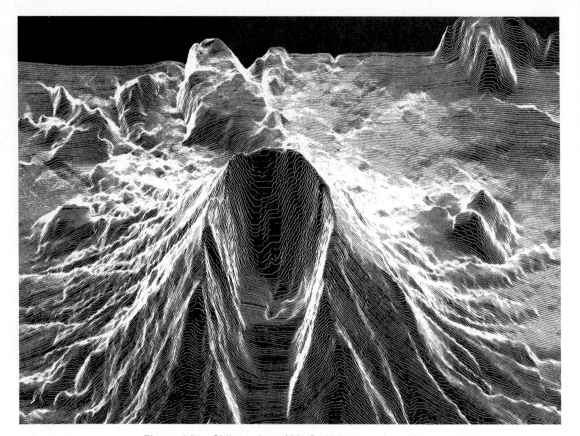

Figure 4.31 Oblique view of Mt. St. Helens produced from a digital terrain model (DTM). (Courtesy of Mark Hurd Aerial Surveys, Inc., Minneapolis, Minn.) This is a portion of one of the winning maps in the Ninth Annual Map Design Competition sponsored by the American Cartographic Association (ACA) of the American Congress on Surveying and Mapping (ACSM).

means that the location of each point in the orthophotograph is virtually planimetrically correct, rather than being radially offset due to altitude differences. The result is a photograph whose geometry rivals that of a map.

The process used in the orthoprojector is based on the type of stereomodel used in stereographic plotters. The reason for this, as discussed above, is that the stereomodel does not suffer from the horizontal displacement problems that afflict individual aerial photos; it is a three-dimensional reproduction of the terrain, not a two-dimensional transformation of it. What is needed, then, is a means of using the information contained in the stereomodel to control the production of the photo print. If this is done, an orthographic projection is obtained, rather than a perspective projection. In essence, this is what the orthoprojector accomplishes.

A typical orthoprojector has two major components. The first unit is a stereoscopic viewer that produces the stereomodel. This is done in the same manner as with a stereoscopic plotter, described above. The second unit is a printmaker, which is similar to a photographic enlarger (Fig. 4.32). It holds the negative from which the print will be made, as well as the photographic paper and the exposure control system. The two units may be connected or may be located in separate rooms.

When a print is made in an ordinary photoenlarger the entire print is made at one time. In the case of the orthoprojector, however, the table on which the exposure is made is covered with a mask that contains a *rectangular slit*. The slit uncovers a very small area of the photographic paper at any one time. It is incrementally moved across the surface of the table so that each small area is exposed, one area after the other, until the entire image has been printed. The size of the slit and, hence, of the area exposed, is varied depending on the accuracy required and on the type of terrain. Typical slits range from 4 mm × 16 mm to 0.5 mm × 2 mm. This means there are literally thousands of individual exposures in one final print. In order to remove planimetric displacement completely, the exposure slit would have to be so small that the entire area exposed at any one time would be at the same elevation. Because this condition is not always met, some error may remain because of elevation differences within the area of the slit.

As the slit moves over the surface of the photographic paper, the operator of the orthoprojector is viewing a stereomodel and a floating mark. The position of

Figure 4.32 Orthoprojector. (Courtesy of Firma Carl Zeiss, Dept. of Geodesy & Photogrammetry, P.O.B. 13 69, 7082 Oberkochen, West Germany.)

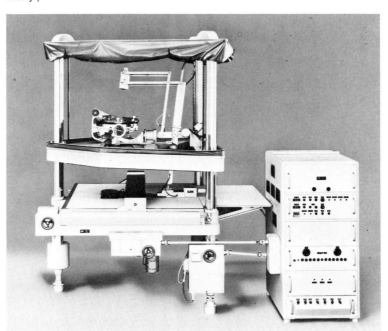

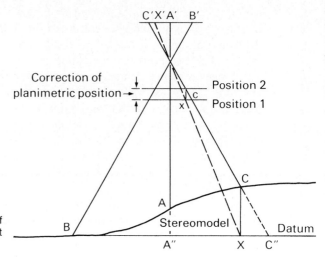

Figure 4.33 Vertical movement of orthoprojector printer to correct planimetric displacement of image.

the floating mark is coordinated with the position of the exposure slit. The operator continuously adjusts the vertical position of the floating mark so that it remains in contact with the surface of the terrain in the stereomodel. As this is done, the distance between the exposure table and the photonegative is automatically kept in adjustment so that it is, in effect, in contact with the surface of the stereomodel at the time of each exposure (Fig. 4.33). This means that the exposures are in the correct planimetric position and, therefore, the overall result is the virtual removal of planimetric displacement from the photograph. The amount of image displacement removed as a result of using this process depends on the elevation differences within the area of the photo. This difference can be quite striking, as the example shown in Fig. 4.34 illustrates.

Analytical orthophotos   The control of the orthoprojector system may be turned over to a device that transforms the original aerial photograph into an orthophoto based on information in digital form—obtained, for example, from an analytical plotter in the form of a DTM. This device, which is known as an *analytical orthoprojector,* uses the information from the DTM to control the process of creating the orthophoto (Fig. 4.35). In this process, each small area of the uncorrected photo is projected through a slit and thence through a prism, mirror, and lens system onto the sensitized film on which the new image is formed. The optical system accomplishes the scale changes and image displacements that are necessary to obtain an orthographic representation of the image. A system of this type is even able to adjust for the average slope of the terrain within the area of the exposure slit, so that the final result is virtually free of even minor position displacement.

Orthophotomaps

The addition of supplementary information, such as place names, a locational grid, contour numbers, and other symbols converts an orthophoto into an *orthophotomap*. Orthophotomaps can be reproduced using standard lithographic printing tech-

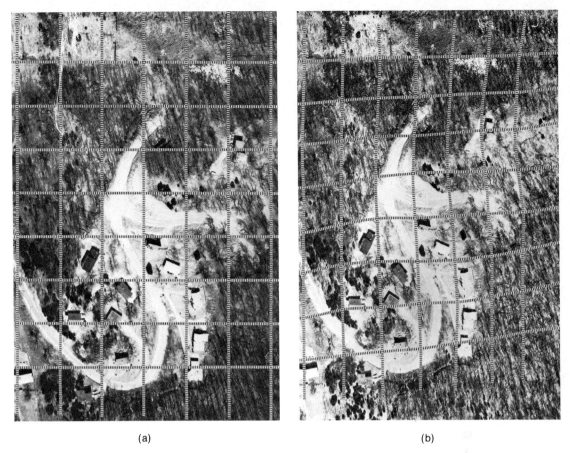

(a)	(b)

Figure 4.34 Effect of removing planimetric displacement: (a) Uncorrected vertical photograph; (b) Corrected orthophoto image. (Photos courtesy of Aerometric Engineering, Inc.)

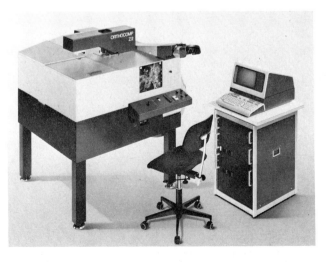

Figure 4.35 Analytical orthoprojector. (Courtesy of Firma Carl Zeiss, Dept. of Geodesy & Photogrammetry, P.O.B. 13 69, 7082 Oberkochen, West Germany.)

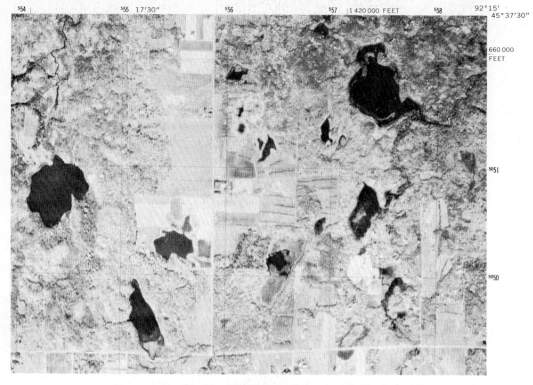

Figure 4.36   Portion of USGS orthophotoquad. (Frederic SE quadrangle, Wisconsin, 1974. Original scale, 1:24,000—illustration reduced.)

niques, and provide, for many purposes, a very effective substitute for a more conventional map.

The USGS, for example, produces orthophoto products. In their terminology, *orthophotoquads* are orthophoto images printed in black and white in standard quadrangle format (Fig. 4.36). Orthophotoquads show photographic detail but cartographic treatment is limited and they do not show contours. The USGS orthophotomaps are refinements of orthophotoquads that include contour lines and names, and are color-enhanced to improve their readability.

RADAR

Radar is an active remote sensing technique involving the transmission of *microwave* signals that are reflected back to a receiver from objects in the viewing area. Aircraft-mounted radar systems are used to provide mappable information regarding the location of objects, the texture of surfaces, the presence of subsurface moisture, the temperature of surfaces, and so on. Radar signals penetrate clouds and haze effectively, a characteristic that allows the acquisition of images under conditions that would prevent the use of other methods, such as aerial photography.

Two of the several types of radar that are in use, *plan position indicator radar* (PPI) and *side-looking airborne radar* (SLAR), are particularly useful for mapping purposes. Plan position indicator radar involves generating a circular pattern of signals from a point-source transmitter. The reflected signals are translated into an image on a televisionlike viewing screen; strong returns result in light tones, and weak returns in darker tones. Once the image is formed, it can be photographed for future mapping use. The plotting of objects within this image is accomplished in terms of their polar coordinates in relation to the location of the apparatus.

For mapping purposes, side-looking airborne radar images have particular advantages (Fig. 4.37). This technique utilizes a longer antenna than the rotating type used with plan position indicator radar, because a longer antenna provides better image resolution. The length of antenna that can be carried by an airplane is limited, however, so a form of SLAR that utilizes an approach called *synthetic aperture* has been developed. In this method, a relatively small antenna transmits a diverging beam of energy. The returns from this beam arrive at the receiving antenna at different time intervals but are sorted out by a computer to obtain an accurate image that is the equivalent of the results that would be obtained by a very long antenna. In addition, SLAR uses Cartesian rather than polar coordinates, so that its mapping applications are improved.

Figure 4.37 SLAR image of San Andreas fault. (Courtesy of Westinghouse Electric Corp.)

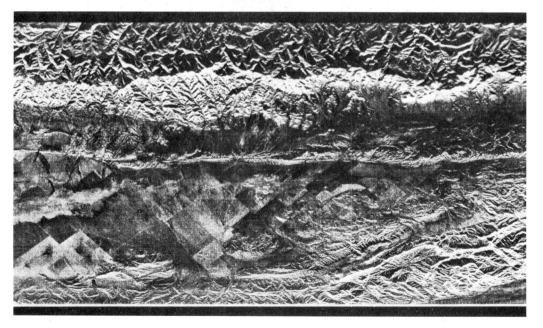

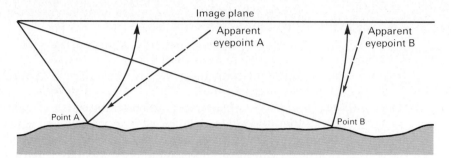

Figure 4.38   Distance relationships in radar image.

A radar image involves different geometrical relationships from those of an optical projection, such as an aerial photograph. In particular, a radar image is recorded in terms of the distance of the object from the antenna. This causes *foreshortening;* that is, terrain that is farther from the radar appears to be seen from directly above, whereas terrain closer to the radar appears to be seen from an increasingly oblique view (Fig. 4.38). Another effect is that of vertical *displacement* of the image toward the source. For example, on an aerial photograph a tall chimney appears to lean away from the principal point of the photo. In a radar image, the same chimney appears to lean toward the radar source because the top of the chimney is closer to the source than is the bottom. In addition, features located behind an elevated area of terrain are hidden from view by apparent shadows on the image.

SCANNERS

Scanners are passive devices that detect and record energy reflected or emitted from objects within their range. They typically operate in one of two patterns; *line scan* (or whiskbroom) and *array scan* (or pushbroom).

In operation, the line-scan type of scanner uses a rotating mirror that views the terrain in continuous strips perpendicular to the line of flight [Fig. 4.39(a)]. The side-to-side aspect of this pattern of viewing leads to the use of the descriptive term, "whiskbroom." As the mirror rotates, it continuously reflects the terrain image so that it strikes a *photoelectric detector* that is sensitive to radiation of the desired wavelength. This generates a signal that is amplified electronically and recorded on magnetic tape. Alternatively, the signal is used to produce an image on a televisionlike device that can be recorded photographically.

Array scanners, on the other hand, are arranged so that a field of view across the line of flight is constantly within view [Fig. 4.39(b)]. Sensors are arranged so that each one scans a line of terrain parallel with the line of flight and the movement along these scanning paths is the origin of the "pushbroom" description. The signal strength received from the terrain is recorded a line at a time, in a manner similar to that of the line scanner.

Scanners are operated from both aircraft and space platforms. Because the

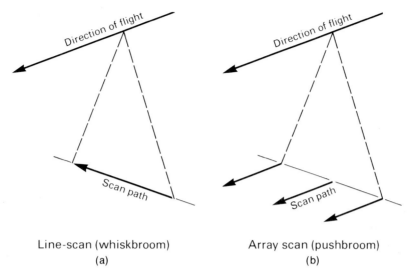

Line-scan (whiskbroom)
(a)

Array scan (pushbroom)
(b)

Figure 4.39 Whiskbroom and pushbroom scanning patterns.

images that are produced are oblique, except for locations directly under the platform, it is not always practical to use them for precise measurements; they are generally more useful for feature identification.

Infrared Scanners

The atmosphere is not uniformly transparent to all wavelengths of energy. *Infrared scanners* are used to detect the longer infrared wavelengths that penetrate the relatively transparent atmospheric *windows* (typically in the 0.7–1.2 μm, 1.5–2.5 μm, 3.0–5.5 μm, and 8–14 μm ranges). The process depends on the detection of the infrared energy emitted by any object—animal, vegetable, or mineral—that has a temperature above absolute zero. The amount of radiation emitted is related to the temperature and surface characteristics of the object; the cooler surfaces within the target area appear as dark areas on the image and the warmer surfaces are lighter. For this reason, one of the principal uses of infrared scanners involves the sensing of temperature differences. These include such relatively obvious applications as the detection of forest fires, the monitoring of volcanic action, or the determination of temperature differences in water bodies caused, for example, by hot effluents or by cool springs. Less obvious applications involve gathering information regarding plant health, determining the status of irrigation moisture, monitoring the decay of sea ice, and counting animal populations.

Microwave Scanners

The operation of *microwave scanners* is similar to that of the infrared scanners described above, but energy in the wavelengths at which they operate penetrates cloud cover more effectively. Microwave scanners are used for such applications as detecting variations in soil moisture content, determining the relative roughness or smoothness of the surface of the sea, monitoring the extent of sea ice, estimating the extent of snow cover, locating oil films on water surfaces, or estimating atmospheric moisture and rainfall amounts, as well as for temperature monitoring.

IMAGERY FROM SPACE

Over a period of several years, some of the information obtained from a variety of space exploration programs has been utilized for mapping purposes. In the United States, for example, the first of the *Landsat satellites,* originally named Earth Resources Technology Satellites (ERTS), began operation in 1972 and was removed from service in 1978. Two additional satellites, which operated during the period from 1975 until 1982, provided limited service into 1983. Landsat 4, launched in July 1982, flies a nearly circular orbit 708 km (438 mi) above the earth's surface with coverage of the entire globe, other than the polar areas, every 18 days. It carries two remote sensing systems; a four-band *multispectral scanner* (MSS) and an experimental system called the *Thematic Mapper* (TM). The TM replaces the *return beam vidicon* (RBV) systems used on Landsats 1–3. The information obtained from the MSS system is normally available to the public within 30 days.[1] Other space missions, such as Skylab and the Gemini and Apollo programs, have also provided data, but not on a continuing, systematic basis. The following discussion, therefore, is based principally on the characteristics of the Landsat program, especially Landsat 4.

Information from space platforms is obtained from a wide range of frequencies of the electromagnetic spectrum, ranging from the relatively little-used gamma ray and ultraviolet portions into the far reaches of the radar portion. Because of the differing effects of *atmospheric absorption and scatter,* which interfere with detection, some wavebands are avoided and others are used more frequently. The wavelength bands used in the multispectral scanners carried by Landsat 4, for example, are the following:

Band 1 (previously Band 4)—green, 0.5 to 0.6 μm;

Band 2 (previously Band 5)—red, 0.6 to 0.7 μm;

Band 3 (previously Band 6)—near-infrared, 0.7 to 0.8 μm; and

Band 4 (previously Band 7)—second near-infrared, 0.8 to 1.1 μm.

Some of the information obtained from space is recorded by instruments that return to earth. In such cases, the processing and interpretation is carried out in a manner essentially the same as that already described for information obtained from similar systems carried aloft by aircraft. More frequently, however, the instruments do not return to earth, so the information that has been collected must be *encoded*

[1]Information is available from the Earth Resources Observation Systems, (EROS) Data Center, Sioux Falls, S.D. 57198.

on board and then transmitted by radio to earth stations for conversion into the required form for interpretation.

Typically, *radio transmission* of imagery requires the image to be formed by the sensing unit within the satellite. The image may consist of an electrical charge built up on a sensitive plate or sensor, or it may be an actual photograph that has been processed on-board. The total image area is then divided into small subunits, called *pixels,* each of which is scanned by the instrumentation (Fig. 4.40). The outcome of this scanning is the recording of a series of signals. These signals are usually *digital values* that represent the strength of the signal, such as the particular shade of gray that is characteristic of the pixel (some systems can record as many as 256 levels). The digital values are then transmitted to an earth station where they are again recorded on a magnetic tape. The recorded values for all the pixels are then reconstituted into a visual image, if desired, or retained in digital form for future processing.

The size of the area included within a pixel determines the resolution of the remotely sensed image and, therefore, the use to which it can be put. If the portion of the target area which is covered by a pixel is 80 m × 80 m, for example, no feature smaller than that can be detected or mapped. As the size of the surface area covered by each pixel is reduced, resolution is improved and the amount of information that is retrieved and mapped is correspondingly increased.

The best *ground resolution* of orbital sensors (that is, the smallest image area that can be delineated) presently ranges around 20—40 m². It is suggested that the resolution from such sensors is probably limited to 10 m × 10 m. Photography with this resolution is planned for the NASA Large Format Camera portion of the Space Shuttle program. This program, which is planned for 1984, will produce stereoscopic images suitable for topographic map compilation at a scale of 1:50,000, with a 20–80 m contour interval.[2]

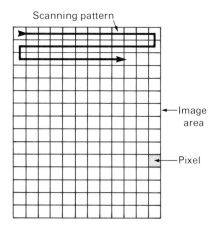

Figure 4.40   Scanning of pixels.

[2]Chester C. Slama, ed., *Manual of Photogrammetry,* 4th ed. (Falls Church, Va.: American Society of Photogrammetry, 1980), p. 966.

Use of Imagery

In the case of the moon and the planets, sensors mounted on spacecraft provide the only usable mapping information, and topographic maps of some of these bodies have been produced using such data. Even on earth, however, increasing use is being made of satellite imagery as systems become more refined. Such imagery has provided information about crop problems, thermal hot spots, ocean currents, weather patterns, and other environmental conditions. In general, most of the applications of this imagery have involved plotting the information to produce thematic maps, or using it as a check on the currency and accuracy of existing maps, rather than using it to produce topographic base maps. As was mentioned above, however, the potential for the application of satellite images to topographic base map production is increasing.

Several advantages are gained from the use of sensors located in space. First, because of the relatively great distance of the satellite from the surface of the earth, the image obtained from orbital positions is nearly orthographic. This means that the horizontal position of features is very nearly correct, even when there is considerable variation in relief. Also, because of the high altitude involved, the images obtained from space cover a wider area. This assists in the identification of extensive features. Such features are difficult to recognize on low-altitude images because their configuration is lost over the extent of a large number of individual images. On a single image that covers a large area, however, the same features often become readily apparent to the analyst. In addition, coverage of extensive areas can be obtained more rapidly and with greater frequency than with other techniques.

An additional benefit from the use of information obtained from instruments mounted in spacecraft is the reduction of the required density of mapping control points. This occurs because of the large ground area covered by each image. Also, the orbit of a spacecraft is highly predictable, so that the position of the camera at the time each image was acquired can be accurately determined. In addition, taking a stellar photo at the same time the image of the terrain is taken provides accurate orientation information. The altitude of the observation platform above the terrain surface can also be obtained by radar or laser distance-measuring devices, often within a range of less than 1 m, which contributes to the accuracy of scale determination.

One problem with using very high-altitude information for the production of topographic maps, in addition to problems with resolution, is that the angle of view is narrow in relation to terrain elevation. This means that very little parallax difference can be measured in adjacent, overlapping photos, and height determination is therefore difficult. For this reason, overlapping angled images are often used instead of vertical views (Fig. 4.41). Such angled images are obtained by using either two sensors, one looking forward and one looking backward, or one sensor that alternately looks forward and then backward. The images obtained by either method can be coordinated to provide views of the same area from two different angles. When this is done, parallax is increased and height information can be extracted by methods similar to those used to measure elevations in normal aerial photographs.

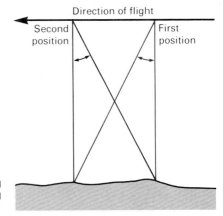

Figure 4.41 Stereoscopic viewing of forward- and backward-facing photos.

Applications Landsat 4 MSS images cover an area of 185 km (115 mi) on a side, with an 80 m × 80 m ground resolution. Because of the earth's rotation and the scanning pattern, these images are parallelograms, not squares, with the outer edges parallel to the orbital track of the satellite. Each of the four wavebands, which are scanned simultaneously, is particularly useful for the detection of certain classes of features. The features emphasized on the MSS bands are as follows:

Band 1—areas of shallow water and of moving, sediment-laden water;

Band 2—cultural features, such as metropolitan areas;

Band 3—vegetation, the boundary between land and water, and landforms;

Band 4—similar to Band 2, but with better penetration of atmospheric haze.

Images from each band may be used individually, or they may be compared with one another to detect objects or surfaces with different signatures (Fig. 4.42). In addition, *false-color composite images* are produced by successively exposing three black-and-white band images onto a single sheet of color film, using different color filters for each. On the false-color composites, healthy vegetation appears in bright red; clear water is black; sediment-laden water is powder blue; and urban centers are blue or blue-gray (Plate 1).

Vidicon Camera

The return-beam vidicon camera (RBV) is a televisionlike device that generally operates in the 0.35—1.1 μm range. Landsat 3, for example, utilized a pair of these cameras, each of which covered a 98 km² image area with a ground resolution of 20–40 m. The RBVs operate by forming an optical image on a photoconductive target surface. This image builds up a charge pattern that is detected by a scanning electron beam. As the beam scans, it generates a digital signal that is transmitted to an earth station for decoding. At the same time as it generates the signal, the

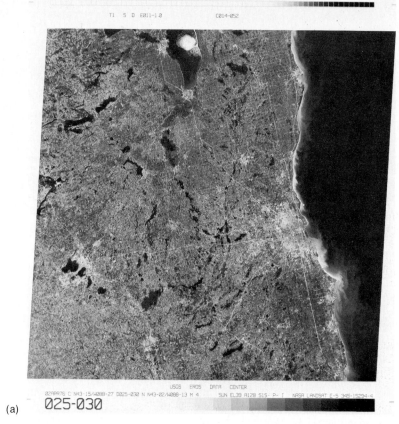

(a)   025-030

Figure 4.42   Landsat images of Milwaukee, Wisconsin, and vicinity, April 2, 1976. (a) Band 4; (b) Band 5; (c) Band 6; (d) Band 7. (USGS EROS Data Center.)

scanning beam also erases the image from the target surface so that it is prepared to receive the next image.

Thematic Mapper

The multispectral scanners used in the Landsat program are of the oscillating mirror (whiskbroom) type. This includes the experimental thematic mapper that is aboard Landsat 4 instead of the RBVs that were carried by Landsats 1–3. The thematic mapper simultaneously scans seven spectral bands over a 185 km wide swath. The ground resolution of the thematic mapper is 30 m × 30 m in Bands 1–5 and 7, which are in the reflected sunlight range, and is 120 m × 120 m in Band 6, the thermal infrared band. The wavelengths of the thematic mapper bands are: Band 1, 0.42–0.52 μm; Band 2, 0.52–0.60 μm; Band 3, 0.63–0.69 μm; Band 4, 0.76–0.90 μm; Band 5, 1.55–1.75 μm; Band 6, 10.4–12.5 μm; and Band 7, 2.10–2.35 μm.

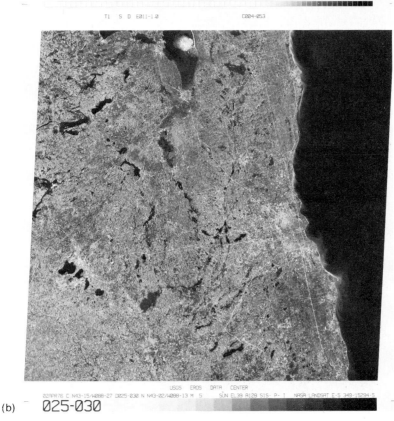

T1 S D E011-10   C004-053

USGS   EROS   DATA   CENTER
02APR76 C N43-15/W088-27 D025-030 N N43-02/W088-13 M 5   SUN EL39 A128 51S- P- I   NASA LANDSAT E-5 349-15294-5

(b) 025-030

Figure 4.42   (*cont.*)

Linear Array Scanners

It is expected that linear array detectors will be used in future programs. It is now possible to arrange as many as 2000 detector elements in a side-by-side array and, by joining arrays, to provide as many as 10,000 detector elements per line. With this type of scanner, an entire line on the ground is imaged instantaneously rather than scanned by a moving beam. This means that the image must be recorded in the time the spacecraft takes to move to the next line of the ground scene. The spatial resolution of this pushbroom type of scanner, at right angles to the ground track, is determined by the spacing of the detector elements. The resolution along the track is determined by the relationship between the velocity with which the platform moves over the earth (ground track velocity) and the time interval between readouts from the sensors. Several arrays can be aligned with one another, with appropriate filters on each array, to provide a multispectral scanning system.

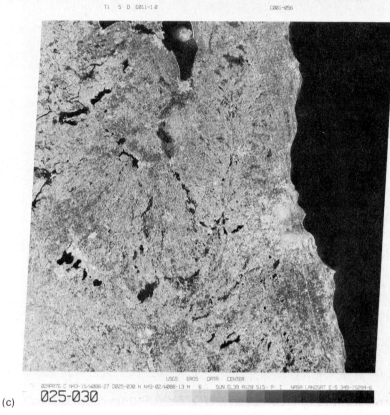

(c) 025-030

Figure 4.42 (*cont.*)

Image Enhancement

Remotely sensed images are often subjected to additional processing called *image enhancement.* Image enhancement involves the use of techniques that either correct the geometric characteristics of the image or improve its visual quality so that it is possible to detect information that was initially hidden or difficult to discern. The types of enhancement performed on Landsat imagery at the U.S. Geological Survey's Earth Resources Observation Systems (EROS) Data Center, for example, include *geometric and radiometric corrections,* as well as *contrast and edge enhancement,* each of which is accomplished by appropriate computer routines.

For each spectral band, the Landsat MSS scans six successive lines at a time, using six individual detectors. Differences in the performance of these detectors often result in an image with a striped appearance. This striping is removed by a digital algorithm in a process called *radiometric restoration.* Geometric corrections include adjustments for variations in the angular velocity of the oscillating scanning mirror, skew distortions due to the earth's rotation and the satellite's orbital move-

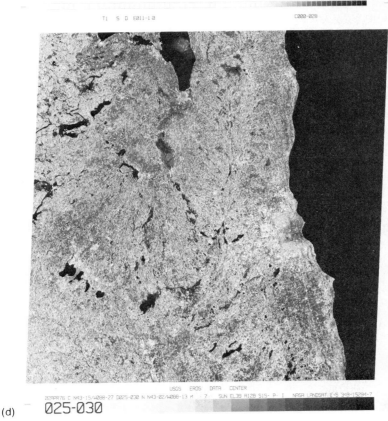

(d) 025-030

Figure 4.42 *(cont.)*

ment, as well as corrections for certain technical characteristics of the detector and transmission system. Contrast enhancement involves stretching the range of gray values to provide maximum contrast. In essence, it improves a low-contrast image by increasing the differences between each of the recorded gray-scale steps as much as possible. This improves the usability of the image because the transitions between one tone and another throughout the gray-scale range are emphasized and more easily identified. Edge enhancement, on the other hand, sharpens the image by emphasizing the transitions from one particular tone to an adjacent tone. This assists in the delineation of areas that differ from one another only slightly in terms of the signal they generate.

Automated Interpretation

The interpretation of scanning images is in many ways similar to the interpretation of aerial photographs. The significance of different image values in different wavebands must be recognized, however, and the differences in image geometry must also be taken into account. Observations gathered by aircraft-based methods, as well as by ground teams, are used to establish ground truth information for the verification of interpretations based on sources located in space.

At the present time, much of the interpretation of remotely sensed images is done by trained analysts. Because of the great volume of information returned by programs such as Landsat, however, computerized methods of interpretation are being developed to assist the human analysts. The scanning of multiband images, for example, can be timed so that photoelectric sensors simultaneously scan a given spot on each image. The degrees of brightness of the images in each band, when correlated to one another, provide a tonal signature for that spot which can be used to automatically place it into an interpretation category.

Change detection is an interpretation technique that, as previously mentioned, involves comparing the images obtained at the same location on two or more successive images. Changes in gray tones at different time periods, for example, may reflect a change in the material or in the surface characteristics present at that location. This technique is used to detect changes in characteristics such as land-use patterns or crop growing conditions. Because of the vast amount of imagery that is accumulated by continuously operating detection and monitoring systems, it is imperative that automated techniques be developed to accomplish this task as well.

Suggested Readings

AVERY, T. EUGENE, *Interpretation of Aerial Photographs* (2nd ed.). Minneapolis, Minn.: Burgess Publishing Co., 1968.

BARRETT, E. C., and L. F. CURTIS, *Introduction to Environmental Remote Sensing.* London: Chapman and Hall; and New York: John Wiley & Sons, A Halsted Press Book, 1976.

BEAN, R. K., "Development of the Orthophotoscope," *Photogrammetric Engineering,* 21, no. 4, (1955), 529–35.

BURNSIDE, CLIFFORD D., *Mapping from Aerial Photographs.* New York: John Wiley & Sons, A Halsted Press Book, 1979. Thorough coverage of the theory and practice of photogrammetry. Mathematics is important to some chapters, but many of the descriptions are of value without mathematics. Useful bibliography for each chapter's topics.

CIMERMAN, VJ., and Z. TOMAŠEGOVIĆ, *Atlas of Photogrammetric Instruments.* Amsterdam: Elsevier Publishing Co., 1970. Excellent photographs and descriptions of most modern photogrammetric instruments.

HAUG, MOIR D., FRANCIS H. MOFFITT, and JAMES M. ANDERSON, "A Simplified Explanation of Doppler Positioning," *Surveying and Mapping,* 40, no. 1 (March 1980), 29–45.

HOLZ, ROBERT K., ed., *The Surveillant Science: Remote Sensing of the Environment.* Boston: Houghton Mifflin Company, 1973.

MOFFITT, FRANCIS H. and EDWARD M. MIKHAIL, *Photogrammetry* (3rd ed.). New York: Harper and Row, 1980.

REEVES, ROBERT G., ed., *Manual of Remote Sensing.* Washington, D.C.: American Society of Photogrammetry, 1975.

SLAMA, CHESTER C., ed., *Manual of Photogrammetry* (4th ed.). Falls Church, Va.: American Society of Photogrammetry, 1980. A compendium of equipment, theory, and techniques of photogrammetry and air photo interpretation.

THOMPSON, MORRIS M., *Maps for America.* Washington, D.C.: U.S. Department of the Interior, Geological Survey, 1979, pp. 17, 135–42, and 169–89.

THROWER, NORMAN J. W., and JOHN R. JENSEN, "The Orthophoto and Orthophotomap: Characteristics, Development and Applications," *The American Cartographer,* 3, no. 1 (April 1976), 39–52.

5

Compilation
and Layout

The survey and remotely sensed data described in the previous chapters provide the basic information for map production. This chapter discusses the considerations involved in the compilation of a map as well as in the organization, or layout, of the map sheet. *Compilation* consists of bringing together, in a coherent manner, a variety of source materials to create a new map. *Layout,* on the other hand, consists of arranging the various map elements in an attractive and orderly manner. The cartographer uses both processes in a coordinated way to organize the information that is included in the map and to ensure that the desired message is conveyed.

COMPILATION

Source Materials

The source materials used in map production must be carefully evaluated. The evaluation is based on the accuracy of the data, the level of detail provided, and the date of the information relative to the purpose for which the map is being compiled.

In many cases, the evaluation of the source material is initially based on the reputation of the individual, agency, or company that produced it. United States Geological Survey (USGS) topographical maps, for example, are prepared to meet specified levels of accuracy. Other factors need to be considered, however, in addition to the reputation of the provider. These include the date of the information, the manner in which it was compiled, and the sources from which it was obtained. In the case of USGS maps, for example, each sheet contains information regarding the types of data used and the dates of the surveys. These facts can be used to judge the suitability of the map for the purpose at hand; for example, 1948 boundaries are of little use in showing population statistics for 1980.

The *copyright* status of the source materials must also be taken into account. When the materials are subject to copyright restrictions it is necessary to obtain permission to use them unless equivalent material is available from an alternative, noncopyrighted source. It is helpful to know that U.S. government maps and statistics can be used without payment or permission as a base, or source, for private work.[1] This is not necessarily true of government products from other countries and is certainly not true of privately produced materials.

Worksheet

The cartographer combines the information obtained from surveys and aerial photographic work with any supplemental information that has been gathered, in order to prepare a worksheet. A *worksheet,* or compilation manuscript, is simply a draft, often drawn by hand, that contains all the information to be included in the final map; it provides a guide for the preparation of the final drawings and other map elements.

A worksheet is needed for either a drafted or a scribed map. The requirements for each process are slightly different, however, so the manner in which the worksheets are prepared also varies slightly. This section discusses worksheets for drafted maps. When scribing is described (Chapter 7), the differences in the preparation of worksheets for scribed maps are described.

Translucent material is useful for worksheet preparation, especially *dimensionally stable drafting plastic* (materials are discussed in the following sections). Translucent material is the most satisfactory because it is often possible to trace some of the elements of the map from an existing original. Tracing is the quickest and most accurate means of transferring information at desired scale and projection (assuming that no copyright violation would occur). The worksheet is prepared at the same scale at which the drafting will be done, so the drafted work is also traced from the translucent worksheet.

Because the various features on the map are to be drawn with different line weights, and a variety of symbols are to be used, some form of *coding* is needed on the worksheet. The most convenient means of coding is to use differently colored lines and symbols to designate the different requirements for the final drafted version. A *specification sheet,* which lists the particular final form that is desired, is also prepared. The instructions may state, for example, that a solid red line on the worksheet is to be drawn as a line 0.2 mm wide, consisting of 3.0 mm dashes separated from one another by 1.0 mm spaces.

The worksheet provides a complete guide for the drafting of the finished map. It must therefore show the accurate placement of all of the lines and symbols that will appear. It also indicates the placement, style, and size of the lettering, and the types of screens or patterns to be used in different areas on the map. It is obvious that accuracy is extremely important; the guidelines must be followed precisely in order to produce the final map and no other information should be added at the drafting stage.

When line drafting techniques are used, the drafted original and therefore the worksheet are usually both prepared at a larger size than the final printed size of

[1]Morris M. Thompson, *Maps for America* (Washington, D.C.: U.S. Government Printing Office, 1979), p. 13.

the map. There are advantages that make it preferable to work at the larger size. One advantage is that the tolerances for line weights and placement are slightly less critical. Photographing the drawings to a smaller size also results in a finer, sharper image on the printed map than would result if the image were photographed at its original size. The amount of reduction utilized varies, but the most common range is a linear reduction of 20 to 30 percent; the result is a final size in which the linear dimensions are 70 to 80 percent of the length of the original. It is not advisable to reduce the image too severely, say beyond 50 percent of its original size, because extreme reduction makes it very difficult to predict the appearance of the final result. As a practical matter, it is obvious that the creation of a larger original involves the use of more materials and frequently increases production time.

A significant aspect of reduction is that the apparent amount of contrast between lines of different weights is reduced as the image size is reduced. It is necessary, therefore, to exaggerate the difference in line weights at the original size if the final, reduced result is to be effective (Fig. 5.1).

Figure 5.1   Effect of reduction on line weight contrast.

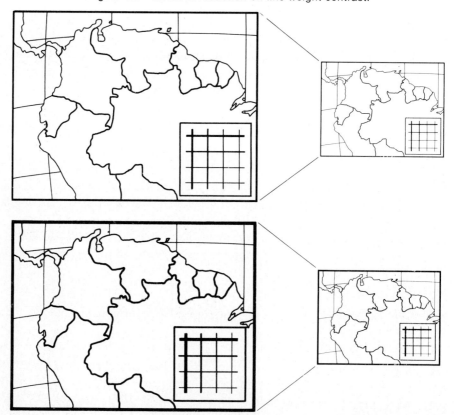

Generalization

Generalization consists of achieving a level of detail appropriate to the purpose of a given map and usually involves manipulating a large amount of detailed information. Every map requires some degree of generalization; even large-scale topographic maps cannot possibly show every detail of the real world they represent. Because of this fact, the cartographer must adjust the content of each map so that it is a useful and recognizable representation of the real world and yet does not overwhelm the viewer with excessive detail. Obviously, the smaller the scale of the map the greater the amount of generalization required. Successful generalization results in the retention of the distinguishing characteristics of the mapped features so that they are effectively represented.

Generalization applies equally to map features and to statistical information. This section is concerned with the generalization of map features; the next chapter deals with methods used in connection with statistical data.

Scale is a primary factor in generalization; in fact, it is even more important than might at first be thought. This is because the *compression of detail* that is required when going from a larger to a smaller scale is not a simple, linear function; in fact, the compression takes place at a geometric rate. If the scale of the map that is being compiled is reduced to one-half that of the original map, for example, the total area available for plotting the information on the new map is only one-quarter of what was available on the original. This means that, unless the original map was very sparsely detailed, it will very likely be necessary to reduce the amount of information included in the smaller map. This reduction in the amount of information reduces clutter and provides space for the linework, symbols, and lettering that must be included and that cannot be reduced beyond some minimum useful size.

One means of generalization involves simply *selecting* and retaining the more critical features on a map and eliminating the less critical ones. If a series of lakes is to be shown, for example, some of the smaller lakes in the group may be eliminated, as scale is reduced, so that the larger features can be retained [Fig. 5.2(a)].

A second technique of generalization requires *simplifying* the shape of the features that are retained on the map. To continue the previous example, the shorelines of the lakes would be made less complex than they were at the original scale. The difficult aspect of this approach is that enough detail must be retained so that the features are identifiable. A coastline with many bays and headlands, for example, should not be reduced to a smooth curve; instead, sufficient complexity should be retained so that the viewer will realize the nature of the actual coastline, even though the individual features are not all retained [Fig. 5.2(b)].

Another step that can be taken is to *combine* two or more similar features into a single symbol. If there are many small wooded areas in a region, for example, two or more of them might be combined to show as one. The difficulty here is to avoid losing sight of the fact that the region is characterized by scattered areas of woodland, separated by unwooded areas [Fig. 5.2(c)]. This approach cannot be used in all situations, however. A group of lakes, for example, should not be combined

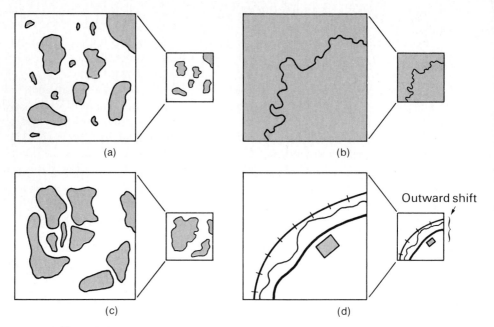

Figure 5.2 Approaches to generalization: (a) Selection; (b) Simplification; (c) Combination; (d) Shifting.

into one large lake. The reason that one combination is acceptable and the other is not is that there are factors that differentiate between the two examples. In the case of the wooded land, the combination involves only one type of phenomenon (vegetation), so the combination is justified. In the case of the lakes, on the other hand, because two types of phenomena are involved (land and water), it is inappropriate to combine them.[2]

Generalization may also require *shifting* the location of certain features. For example, if a road, a railroad, and a river are crowded into a narrow valley, the purpose of the map may make it necessary to retain all of them. Because of the need for legibility, however, the weight of the linework on the map must be sufficient to be distinguishable and there must be sufficient space between the lines to keep them from running together. It may be necessary, therefore, to exaggerate the size of the features and to shift their location slightly in order to gain space. This combination of techniques may make it possible to obtain a legible result, even though the features lie in a slightly shifted position and occupy more space than they would if they were represented to precise scale [Fig. 5.2(d)].

No really useful rules exist for deciding on the best generalization techniques in a given situation. In most instances, generalization involves the application of more than one of the suggested approaches. The cartographer's judgement is crucial

[2]J. S. Keates, *Cartographic Design and Production* (New York: John Wiley & Sons, A Halsted Press Book, 1973), p. 27.

to the selection of an appropriate level of generalization and of the best means of obtaining it.

Scale Change

It is frequently necessary to change the scale of one or more of the source maps that are used in compiling a new map. This is because existing maps may not show the desired area at a size that conveniently fits the space available for the new map. Also, the needed information may be available on maps that are at different scales. Whenever one or both of these situations prevails, some method of *scale change* must be employed to bring all of the materials to a common compilation scale.

Several methods of making scale changes are available but, regardless of which is chosen, it is always important to use sources that are at the same scale as the compilation sheet or, preferably, larger. This is because size reduction during compilation reduces the inaccuracy and generalization that inevitably exist in any source map. If source maps are enlarged instead of being reduced, any errors that may have crept into them are exaggerated. It is also inappropriate to enlarge any generalizations introduced during the compilation of the source map. In short, the enlargement of source materials, rather than their reduction, can result in a distorted final map (Fig. 5.3).

Similar figures   Although it may seem archaic when it is described, the method of *similar figures* is an accurate and useful means of transferring information from a source map to a compilation drawing. It is often relatively time-consuming, however, when compared with other techniques.

The method of similar figures has one especially useful characteristic; it permits the cartographer to plot the changes in shape that are needed when the source map and the compilation projections are different from one another. When different projections are involved, the shapes of the features on the map must change in order to conform to the changes in the shape of the graticule. With the exception of computer-assisted techniques, none of the other methods of scale change can easily accommodate changes in shape.

Figure 5.3   Distortion introduced by enlarging a generalized original.

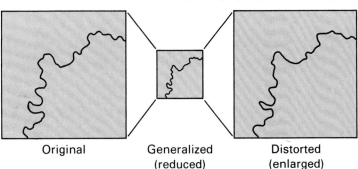

Original   Generalized   Distorted
(reduced)   (enlarged)

The simplest example of the method of similar figures involves the use of a square *reference grid;* this is so common, in fact, that the method is sometimes called the method of squares. The first step in transferring detail from a source map is to draw a grid of reference lines over it. These lines may be drawn directly on the map, or they are drawn on a translucent overlay if the original must be protected. The spacing of the lines must be sufficiently close that major features on the map are, on average, fairly close to one of them. The spacing should not be so close, however, that excessive time is spent in drawing a framework that will go partially unused (supplementary reference lines may be added in areas where more detail is needed). A similar set of grid lines is drawn on the compilation sheet. Here, however, the spacing between the lines is reduced in proportion to the scale relationship between the source map and the compilation. If the source map is at a scale of 1:50,000, and the compilation is to be drawn at a scale of 1:100,000, for example, the grid lines on the compilation will be spaced half as far apart as the grid lines on the source map.

Once the reference grids are established, the compiler transfers the required detail from the source map to the compilation drawing. This is done by visually noting the relationship of the details on the source map to the reference grid. Guides such as the locations at which a line crosses the reference grid, and the angle at which the crossing occurs, assist in the process of properly copying the source map. These relationships are duplicated at the reduced size by drawing the required information into the appropriate square on the compilation drawing (Fig. 5.4). Of course, the compiler must be careful to copy the detail into the correct square on the compilation sheet; otherwise, a complex line may suddenly fail to line up with other lines on the map.

The process of obtaining the correct spacing between features is sometimes speeded up by using *proportional dividers.* The dividers are first set to match the scale ratio between the source map and the compilation drawing. The larger end of the dividers is then set to match the space between the features on the source map and the smaller end is used to transfer the reduced spacing to the compilation drawing.

When an intricate portion of a feature is transferred, the grid squares in its vicinity are subdivided by as many supplementary lines as are needed to provide an

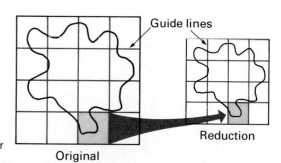

Figure 5.4 Reduction by similar squares.

Guide lines

Reduction

Original

accurate guide for the placement of the detail. The only requirement is that both the source map grid and the grid on the compilation sheet are to be divided into the same number of units, so that there is a one-to-one relationship between the two reference grids.

Although the description thus far has indicated that a square grid is used for transferring detail, other patterns may be more useful in certain situations. A linear feature, such as a river and its tributaries, may be transferred by using a set of guidelines that cross one another at angles chosen to match the general trend of the feature [Fig. 5.5(a)]. The advantage of this approach is that the main characteristics of the linear pattern, such as the angles of crossing or joining, or the proportions of line lengths, may be more quickly matched by using figures other than squares. The choice of the particular method or combination of methods to be used in each case is a matter of experience and judgment.

Perhaps the most useful aspect of the method of similar figures is that it accommodates the changes of shape that occur when the map projections used on the source map and the new map differ. When changing projections, it is usual to use the graticule on the source map as the reference grid and the graticule of the new projection as the plotting grid [Fig. 5.5(b)]. It is then a relatively simple matter to proportionately subdivide the spaces between the lines of the graticules on both the source map and the worksheet. In this case, the proportions involved differ from grid zone to grid zone and may even vary within one zone. This means that care and judgment are required when transferring the detail from a source on one projection to a worksheet on another projection.

It is helpful to copy only one small area at a time, introducing the comparatively small shape changes that are needed in order to have the lines cross at the appropriate reference points. Although a certain amount of distortion is introduced in each small area, the overall effect is a reasonably accurate representation of the larger shapes. The finer the mesh of latitude and longitude lines, the more accurate

Figure 5.5 (a) Reduction by similar figures. (b) Change of shape (projection) using similar figures.

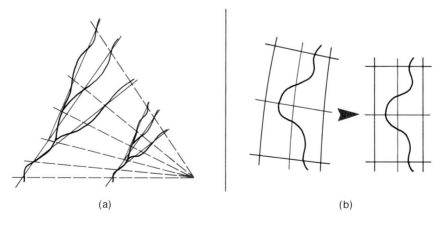

(a)   (b)

the results. Again, however, the mesh should not be so fine as to be overly time-consuming to plot or too confusing to use; the appropriate spacing will become apparent with experience in using the method.

Optical projectors Optical methods of scale change involve the use of a device that projects the image of an original, such as a source map, onto the compilation sheet. The required portion of the *projected image* is then traced onto the work-sheet. This method allows the tracing to be done quite speedily and is particularly useful when no change in projection is required. As with other methods, it is preferable to reduce the size of the image from the source map to the worksheet, so that any errors that exist are not enlarged.

In a typical *optical projector* [Fig. 5.6(a)], the source map is placed against a glassed-over opening and bright lights behind the opening illuminate it [Fig. 5.6(b)]. The map image is then reflected by a mirror through a lens and onto a table surface. The size of the image is adjusted by moving the head of the device closer to the table, or farther away, and focus is maintained by raising or lowering the lens. Some projectors incorporate a mechanism to keep them automatically in focus as the image size is adjusted, and some must be adjusted for focus by the operator. In either case, once the image is projected at the desired scale, compilation is a simple matter of placing the worksheet on the table and tracing the desired portions of the image. To be certain that the information is plotted in the correct location on the compi-

Figure 5.6 (a) Optical projector, used for making scale changes. (Courtesy of Artograph Inc.) (b) Operation of optical projector.

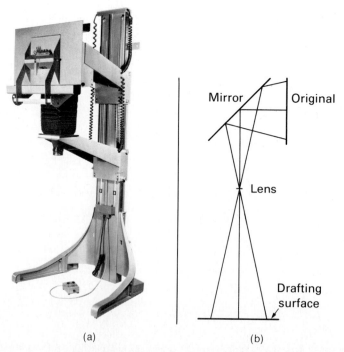

(a)

(b)

lation sheet, appropriate guides, either squares, or lines of latitude and longitude, are used.

Photographic processes   The term *photographic* is used here to apply to the use of any *photomechanical method* by which the scale of a source map is changed. It includes, therefore, the *photostatic process* (see Chapter 7), which produces a paper negative, as well as regular photography, which produces a film negative or, if desired, a paper negative. The main disadvantage of a paper negative for this purpose is the shrinkage that occurs when the paper dries. This can result in an unacceptable amount of error in the image. A film negative, therefore, is usually preferred and, if maximum accuracy is required, a stable-base film is used.

The type of film emulsion used is also important if the source map is in color. If the emulsion is *orthochromatic,* any features in light blue on the original will fade out on the negative. Other colors may also fade to a greater or lesser degree, so some portions of the negative may be difficult to use. Panchromatic film sometimes produces a more satisfactory negative. It is also possible to introduce filters, or to vary the exposure and development of the negative, in order to retain information that would otherwise drop out in the photographic process. These results are quite variable, so consultation with an experienced and sympathetic camera operator is frequently the best way to acquire a usable image in the face of difficulties with colors. Miracles are not possible, however, and it may not be feasible to capture some color combinations.

The size of the photographic image is adjusted so that its linear scale is the same as the worksheet scale. The desired size is specified by determining the percentage of reduction from the original size. Alternatively, a scaling line is drawn along the edge of the source map to indicate the desired size change.

The resulting photo is a negative copy of the original; it will be right-reading if a photostat machine is used, and wrong-reading if a camera is used. This negative, after being processed and dried, is placed on a light table, face up or face down as required. The worksheet material is then placed over the negative and the desired information is traced onto the worksheet. The same negative is, of course, available for future checking or revision, which can prove very useful.

Photographic techniques, like projection techniques, are useful when no change in map projection is required, because the size of the entire image is changed proportionately in all directions when it is photographed. They have an additional advantage, too, in that a permanent record of the reduced image is produced.

Pantograph   The *pantograph* is a mechanical device that uses an arrangement of adjustable linkages to transfer the movement of a tracing point to a pencil point (Fig. 5.7). As the tracing point is moved over the source map, the pencil point moves a proportionately greater or lesser distance depending on the setting which is used. The motion of the pencil point duplicates the shapes of the original, but at the new scale.

In general, pantographs are not ideally suited to map compilation because any friction in the linkage leads to distortions in the final result. This problem is less serious when the image is being reduced in size, which is the preferred situation.

Figure 5.7 Pantograph. (Courtesy of Kratos/Keuffel & Esser)

Elaborate suspension systems have been developed in an attempt to circumvent the friction problem, but they are quite expensive. In some situations, the results obtained are sufficiently accurate to warrant the use of a pantograph.

Computer-assisted techniques The computer provides a considerable capability for rapid and accurate scale and shape changes. The methods and problems involved in using these computer-assisted techniques are described in Chapter 11.

LAYOUT

A cartographer's creative freedom is necessarily limited by certain rigidities inherent in maps. The shapes of coastlines, rivers, national boundaries, and similar features are not matters of choice, although the patterns of map projection graticules sometimes are. Many aspects of map design, nevertheless, are susceptible to creative treatment. If these aspects are properly handled, the end result is enhanced. All things being equal, an attractive map is certainly preferable to an unattractive one. This is not simply an aesthetic judgment; experience indicates that an attractive product is more likely to be readable and is also more likely to be consulted in the first place.

Although cartographers are usually not trained as artists, there is a definite place for artistic sensibilities and considerations in the cartographic process. Indeed, it is recommended that anyone interested in cartography study art; two-dimensional design, the use of color, and the design and application of lettering are among the topics that are particularly useful. A grounding in artistic principles, as well as experience in applying them, is an invaluable aid to the production of attractive, readable, and usable maps.

This section is not meant to provide a short course in art; it simply presents some general design principles that should be kept in mind during the process of creating a map. These are selected on the basis of their immediate usefulness to the cartographer.

Balance

The consideration of *balance* ensures that the major map elements will be placed within the available space in an organized and visually pleasing manner, whether the layout is formal or informal. Certain limits on the cartographer have already been mentioned. It is usually possible, however, to shift certain of the map elements to alternative locations, in order to improve the balance, without conflicting with the accuracy of the map.

Formal design calls for the *symmetrical balancing* of similarly sized and shaped elements around a balance point. This approach is used rather frequently in the general organization of map series sheets. Many projections used for map series are symmetrical around a central meridian and, to that extent, provide a logical starting point for a formally balanced design. In a map series, there is also a strong incentive to work with formal balance because the main supporting elements, such as title, scale, and notes, must be repeated on each map of the series. It would be rather disorganized and therefore disconcerting to the user to have these elements appear in a different location on each map. It is virtually impossible, furthermore, to judge what variations would best accommodate the differing contents of the different maps in the series. The result is that a symmetrical layout is the most suitable compromise.

A typical symmetrical arrangement calls for centering the title at the top of the sheet, centering the scale at the bottom, and arranging the notes around the perimeter. This leaves all of the area within the borders of the map for the map itself [Fig. 5.8(a)].

Individual maps are not as susceptible to formal design incentives because the repetitive nature of a map series is not present. There is frequently a rather stilted feeling and a lack of interest about a formally balanced layout that may cause it to be consciously avoided. These factors are reinforced by the fact that the features shown are usually not symmetrical and, often, the portion of the projection that is used is not the central, symmetrical portion. The shape of the region being mapped tends to suggest locations for such elements as the title and legend. These can often be conveniently placed in open areas of the map and, as a result, are not usually balanced around the map center line. Because of these factors, many single map designs incorporate an *informal balance.*

In informal balance, the major map elements are considered as individual masses, with the size of each corresponding to its weight. The elements are placed

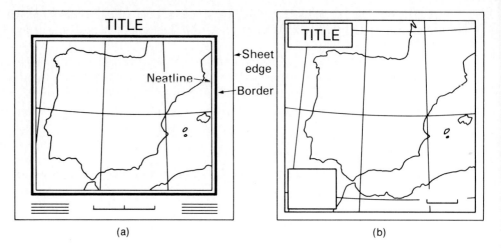

Figure 5.8 Typical arrangements of map elements: (a) Formal (symmetrical); (b) Informal.

so that there is a general but nonsymmetrical balance among them. A large element, such as the title and legend box, for example, may be balanced by two or more smaller elements, such as the north arrow and scale, on the other side [Fig. 5.8(b)].

For either formal or informal balance, *thumbnail sketches* provide a practical way to test several possible designs for a particular map project before the detailed planning and layout are undertaken. A thumbnail sketch is simply a small-scale drawing, done with a minimum of detail (Fig. 5.9). In series of such sketches, various positions, sizes, and styles of map elements are tried, in order to arrive at the most pleasing solution. Working at a small size allows several ideas to be worked out without a large expenditure of time. The more suitable layouts are then developed in more detail, at a larger size, in order to make the final selection.

Map Elements

Most maps contain a common set of elements, such as neatline and border, title, legend, scale, and north arrow. The following sections discuss a variety of ways of handling these elements from the standpoint of both design and placement.

Neatline and border   A *neatline* is a fine line that is sometimes used to provide a definite frame, or edge, at which the various elements of the map terminate. It is not always necessary to use a neatline and it is up to the cartographer to decide when one is needed. It is perfectly possible, for example, to simply terminate the map along an edge without having a bounding line. It is also possible to have the map run completely off the page, so that the edge of the page itself is the terminating line. This type of treatment is called a bleed and its use is limited to those occasions when it can be accommodated by the printing process.

Although the neatline is usually the edge of the mapped area, it is sometimes desirable for a portion of the map to extend beyond it. This is commonly done to

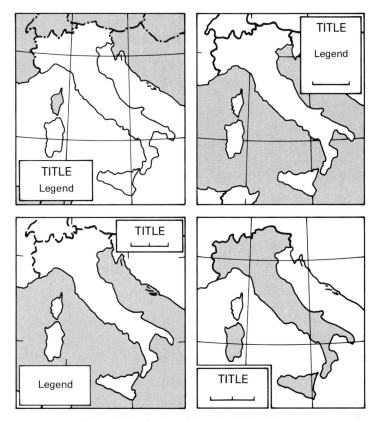

Figure 5.9   Series of thumbnail sketches.

allow a small extension, such as a peninsula or an island, to be included without squeezing a larger map area into the same space (Fig. 5.10). This has the advantage that the map can be drawn at a larger scale than would otherwise be possible or, alternatively, a slightly larger area can be shown.

Figure 5.10   Scale improvement obtained by penetrating neatline and border with map detail.

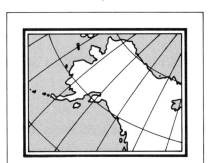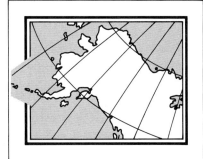

A *border* is an additional line, or set of lines, drawn outside the neatline and parallel to it. When a border is used it may range from a simple single line, usually heavier than the neatline, through a complex decorative treatment [Fig. 5.11(a)]. The tendency in modern cartography is to use rather simple borders, instead of the ornate concoctions sometimes used in the past. Several types of borders are commonly encountered.

The simplest type of border is a single wide line that acts as a neatline as well as a border; indeed, it might be considered to be a thick neatline. The next simplest type is a combination neatline and border, which consists of a heavy outer line and a fine inner line. A slightly more complex version has a wide outer line and a fine inner line, combined with a neatline.

There is one special type of border that is somewhat time-consuming to draw, but which can be very useful; this type consists of alternate black and white bands. If properly used, the change in color indicates the grid interval. A banded border is particularly helpful on navigational charts or reference maps because it makes it simpler to find locations by reference to latitude and longitude. This type of pattern is sometimes used for purely decorative effect without any relationship to the lines of latitude and longitude; in such cases the effect is misleading and its use is questionable.

Neatline and border arrangements are sometimes drawn to accommodate the numbers that identify the lines of latitude and longitude [Fig. 5.11(b)]. Alternatively, the grid numbers are placed inside the neatline, in a break in the grid lines themselves [Fig. 5.11(c)].

Borders usually look best when their sides are parallel to the central meridian of a symmetrical projection. If this is not done the map often appears to be tilted. The placement of the borders around a nonsymmetrical projection, or around an area that is away from the central meridian of a symmetrical projection, has to be decided on the basis of the shape of the mapped area and the placement of the other map elements.

Legend and title   Almost all maps require a *title,* and many require a *legend.* When they are used, these elements must be carefully worded. There is a need for completeness and accuracy in legends and titles; but there is also an opposing need to avoid using excessive amounts of map space. If the title and legend wording is not complete, there is a very real risk that the user will be misled regarding the content

Figure 5.11   (a) Typical borders. (b) and (c) Two treatments of neatline and border in relation to latitude and longitude designations.

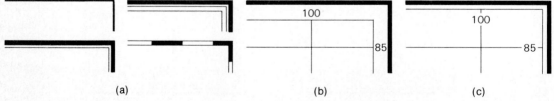

(a)   (b)   (c)

of the map. At a minimum, the title should identify the mapped region and, if it is a special-subject map, the topic that is displayed, as well as the date of the data. It is not necessary, on the other hand, to have a title include the superfluous words, "Map of . . ."!

The location of the title varies considerably in relation to the border and to other map elements; four typical placements are shown in Fig. 5.12. These include free-standing locations, either outside the map border or in a blank area inside the neatline. Alternatively, the title may be placed within a cartouche or title box; if this is done, the box is almost invariably placed within the neatline.

The map legend should fully identify any symbols that require explanation. Symbols that identify types or sizes of settlements, types of vegetation, or any such specific subjects, should be explained in the legend. This is simply because, without a legend, the viewer has no way to know the meaning, on the particular map, of a solid red dot, a green line, or whatever other special symbols are being used. It is not necessary, however, to include a coastline, a graticule line, or any other such easily recognized symbol unless special categories are being distinguished from one another.

The arrangement of the legend items is important to the success of the map as a communication device. If the arrangement is logical and attractive, the user can refer to it easily and interpret it accurately. If the legend is not well arranged, on the other hand, it may be very ambiguous and not at all helpful. There are three keys to the successful arrangement of a legend: grouping, hierarchy, and symmetry.

Grouping means simply locating together all of the legend items that describe a particular category of features. All symbols that describe terrain features, for example, should be in one group, all aquatic features in a second group, all cultural features in a third group, and so on.

Within each legend category, the individual items are arranged in a logical order; this order often implies a *hierarchy* of importance. If several symbols are used to specify cities of different sizes, for example, it is preferable to arrange the symbols in sequence, from smallest to largest (or from largest to smallest). Such a clear-cut hierarchy may not always exist and, if that is the case, the cartographer simply establishes a logical sequence. It is preferable to keep the hierarchical ordering consistent from category to category. If city sizes are arranged from smallest to largest, for example, then boundaries should be in a sequence from less important

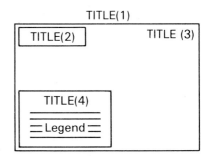

Figure 5.12 Typical title locations.

to more important (county, state, and international), or rainfall data from lesser to greater amounts.

Adhering to a logic of the type described is of considerable assistance to the viewer who has only the information provided by the cartographer, combined with any previously acquired experience, to sort out the message that the map is meant to convey. Even the physical arrangement of the individual items in the legend assists in making the map readable; it is usually preferable to arrange the legend in a rather *symmetrical* manner. The layout shown in Fig. 5.13 provides an example of one of many possible ways to arrange a legend. The factors taken into account in this layout include the relationship of the boxes, lines, and symbols to one another and to their labels, as well as the spacing of the materials in relation to the outline of the legend box. It is not necessary to label the legend with the word *Legend* or *Key*—that identification is self-evident.

Items such as the legend and scale are either placed separately or included within the title box. The placement depends upon the distribution of the available space, and it is often best to group these items in order to keep the number of individual components down, thus avoiding visual clutter. If a box is used, the manner in which it is arranged, including the use of a neatline, or neatline and border, is designed in consonance with the design of the same elements as they were used on the map itself. (See the section on insets, below, for additional suggestions.)

Graphic scales   There is a variety of styles of *graphic scales,* ranging from simple to complex [Fig. 5.14(a)]. The usual modern standard is to select the less ornate, with the emphasis on making the scale as functional as possible.

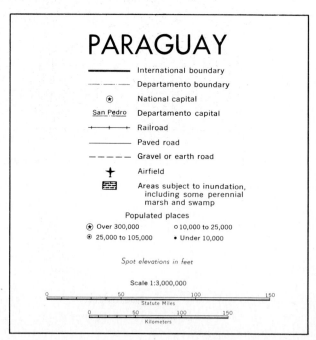

Figure 5.13   Typical legend arrangement.

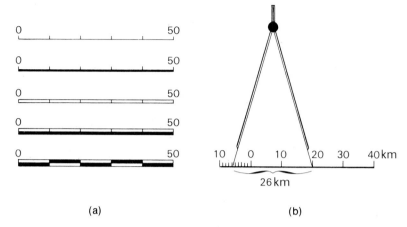

(a)   (b)

Figure 5.14 (a) Typical graphic scales. (b) Use of scale with subdivided portion.

There are two types of scale division. In one case, one of the major divisions of the scale is subdivided into smaller units; in the other case, a set of subdivided units is added at the end of the scale. The latter type is probably the most useful on large-scale maps because it simplifies the taking of the measurements that are frequently made on such maps. The distance is transferred from the map to the scale, or vice versa, using dividers or a paper strip; the major units are measured first, and the minor units are added to give the total distance [Fig. 5.14(b)].

The scale is frequently located in a position centered below the map title or within the legend box. Alternatively, it is placed in a blank area of the map.

Graticules and grids A cartographer may choose to use a full latitude and longitude graticule, a graticule on water areas only, short lines (ticks) only, or a combination of a water area graticule with ticks on the land areas (Fig. 5.15). Circumstances may dictate one or the other arrangement but frequently the selection is simply a matter of preference. The same choices are available for showing a locational grid, such as a Universal Transverse Mercator (UTM), military, or state plane coordinate grid.

A full grid or graticule is more likely to be used on a reference map such as

Figure 5.15 Different treatments of graticule.

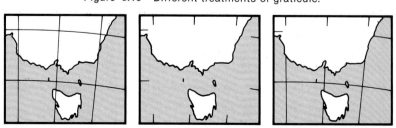

a topographic map, navigational chart, or atlas map. In such cases, the user is frequently locating map features by use of an index and coordinates or, conversely, determining the coordinate location of selected features. In either case it is helpful, and is usually more accurate, to have the grid or graticule lines on the face of the map. There are situations, however, in which showing the full graticules and grids is confusing. On USGS topographic maps, for example, there are four reference systems: latitude and longitude, township and range, state plane coordinates, and UTM. In this case, in order to reduce clutter, the township and range lines are shown on the face of the map but the other systems are indicated only by ticks. In other cases, where the use of coordinates is not so important, the type of arrangement is selected more on the basis of appearance and less on the basis of utility.

The use of a *water-only grid* or graticule reduces the clutter on the land area, which usually contains most of the map symbols and typography. This helps to improve the readability of the map. A water-only grid also helps to reduce the figure-ground problem, discussed later in this chapter.

Insets   An *inset* is a smaller secondary map that is shown in conjunction with the primary map. There are several types of insets, classified in terms of their content and their relationship to the main map. There are many different ways of handling the design of insets. In general, insets are treated as independent maps with their own border, title, legend, grid lines, and scale. The exception, as will be noted, is the inset that shows related areas at the same scale as the main map.

One type of inset presents an *enlargement* of an important area of the main map. The layout of a major city, for example, may be included with a state map [Fig. 5.16(a)].

A second type of inset is a *locating map*. This type is designed to assist the map user in visualizing the location of the mapped area in relation to a larger, more easily recognized, region. An example is a map showing the location of the region that is the subject of the main map in relation to national boundaries [Fig. 5.16(b)]. This type of inset is usually rather simple and may consist of very little but an outline map of the major region and a spot symbol identifying the map area with appropriate names added.

A third type of inset shows a *related area* that is located outside the limits of the main map. A typical example is a map of the contiguous states of the United States with insets of Hawaii and Alaska added. It is usually preferable, so that comparisons can be more easily made, to show the related areas at the same scale as the main map. As in the example cited, however, the size of the subsidiary areas (Alaska and Hawaii) relative to the size of the principal area (the United States) may make it difficult to show them at the same scale as the main map. The decision regarding scale is made on the basis of the importance of the inset areas to the topic being presented, as well as the available space. This type of inset is considered to be an element of the main map, if both are at the same scale. It need not, therefore, be set off with its own border; frequently, only a neatline is used to provide some separation [Fig. 5.16(c)].

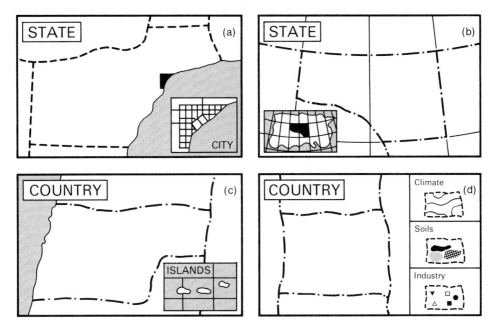

Figure 5.16 Types of insets: (a) Portion of main map at larger scale; (b) Location of main map; (c) Related area; (d) Special subjects.

Finally, *special-subject* insets are often desired. This type of inset is exemplified by a distribution map of crop types, a map of a transportation network, or a map of population densities. This type of inset typically shows the same area as the main map but at a smaller scale [Fig. 5.16(d)].

Legibility

A requirement of major importance for any map is that the user be easily able to see and interpret the information being presented. In order to judge the best way to meet this need for *legibility,* the cartographer must have some idea of the normal conditions under which the map will be viewed. Viewing conditions range from a well-lighted table in the library, with a magnifying glass readily at hand, to the interior of an airplane cockpit, with only a red night-light for illumination. Under such contrasting conditions it is obvious that the entire structure of the maps produced—not only the content but the colors and line weights, typography, and symbol styles and sizes—needs to be markedly different. Consideration of several design elements assists in the production of legible maps.

Contrast A map drawn with lines that are very similar in width is visually very dull and uninteresting. More importantly, however, it is also very difficult to distinguish between the different elements of such a map [Fig. 5.17(a)]. Visual interest is provided, in part, through the use of *contrast:* contrast between line weights,

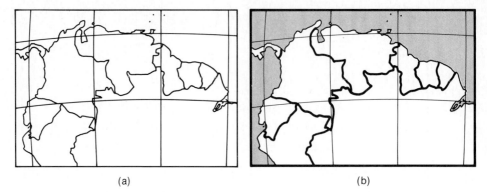

(a)   (b)

Figure 5.17 Contrast by variation in line weight and provision of tone.

tones, and colors. Not only does contrast provide visual interest, it also contributes to the important task of separating the different map features from one another. For example, differences in line weights can help the viewer distinguish between the linear symbols that represent such features as coastlines, roads, rivers, railroads, and pipelines [Fig. 5.17(b)].

The figure-ground problem   A map user may encounter difficulty in distinguishing the image of the area that is the subject of the map from its background. This *figure-ground problem* occurs when a map lacks sufficient contrast between the subject, or foreground, and the background against which it is seen. The problem occurs most frequently when the shape being shown is not a familiar one. In Fig. 5.18(a), for example, it is not immediately apparent whether the shape that is shown is a lake or an island. Adding a tone to the water area, however, makes it apparent that a lake is being represented [Fig. 5.18(b)]. The figure-ground problem is also reduced by using a water-only grid, by the use of color, or by labeling.

Pattern selection   Different *patterns* of lines, dots, or other symbols are frequently used to distinguish one area on a map from another. This is appropriate when nominal categories are being distinguished (see Chapter 9). A line pattern might show areas devoted to wheat cultivation, for example, whereas a dot pattern might be applied in areas of irrigated agriculture.

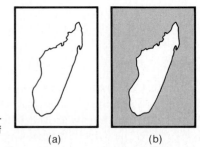

Figure 5.18 Figure-ground relationship improved by introduction of tone.

(a)   (b)

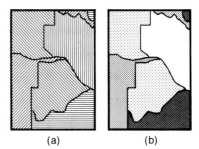

Figure 5.19 Irritating line patterns and more suitable dot values.

(a)   (b)

Unfortunately, however, there are problems associated with using such patterns. The most difficult aspect is that patterns distinct enough to be easily distinguishable from one another may be unattractive to the eye and may even interfere with the readability of the map. It is necessary, therefore, to select patterns that are distinct enough to be readily identifiable but not so strong as to dazzle the eye of the viewer.

An example of extreme visual conflict is a herringbone arrangement of parallel line patterns [Fig. 5.19(a)]. There is little doubt that the various areas in this example are easily distinguishable. The problem is that the eye is pulled back and forth by the strong line patterns and the map is very unattractive and difficult to view. One way to reduce this problem is simply to select less bold and obtrusive patterns in the first place. A second way is to screen the patterns so they are values of gray (or of a color, if that is possible) and therefore have a reduced visual impact. Third, and most satisfactory, is to use a dot pattern, or a screened gray value [Fig. 5.19(b)]. Any of these alternatives runs the risk that the patterns will become so subdued that the viewer will not be able to readily distinguish between them; the goal, of course, is to achieve a suitable balance between the two extremes.

Screen (value) selection   *Gray values* are often used to distinguish one area on a map from another. A water area, for example, may have a light gray value printed on it, whereas the land area may be left white. More importantly, however, gray values are also used when differences in quantity are being represented—for example, on choropleth or dasymetric maps, which are discussed in Chapter 9. The underlying idea in this application is that, as the quantity that is being indicated increases, the value associated with it should be darker.

The idea of using gray values to represent quantitative information implies that the best way to depict a continuous range of quantities is to use a continuous range of values.[3] If this were done, the generalization required by grouping into categories would be avoided. As a practical matter, however, most maps use a discrete set of values to represent different generalized levels of information. There is no specific optimum number of categories to use in order to minimize confusion between categories. In general, however, a range of from four to seven values is

[3]For example, Waldo R. Tobler, "Choropleth Maps Without Class Invervals?" *Geographical Analysis,* 5, no. 2 (July 1973), 262–65.

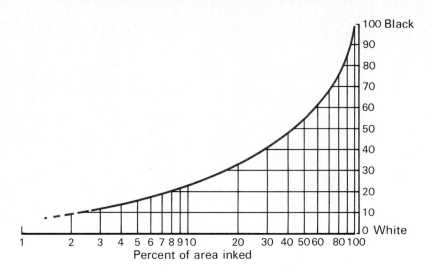

Figure 5.20   Relationship between percent of area inked and apparent gray value. [Source: Robert L. Williams, "Map Symbols; Equal Appearing Intervals for Printed Screens," *Annals of the Association of American Geographers,* 48, no. 2 (June 1958), 132–39, with the permission of the Association of American Geographers.]

frequently suggested. The manner in which these categories are developed is discussed in Chapter 9.

The gray values used on different areas of the map must have sufficient contrast to allow the viewer to distinguish between them and must provide an indication of the quantity being mapped. The idea is that a series of evenly graded gray-value steps will indicate evenly graded category changes. Assume, for example, that six categories are to be represented, with the values 0 percent, 20 percent, 40 percent, 60 percent, 80 percent, and 100 percent. White would then represent the 0 percent value and black the 100 percent value, and appropriate percentage screens would represent the other values. Unfortunately, most viewers would not distinguish these even-percentage gray values as representing equal-category steps.

The problem of how to assign appropriate gray values to represent specific percentages has been the subject of considerable research. The graph shown in Fig. 5.20 represents a useful scale of values that has come out of this research.[4] To use this graph as a guide, the percentage value that is to be represented is located on the scale at either side of the graph and a horizontal line is drawn from that value

[4]George F. Jenks and Duane S. Knos tested several approaches to selecting values, as reported in "The Use of Shading Patterns in Graded Series," *Annals of the Association of American Geographers,* 51, no 3 (September 1961), 316–34. They found the curve developed by Robert L. Williams, "Map Symbols: Equal Appearing Intervals for Printed Screens," *Annals of the Association of American Geographers,* 48, no. 2 (June 1958), 132–39, to be most effective. Further discussion is provided in Arthur H. Robinson, " 'The Curve of the Grey Spectrum': A Review," *Annals of the Association of American Geographers,* 49, no. 4 (December 1959), 457–60; and Robert L. Williams, "Map Symbols: 'The Curve of the Grey Spectrum'—An Answer," *Annals of the Association of American Geographers,* 50, no. 4 (December 1960), 487–91.

to intersect with the curve on the graph. A vertical line is then drawn from the intersection to the horizontal scale and the required percentage of area inked (screen percentage) is obtained.

It should be noted that it is frequently very difficult to maintain accurate screen values during the printing process. This is because of ink spread that results from slight variations in exposure and development during film and plate processing, as well as differences in ink density, paper surface, moisture, and mechanical problems with plates and rollers. These factors also make it prudent to limit the number of values used on a single map because the theoretical values obtained from the graph are not necessarily the values that will actually be printed.

The most effective way to produce the required gray values is to use a flat tint screen. If this is not possible, preprinted patterns of dots, lines, or other symbols that give an impression of a gray value may be used. Of the choices available, dots seem to be especially effective. A uniform textural appearance is also preferred, although this is difficult to achieve with preprinted symbols.[5]

Simultaneous contrast   Even if equal steps of gray value are achieved, there is an additional perceptual problem. This problem is illustrated by viewing a patch of gray, first against a white background and then against a black background. Against the white background, the gray is perceived as having a particular value [Fig. 5.21(a)]. The same gray seen against the black background is perceived as having a lighter value, simply because of the difference in contrast between it and the background [Fig. 5.21(b)]. This apparent change in value is known as *simultaneous contrast*. Although gray values are discussed here, the same problem applies to the use of colors (Plate 2).

On a map, the problem of simultaneous contrast arises because each gray value is likely to appear at a number of locations on the map. At each location it will

Figure 5.21   Effect of simultaneous contrast. The central gray value is the same in both portions of the figure.

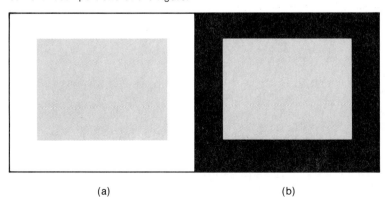

(a)   (b)

[5]Jenks and Knos, "The Use of Shading Patterns in Graded Series," presents the results of the testing of user perceptions of a variety of preprinted shaded sheets. They include a key that allows the selection of preprinted patterns that most closely match a list of desired percentages of area to be inked.

probably be adjacent to a different combination of gray values and, as a consequence, will appear to have a different value at each location. When the map reader attempts to relate the value to the legend, it is difficult to be confident of its interpretation because, again, the surrounding tones will be different.

In order to reduce the problem of simultaneous contrast, it is usual to limit the number of categories and hence the number of values that are used on a given map. This makes it possible to maintain greater differences between values, with the result that it is less difficult to differentiate between them regardless of their location in relation to other gray values.

TYPOGRAPHY

The lettering placed on a map provides the main means of communication between the cartographer and the map user. The type must be readable as well as suitable in style, and it must be placed so that the overall appearance is pleasing and the identification of the map features is clear. The appearance of even the most expertly drawn map is enhanced or spoiled depending on the skill with which the typography is selected and placed.

The following section deals with the selection of type styles and sizes, as well as the positioning of lettering on the map. The materials and processes used to apply the lettering are described in the next chapter.

Size

A piece of movable type of the sort in use when type sizing conventions were developed is shown in Fig. 5.22(a). (The same basic sort of type is still in use today, although other forms have taken its place in many applications.) Printing practice designates type sizes on the basis of the measurement of this type body. The unit of measurement is called a *point,* and is 0.013837 in. long (approximately 1/72 in.).

Figure 5.22 (a) Dimensions of movable printing type. (b) Different size characters on same size type body.

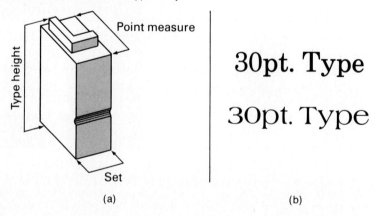

(a)   (b)

A raised representation of the individual letter, number, or other symbol is cast on the top of the lead alloy type body so that its printing surface is at what is called *type height*—0.0918 in. high. The *width,* or *set,* of each piece of type varies, depending upon the amount of space needed to accommodate the symbol itself, as well as the additional space needed to prevent adjacent letters from touching one another. The remaining dimension, which is used for the specification of type size, is the depth of the type body. This dimension is designated on the diagram as the point measure.

The point measure of type is based on the size of the type body and not on the size of the letter itself. Three factors determine the actual size of the letter that is cast on a particular size type body. The first of these is the *x-height,* which is the height of the lowercase (that is, the noncapital letter) *x* in a particular face. The second factor is the length of the *ascenders* (such as in the letter *d*) and *descenders* (such as in the letter *p*). The final factor is the amount of space allowed between lines. Because the proportions of different type styles vary considerably, the actual size of the character that is cast on, say, a 24-point body also varies [Fig. 5.22(b)].

One of the principal factors that determines the readability of the type on a map is size; if the letters are too small it will obviously be difficult to read them and the effectiveness of the map will suffer as a result. Some maps, such as detailed atlas reference maps, have been produced using very small type, with the expectation that the viewer will use a magnifying glass, if necessary, in order to read the lettering; the concept behind this approach is that having the detail available is more important to the user than ease of viewing. This is normally not a very desirable approach, however, and it is more usual to design the map so that the average user can read it without viewing aids.

Although no absolute rule can be set for determining minimum desirable type size, some guidance is available to aid in the selection process. The most important factors involved are the ability of the normal eye to resolve an image, combined with the distance at which the viewing is to take place; there is obviously a difference between the minimum acceptable type size for a map that is to appear in a book and what is acceptable for a classroom wall map. Consider, for example, the standard eye chart that is used in eye examination procedures; at the prescribed viewing distance the progressively smaller type sizes are increasingly difficult to distinguish. If one moves closer to the chart, however, it becomes easier to discern the smaller letters. This is because the light rays coming from each of the letters on the chart converge at the eye at an angle that is the product of the size of the type in relation to its distance from the viewer. Obviously, the farther away the image, or the smaller its size, the smaller the angle at the eye and the more difficult it is to resolve the image. The smallest angle that results in a distinguishable image is called the *minimum angle of acceptance.*

Experiments have been conducted to measure the resolving power of the eye. These experiments involve constructing a grating of black lines on a white background. When the grating is relatively close to the eye the individual lines can be seen. As it is moved farther away, however, a point is reached at which the lines disappear and the grating appears as a tone of gray. The *angle subtended at the eye* by the spacing between the lines, at the point where they are just resolvable, is called the *resolving power of the eye*. This resolving power varies from person to person, but the average ability is used in describing normal vision: the familiar "20/20." The numerator of this measure is the viewing distance at which a standard line on the eye chart is visible to the viewer. The denominator is the distance at which the details that are just visible subtend 1 minute of arc at the eye. Although some persons, under ideal viewing conditions, can discern detail that subtends only 1/2 minute of arc, a 1- or 2-minute standard is a safer guide for assuring readability under all conditions.

The idea of the minimum angle subtended at the eye can be put to practical use, because type sizes can be selected so that the combination of size and normal viewing distance results in an image that is within the resolving power of the eye. If a specific size of type can be comfortably resolved at a *viewing distance* of 18 in., and the viewing distance is increased to 180 in. (10 times the original viewing distance), the type used will have to be ten times as large as the original. If this is done, the light rays will come together at the eye at the same angle and therefore be equally visible.

Sizes smaller than 6-point are frequently not suitable for viewing at normal reading distance. The readability characteristics of different type styles do vary considerably, however. It is imperative, therefore, that the cartographer review actual type samples to determine the size needed for a particular application, rather than depend upon the designated point size to be an accurate indicator of type readability.

Not all styles of type are available in all sizes. The most common sizes are 6-, 8-, 10-, 12-, 14-, 18-, 24-, 30-, 36-, 42-, 48-, 60-, and 72-point. Some styles are also available in 5-, 7-, 9-, and 11-point, and, less frequently, in 4-, 13-, 16-, 20-, 28-, 54-, 84-, and 96-point, or in other, special sizes. Some of these sizes are shown in Fig. 5.23.

A small size letter in a particular style is usually not simply a photographic reduction of a larger letter of the same style; instead, the proportions of the various components, such as serifs, thick-thin contrast, and *x*-height, are often varied slightly by the designer in order to give the best appearance at each particular size. For this reason, extreme enlargements or reductions of map originals that include typography should be avoided whenever possible.

Styles

A multitude of type *styles,* perhaps as many as 30,000 has been designed since Gutenberg invented the occidental version of movable type. Many of these styles are potentially available to the cartographer; a typical *type style book* for a large printing house illustrates literally dozens. In practice, however, only a relatively small selection from the available styles is usually used. This is, in part, because certain styles seem to be suited to map applications and, in part, because of conventions of typographic usage that have developed over the years.

6pt. Type
7pt. Type
8pt. Type
9pt. Type
10pt. Type
12pt. Type
14pt. Type
18pt. Type
24pt. Type
30pt. Type
36pt. Type

72pt. Type

60pt. Type

48pt. Type

Figure 5.23   Typical range of type sizes.

The discussion in this section focuses on a description of the principal style variations that are available and on the ways and means available for applying typography to maps. There is no generally agreed on, comprehensive system for the classification of type styles, apparently because of the difficulty of adequately taking the variety of characteristics involved into account. Several aspects of typography can serve as a starting point for the discussion of type styles, however. These include the presence or absence of serifs and thick-thin contrast, vertical or slanting alignment, upper- or lowercase letters, boldness, and width.

Roman   *Roman* type styles consist of vertical letters with small terminating lines, called *serifs,* at the extremities of the main lines of the letter. These serifs may be straight, curved, tapered, squared off, or wedge-shaped, with each variation contributing to the distinctive appearance of the particular style (Fig. 5.24).

Figure 5.24   Selected types of serif.

Square   Bracketed   Unbracketed

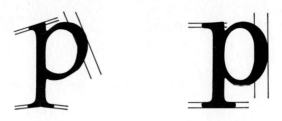

Old face (diagonal stress)   Modern face (vertical stress)

Figure 5.25   Placement of stress in old face and modern type styles.

Some of the Roman styles are drawn using lines of uniform weight; others, however, have a greater or lesser amount of contrast between the line weights of the different strokes that make up the letters. Styles that have the maximum line width of the thick portion of the letter (called *stress*) set vertically are called *modern faces,* whereas those that have a diagonal stress are called *old face* or *old style* (Fig. 5.25). This placement of stress gives the modern faces a more vertical appearance than is true of the old-style faces.

Sans serif   The *sans serif* category includes all of the styles which, as the name suggests, lack serifs. Sans serif styles frequently have little or no thick-thin contrast.

Italic   Type styles drawn on a slant are called *italic.* Most Roman and sans serif styles are produced in both vertical and italic versions. It is sometimes suggested that the italic version imparts a sense of movement to a line of type.

Upper- and lowercase   Most type styles are available in capital and noncapital letters. In the early days of printing the individual pieces of type were kept in two separate type cases; the capital letters were stored in the upper case and the noncapitals in the lower. This arrangement resulted in the identification of the capital letters as *uppercase* and the noncapitals as *lowercase*—terminology that continues in use today.

Small capital letters are also available in some styles. These are uppercase letters that have the same design as the regular uppercase letters, and are on the same size type body, but are smaller in overall size.

Boldness   Another variable in type style is the weight, or *boldness,* of the individual strokes that make up the letter, relative to the size of the letter. A style that has similar characteristics of proportion, thick-thin contrast, and presence or absence of serifs may also be available in a variety of line weights. Although the exact terms that are used differ, the variations that have lines finer than the "normal" version are called *light,* or lightline, and those with a heavier line than normal are called *bold,* or heavy. Letters with the heaviest lines are called *extra bold,* or black, whereas intermediate weights are called *demibold,* or medium [Fig. 5.26(a)].

Width (set)   Type styles are also distinguished from one another in terms of the overall width, or set, of the individual letters. This is true of each separate style,

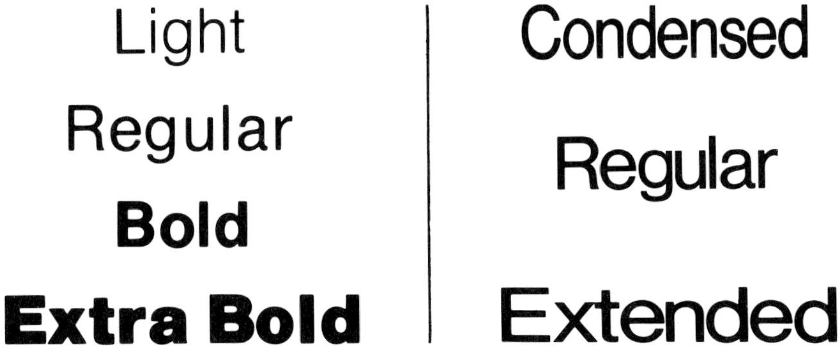

Light

Regular

Bold

Extra Bold

Condensed

Regular

Extended

(a)   (b)

Figure 5.26   Variations in the boldness and width of type faces.

with some being rather extended in form and others narrower; it is also true of variations within a particular style. Letters of a particular general style may be available in the "normal" width as well as in a narrower (*condensed*) version and wider (*extended*) version [Fig. 5.26(b)].

Type Design

Each of the specific styles is identified by a name or style number. Sometimes the name is that *of* the designer, and sometimes it is a more or less descriptive name given *by* the designer. Although the user will ultimately learn to identify the desired style by its name, it is more useful at the beginning simply to consider the characteristics desired and to select the type on that basis. This is done by obtaining a set of samples of the styles and sizes that are most likely to be used and keeping them at hand for use in making selections for particular applications.

Type fonts   A *font* of type consists of a complete range of characters in a given style and size, consisting of capital, small capital, and lowercase letters, and numerals, joined letters, and assorted signs that have been designed for that style.

Examples   At this point, examples of several commonly used type styles are provided. These illustrate the major categories and style variations that have been mentioned (Fig. 5.27).

Selection

One problem with type styles they are meant either for text use, such as on the pages of a book, or for decorative purposes. Book styles are designed for situations in which there is a mixture of capital and lowercase letters, and where the letters are spaced relatively closely and are arranged in parallel horizontal rows. On maps, however, lettering is often done in all capital letters, spaced out over a large area,

Americana

Regular   *Regular Italic*   **Bold**   **Extra Bold**

Schoolbook

Regular   *Regular Italic*   **Bold**   ***Bold Italic***

Times Roman

Regular   *Regular Italic*   **Bold**

Univers

Light   *Light Italic*   Medium   *Medium Italic*
Bold   ***Bold Italic***

Eurostile

Regular   Extended   **Bold**   **Bold Extended**

News Gothic

Regular   Condensed   *Condensed Italic*   **Bold**   **Bold Condensed**

Figure 5.27   A variety of typical type faces.

curved to follow the trend of a particular space, and placed in a variety of orientations. Book styles, therefore, are not necessarily well suited for map use. Decorative styles, on the other hand, tend to be visually complex and therefore relatively difficult to read. They also divert attention away from the map itself. The cartographer must therefore keep the map situation in mind when selecting type for particular applications. Experimentation with different styles, or combinations of styles, is helpful. It is also helpful to observe carefully the typographic combinations found on attractively produced maps—the good work done by others provides ideas that will improve one's own maps without resorting to copying.

It is common practice to use different type styles to distinguish among various categories of map features. An italic type face with serifs, for example, can be used for the names of water bodies, a sans serif vertical face for city names, and so on. Given the large variety of available styles, it is possible to use an entirely different face for every type of feature. To go to this extreme, however, is obviously a mistake because it creates a jumbled, unattractive mass of typographic styles. In order to avoid this kind of result, the cartographer confines the typography on any given map to a limited range of styles.[6] Carefully worked out variations in size, capitalization patterns, and italic versus vertical styles are used to distinguish between categories of features.

Placement Once appropriate type styles are selected, the cartographer must decide where each individual name is to be placed on the map. The main goal of type placement is that the feature being named is readily identifiable. Maps are frequently rather complex in nature, with many lines, tones, and symbols involved. Because of this complexity, a vast number of decisions must be made regarding type placement. Each of these decisions also influences other placements. In order to deal with this complexity effectively, it is helpful to be aware of some general *conventions* that have developed over the years regarding type placement. Several of these conventions seem to have their origins in the left-to-right reading pattern of westerners. In fact, whenever a question arises as to the best solution to a particular type placement problem, it is helpful to keep reading habits in mind.

Conventions provide a useful guide for the planning of the placement and alignment of type on a map.[7] It must be remembered, however, that in some situations it is impractical to adhere to them fully. When this occurs it is necessary to put aside the convention in order to accommodate to the situation.

Each piece of type that is placed on the map must be readily associated with the feature that it identifies. In addition, it must not interfere with the other names or with map symbols. Ideally, for example, type should not fall across a line symbol. In practice, however, this is often impossible to avoid completely. When the type must fall across a line it is common practice to interrupt the linework so that the type is clearly visible [Fig. 5.28(a)]. When the line is very fine compared to the lines in the type, or when the line is in a lighter color, it is possible to print the linework without interruption.

The starting point for type placement is the convention that type should, in general, be aligned horizontally. If a straight line of type is placed on a slant, the viewer has the uncomfortable feeling that it has been accidentally misplaced [Fig. 5.28(b)]. This seems to be related to the expectation that lines of type will be arranged horizontally as on the pages of a book. When curved parallels appear on the map, however, the curvature of the graticule is often strong enough so that the viewer is more comfortable if the "horizontal" lines of type are arranged on a curve, parallel to the lines of latitude [Fig. 5.28(c)].

When type cannot be placed horizontally, it should usually be aligned on a

[6]An interesting guide to acceptable combinations of styles, although not specifically for maps, is given in Allan Haley, *Photo Typography: A Guide to In-House Typesetting & Design* (New York: Charles Scribner's Sons, 1980), pp. 60–61.

[7]See, for example, Eduard Imhoff, "Positioning Names on Maps," *The American Cartographer,* 2, no. 2 (October 1975), 128–44, an English translation of "Die Anordnung der Namen in der Karte," *International Yearbook of Cartography,* 2, (1962), 93–129.

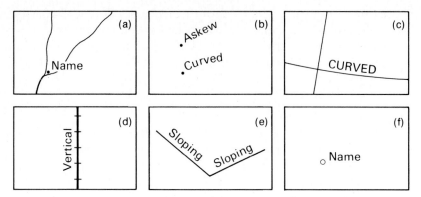

Figure 5.28   Type placement conventions. (See text for explanation.)

curve. The main exception to this rule occurs when the type is aligned with a straight-line feature that is not itself horizontal.

A second convention is that vertically placed type should be turned so that it can be read from the right side of the page [Fig. 5.28(d)]. Vertical type cannot be easily read with the map held horizontally and, for this reason, the user will usually turn the map in order to read it. Turning all of the vertical type in the same direction ensures that the viewer will not be irritated by finding it necessary to swing the map first one way and then the other in order to read it. Related to this is the third convention: If lettering is on a diagonal it should be placed so that it will "fall on its feet" if it is swung into horizontal position [Fig. 5.28(e)]. If this is not done the viewer will feel that the type is upside down, which is very distracting and difficult to read.

As each name is put on the map the cartographer must decide where it should be placed in relation to the map feature that is being identified. The main goal, of course, is to make it easy to associate each map feature with its name; nothing is more irritating to a map user than encountering several names and symbols on a map and being unable to tell which name applies to which symbol. The rules for placement vary, depending on whether the feature being identified is a point, a line, or an area.

The placement of type relative to point symbols is best done in accord with the left-to-right convention of reading. This suggests that the point symbol should be seen first and its identification should be located immediately to its right. In addition, however, the symbol itself should not be confused with the lettering and, therefore, the type is aligned slightly above the center of the symbol [Fig. 5.28(f)].

The ideal placement is frequently impossible because of the occurrence of other symbols, lettering, linework, and other features, so alternative locations must be considered. A suggested order of preference for various placement options is shown in Fig. 5.29(a) and (b). In addition, if space is particularly tight, it is possible to curve the lettering [Fig. 5.29(c)]. If even curving the type does not allow names to be unambiguously associated with the proper symbols, it is possible to use leader lines to indicate the connection [Fig. 5.29(d)].

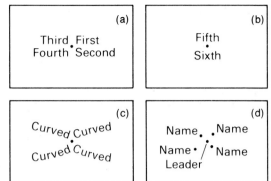

Figure 5.29 Preferred sequence for placing names around point symbols.

The type that identifies a linear symbol should be placed parallel to it. The type should not be placed so as to follow every minor wiggle in the line, but should be aligned with the general linear trend in a smooth curve [Fig. 5.30(a)]. The type can be either above or below the symbol, although placement above is somewhat preferred.

Type that identifies an areal feature is best placed within the feature if there is sufficient space. The type should be aligned so that it follows the general trend of the feature. It is also helpful to space the name out over most of the length of the feature being identified [Fig. 5.30(b)]. When this is done, however, the individual letters in the name should not be so far apart that the viewer sees only the separate letters and fails to connect them into the total name. An alternative to excessive spacing-out is to reduce the spacing and to repeat the name [Fig. 5.30(c)].

Placing the name within the feature assures a minimum of confusion as to what is being identified. Such placement also emphasizes the general extent of the feature. If the type must be placed outside the feature, and the feature is relatively linear, the type is aligned along its trend. If the feature is compact, the type is placed horizontally beside it, in the same manner as type that identifies a point symbol [Fig. 5.30(d)].

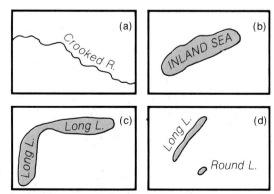

Figure 5.30 Additional type placement conventions: (a) Label for irregular line; (b) Within areal symbol; (c) Repeated, within elongated areal symbol; (d) Outside areal symbols.

NAME SELECTION

It is sometimes difficult to determine the correct name to be attached to a particular place or feature on a map. This is because names are changed, or the same name is rendered differently on different sources. Local usage also differs at times from the officially recognized version or, in some cases, the official name is simply not well known. Because of language differences, the problems related to naming are most difficult on maps of other countries.

Names within the United States

The *Board on Geographic Names* (BGN) is the authority charged with establishing the official name of a settlement or a natural feature in the United States, especially when clarity is lacking or a dispute is involved. The decisions of the BGN are made available through the publication of official gazetteers.

The United States Geological Survey (USGS), in cooperation with the BGN, has published a *National Gazetteer* (1982), which contains the names of over 1.5 million United States places, cultural features, and natural features. The listings include the following information about each feature in addition to its name: type of feature; geographic coordinates; elevation, if appropriate; the date the name became official; and the names of USGS maps on which the feature can be located. Other gazetteers are issued by the BGN, as well as by other agencies, both public and private. A recent edition of one of these gazetteers provides consistent name information. If a gazetteer is not available, a recent edition of an atlas published by a reputable cartographic establishment or a national postal guide is usually a reliable guide.

The decisions of the BGN provide the official names used by U.S. government agencies. While there is no legal requirement that private map producers follow their recommendations, there is no doubt that it is helpful to do so in order to reduce confusion. If it is desired to include an alternate name on a map for some reason, it can be placed in parentheses and located below or beside the BGN-approved name.

Foreign Names

The selection of names for features outside the United States is sometimes difficult. It is rather common, for example, to use an English-language name for many cities, such as Vienna or Rome—even though the inhabitants of those cities know them as Wien and Roma—so the cartographer must decide which name to use.

Although the problem of selecting an acceptable standard rendering is difficult enough if the country involved does not use the English language, it is even more difficult when the language does not use the Roman alphabet or does not have a written form. The English rendering of non-English place names by early explorers and travelers was not always successful and frequently was not consistent; in fact, the local name was often simply ignored and an unrelated English name substituted.

It is not unusual, therefore, to encounter a variety of names and spellings for the same place or feature.

An example of the problems involved in the selection of foreign names is the case of the city of Guangzhou in China. Guangzhou is the currently accepted name of the city which is better known in the United States as Canton. Other spellings for the name of this city have included Kwangchow and Kuang-Chow. The problem is that the original untransliterated Chinese version of the name of Guangzhou is meaningless to most English language map users and the currently accepted spelling is certainly unfamiliar. In order to reduce confusion, it is only realistic that the well-known English version be given some recognition. One way to handle such cases is to use the official version with the popular version added in parentheses: "Guangzhou (Canton)."

Many of the earth's physical features have been named by several countries and, in such cases, the name is based on that country's own language and historical background. The consistent naming of such features obviously requires international cooperation. One example is the Skagerrak, which washes the shores of Norway, Sweden, and Denmark. These three nations have adopted a single spelling, which, therefore, should logically be the international standard. Another example is Antarctica, where many nations have interests. It is an obvious area for international cooperation, as is the naming of features on the moon and other extraterrestrial bodies.

International cooperation is necessary to reduce the confusion resulting from applying more than one system of *transliteration* and *Romanization,* or other sources of alternative names. The United Nations, therefore, is involved in efforts to standardize the treatment of geographical names.[8] For maps made in English, the basic rule that is observed is that the actual local name of the feature is preferred when a Roman alphabet is used. Otherwise, a standardized Roman-alphabet transliteration is acceptable.

The BGN determines the proper names to be applied to foreign entities by U.S. government agencies. Because of the difficulties involved in foreign place names, the decisions of the BGN, which take into account the UN recommendations, should be used as a guide for private map producers as well. Again, a recent gazetteer or atlas provides a guide to proper usage.

Suggested Readings

BOARD, CHRISTOPHER, "Map Design and Evaluation: Lessons for Geographers," *Progress in Human Geography,* 4, no. 3 (September 1980), 433–37.

[8]United Nations Group of Experts on Geographical Names. An indication of the range of concerns addressed by this group is provided in *Second United Nations Conference on the Standardization of Geographical Names,* London, 10–31 May 1972, vol. 1, *Report of the Conference* [New York: United Nations, Department of Economic and Social Affairs, 1974 (E/CONF.61/4)].

CASTNER, H. W., and G. McGRATH, eds., *Symposium on the Influence of the Map User on Map Design*. Kingston, Ont.: Department of Geography, York University, 1971.

KEATES, J. S., *Cartographic Design and Production*. New York: John Wiley and Sons, A Halsted Press Book, 1973.

6

Map Production: Pen and Ink

This chapter deals with the pen-and-ink drafting and construction of a simple one-color map, based on the compilation and design work described in the previous chapter. The chapters immediately following this one expand on these basic concepts and describe map scribing, photography and reproduction, and the procedures involved in adding shades of gray and color to the final map. Descriptions of tools and materials are included at different stages of the discussion. This is because particular types of tools and materials are suited to some of the procedures described and not to others.

LINE DRAFTING

Pen-and-ink line drafting was, for a long period of time, the predominant method of producing map originals. This method is still in use today, although the specific tools and materials that are utilized have changed over the years and, as will be noted, other techniques have become extremely important. Despite the existence of these other techniques, much of the current practice can easily be related to and compared with the basic line-drafting methods. A discussion of line drafting is, therefore, an appropriate way to begin an explanation of the variety of processes used to produce maps. The materials and tools available for drafting are discussed first and the manner in which the actual preparation of the drawings is accomplished is then described.

Materials

Drawing media   The historically customary medium for line drafting is smooth, hard-surfaced paper, which is capable of accepting either pencil or ink lines. Paper is derived from either vegetable fibers (most commonly wood), rags, or a combination of such materials. A filler may be added to give the paper a smooth finish suitable for pen-and-ink use. Finally, other processing can be carried out in order to obtain the desired type of finish.

Because of its fibrous composition, paper absorbs moisture from a relatively humid atmosphere and gives up moisture to relatively dry air. As the moisture content of the paper changes, which is inevitable in all but the most closely controlled environments, its fibers shrink or swell, causing the overall size of the sheet to change accordingly. The papermaking process also tends to align the fibers in one direction, thus giving the paper a grain; this results in greater shrinking or swelling taking place across the grain than in the direction of the grain.

Under certain conditions, such as when a simple monochromatic drawing is being done, good quality paper is an entirely satisfactory drafting material. For drafting purposes, a smooth, densely finished, opaque paper is usually preferred, although thinner, more translucent paper may be used when it is necessary to trace an image. Unfortunately, however, paper's lack of *dimensional stability* frequently renders it unsuitable for use in modern mapping applications. To the cartographer, one aspect of the importance of the stretching or shrinking of the paper is simply that a map drawn on paper changes scale slightly as the paper changes size, thus affecting its accuracy. A second, perhaps even more important aspect comes into play if more than one drawing is required for a single final map—which is frequently the case (see Chapter 8). In this situation, maintaining the correct relationship between the various drawings becomes virtually impossible as each individual sheet independently changes size.

The problems resulting from dimensional instability are so serious that there has been a continuing search for stable drawing materials to take the place of paper. Over the years, for example, images have been scribed on sheets of glass, or have been drawn on paper bonded to a metal plate in order to obtain a more stable image. These materials, however, were so expensive and difficult to work with that, in recent years, their place has been taken by specially developed plastic materials, particularly *polyester film*. This type of plastic is treated so that it stays very close to a constant size over a wide range of temperature and humidity. It is therefore possible to maintain fine tolerances in the alignment of drawings done on *stable-base plastic*.

Plastics used for drafting purposes are treated so that their surface is receptive to pencil, or to pencil or ink.[1] Some materials are clear whereas others are translucent. They can also be coated with different sensitizing materials, or scribing coatings, for use in a variety of applications in addition to drafting. Some of these applications are described in connection with scribing and map reproduction processes (Chapter 7).

Pencils and inks   At times, such as during the compilation of a map worksheet, the cartographer may work in pencil because of the clear but easily erasable image that is produced. When the work is being done on paper there is no particular problem involved in the use of pencil. As a general rule it is preferable to use a relatively hard lead, sharpened to a fine point, which produces a clear, sharp image that will not smudge easily. The amount of pressure applied to the pencil should be moderate so that the image can be erased without damaging the surface of the paper.

The *grained surface* of plastic drafting materials also accepts a pencil image,

---

[1]For example: Stabilene, Keuffel & Esser Co.; Draftrite, Direct Reproduction Corp.; Cronaflex UC-4, E. I. DuPont deNemours and Co., Photo Products Dept.

but the lines tend to rub off the plastic surface rather easily. A better-quality line, which will not rub off as readily, is obtained by using special pencils designed for use on plastic. The special pencils are still easily erased, using a soft eraser, and the drawing surface is not damaged by the erasure.

The reproduction of map drawings depends upon the use of sharp black originals (see Chapter 7). *India ink,* which consists of finely divided carbon black dispersed in water with a stabilizer added, is used for final drawings, instead of pencil. It provides the type of image required for reproduction purposes and has long been the standard drafting ink. India ink has the additional advantage of being indelible when it is thoroughly dry—that is, it does not dissolve in water—so that the image is stable and long-lasting as well as solid black.

The initial use of plastic drafting media created a difficulty in terms of ink selection because when India ink dried it tended to flake off the smooth surface of the plastic. For this reason, inks were developed with a proportion of solvent added so they would slightly dissolve the surface and would thereby be bonded to the plastic. This type of ink was difficult to use because it tended to soften the plastic parts commonly used in drafting instruments. Perhaps more importantly, the solvent evaporated very rapidly with the result that the ink dried quickly and tended to clog the instruments. Both of these problems have been reduced by modifying the composition of the ink. The simplest solution that has been perfected, however, is the treatment of the drafting medium, either mechanically or chemically, in order to provide a grained surface. This has made it possible to use regular India ink instead of solvent ink, because a mechanical bond is created as the ink dries on the grained surface of the plastic. For most purposes, the chemical etching of the surface by a solvent is no longer necessary.

Another advantage of using India ink in combination with a grained surface is that the erasure of the image is easily accomplished, using a soft, slightly dampened eraser or a moist, cotton-tipped swab. Care must be taken with some materials, however, to avoid rubbing off the matte surface. Some experimentation will establish how much of a problem this is on the particular material being used. Because the surface is not damaged by the erasure, a replacement line can be drawn over the erasure without difficulty. This contrasts with the situation when solvent ink is used, because the solvent partially dissolves the surface as it is applied and it is virtually impossible to remove the dried ink without damaging the surface of the plastic.

Plastic is an improvement over paper when the erasure of an India ink line is required, because the ink penetrates the surface of paper to a certain extent when it is applied. The result is that it is rather difficult to erase an ink image from paper and the friction involved in the erasure of the image frequently loosens some of the fibers, thus damaging the surface of the paper. This makes erasure difficult, and reinking even more so, because the ink tends to run along the loosened fibers, creating a blurred image.

If a multicolored image is desired, as might be the case when a worksheet is being created, colored inks or pencils can be used on the grained drafting plastic, as well as on paper. Because some colored inks tend to spread when they are applied, however, the resulting lines may not have sufficient accuracy and definition.

There is, today, a wide variety of products on the market. The various possible combinations of these materials should be explored, with the help of a drafting supply house, when questions arise as to the best combination to use. The materials should also be tested for compatability before they are used.

Tools

The cartographer uses the same types of drafting instruments as those used by workers in the other professions that utilize drafting skills. In cartography, however, there tends to be a greater emphasis on the types of tools needed for the preparation of final drawings suitable for photographic purposes. In this section, the most commonly encountered tools are described. A few of the more specialized tools, such as scribing instruments, are described later when the specific process for which they are used is discussed.

The first requirement of any cartographer is to have available a *flat drafting surface* that is large enough to accommodate the drawings that will be produced— and map drawings are often rather large. Obviously, the selection of an appropriate size for the drawing board or table and other items of equipment is a function of the size of the jobs that will be encountered in a particular office.

For some purposes a *light table,* which consists of a translucent glass or plastic sheet placed over a light source, is more useful than a wood-surfaced drafting table. This is particularly true when it is necessary to trace from source documents or worksheets, to align or opaque film negatives, or to scribe images. (Work with negatives and scribing is described in Chapter 7.) Some cartographers work exclusively on a light table whereas others work on a drafting table but almost always have access to a light table as well.

One edge of the drawing surface must be perfectly straight in order to provide accurate alignment for the *T square.* A T square consists of a long, straight blade, attached at right angles to a shorter crosspiece that is used to hold the straightedge portion in constant alignment (Fig. 6.1). The T square is normally aligned on the left edge of the drafting surface and is used to provide a guiding edge for pencil, pen, or scribing tools as horizontal lines are produced. Only the upper edge of the T square is used for this purpose as there is no guarantee that the lower edge of the instrument is exactly parallel with the upper edge. The upper edge of the T square

Figure 6.1 T square. (Courtesy of Kratos/Keuffel & Esser.)

also provides a guiding edge for triangles, lettering templates, and other tools that must be kept in accurate alignment.

The T square is used only for horizontal alignment. It is not placed on the upper or lower edge of the drafting surface when vertical lines are to be drawn because it is very unlikely that the edges of the surface are perfectly square with one another.

Some workers use a long straightedge, which is attached to the drawing table through a system of lines and pulleys, in place of a T square (Fig. 6.2). In this arrangement, the straightedge moves up and down the table, with the upper edge always parallel.

When long, straight lines must be drawn between points on a map that are not horizontally aligned, it is more convenient to use a *straightedge* than to use a T square. A straightedge is, for all practical purposes, a T square without the aligning crosspiece.

When great accuracy is required, such as in laying out projections, setting margins for the sheets of a map series, or aligning the pages of a book or atlas, a *line-up table* is an indispensable tool (Fig. 6.3). A typical line-up table has two movable guide rails arranged at right angles to one another. The guide rails traverse across a light-table surface; one moves from left to right and the other moves from top to bottom. The guide rails move in geared tracks, so that they remain parallel as they move, and they are positioned accurately through the use of scales that are attached to the tracks. An instrument holder, which holds a pencil, pen, or scribing point, slides along each guide rail. The distance that the instrument moves is controlled by adjustable stops on the guide.

Figure 6.2 Parallel straightedge. (Courtesy of Kratos/Keuffel & Esser.)

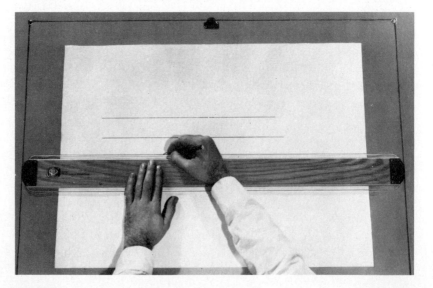

Figure 6.3 Line-up table. (Courtesy
of nuArc Company, Inc.)

Straight lines, with accurate right-angle intersections, can be rapidly drawn by
working on a light table with a precision grid positioned under the drawing material.
Some drafting films are provided with a *preprinted grid,* printed in nonreproducing
blue, which is suitable for this purpose. When prints or photographs are made from
a drawing done on such film the grid does not show in the final product.

Drafting triangles are thin, stiff sheets of plastic or metal that are used to draw
vertical lines and lines at angles. Most triangles are fixed, with 30-, 60-, and 90-
degree angles, or with a 90-degree angle and two 45-degree angles (Fig. 6.4). Triangles that can be adjusted to various, nonstandard angles are also available. For
the sake of convenience, triangles are made in a variety of sizes. When vertical lines,
or lines at one of the standard angles, are to be drawn, one edge of the triangle is
held tightly against the T square. The appropriate vertical or slanting edge is then
used as a guide for drawing the lines. Alternatively, the triangle is placed, as needed,
to serve as a short straightedge.

For some purposes, such as cutting film or paper, metal tools (triangles,
T squares, and straightedges) are preferred. This is because plastic tools are easily
nicked by knives or razor blades and therefore should not be used to guide cutting
tools.

A specially hinged arrangement of straightedges, called a *drafting machine,* is
available to draw both horizontal and vertical lines. A drafting machine can also
be set to draw lines at any desired angle, not just the standard 30-, 45-, or 60-degree
angles (Fig. 6.5). Drafting machines are commonly used in engineering and archi-
tectural drafting offices; they do not, however, seem to have come into common
use in cartographic establishments although they appear to be useful accessories.

A *ruling pen* is the traditional instrument for the pen-and-ink drafting of
straight lines or smooth curves [Fig. 6.6(a)]. Because of the arrangement of its blades,

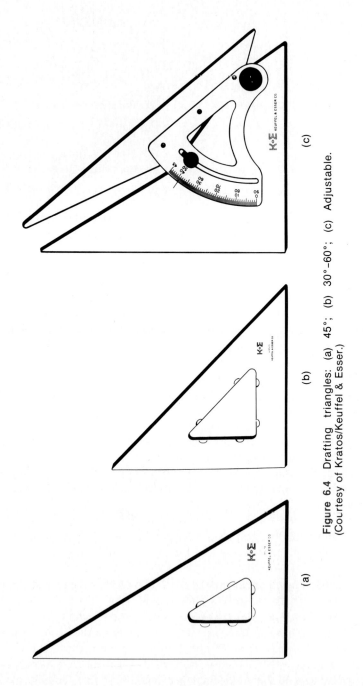

Figure 6.4 Drafting triangles: (a) 45°; (b) 30°–60°; (c) Adjustable. (Courtesy of Kratos/Keuffel & Esser.)

Figure 6.5   Drafting machine. (Courtesy of Kratos/Keuffel & Esser.)

the ruling pen is always used against some type of straightedge or curved template. The spacing between the blades is adjustable, using a small knurled screw, so that line widths may be changed as desired.

A special ruling pen with curved blades and a pivoting handle is used, without a guiding straightedge or template, to draw irregular lines. A version with two sets of blades is used for drawing parallel irregular lines [Fig. 6.6(b)]. The single-blade version is called a *curve pen* and the double-blade version is called a *railroad pen.*

Straight pens, or quill pens, are the traditional instrument for drawing irregular lines, such as streams or contour lines. Such pens are particularly useful because a skilled worker can vary the line weight the pens produce. This is achieved by changing the pressure on the tip of the pen; the greater the pressure the greater the

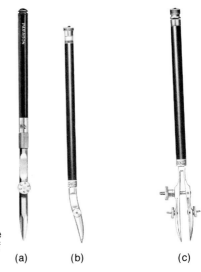

Figure 6.6   (a) Ruling pen; (b) Curve pen; (c) Railroad pen. (Courtesy of Kratos/Keuffel & Esser.)

(a)   (b)   (c)

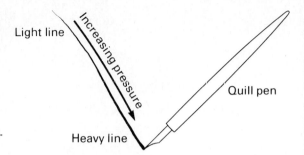

Figure 6.7 Effect of pressure difference on line weight.

spread of the tip and, consequently, the greater the width of the line. An example of the use of this technique is the tapering of a river from a fine line in the upper reaches of the stream to a broader line at the mouth (Fig. 6.7).

In recent years, both ruling pens and straight pens have largely been replaced by a variety of *reservoir pens*. As the name suggests, these pens consist of special interchangeable tips attached to a reservoir that holds a supply of ink sufficient to draw a great many feet of linework (Fig. 6.8).[2] These tips each draw a line of a specific width, so a series of tips is required—one for each width which is to be drawn. Some of the tips used on these pens are similar to ruling pen tips and they are used in conjunction with T squares, triangles, straightedges, and curves. Many of the tips are tubular, which means that they draw a constant-weight line in any direction. Tubular tips are used with straightedges or curve templates, or they are used freehand in the drawing of irregular lines, such as coastlines. If the effect of a tapered line is desired, progressively wider tips are used as the drafting of the line proceeds from the fine to the heavy portion.

Scales are accurately divided "rulers" used for establishing the lengths of lines or for measuring the size of various map features. There is a large variety of scales available, with different scale units and overall lengths; the specific type needed is determined by the type of work being undertaken. It is usual, however, to have scales available in both English and metric units. Some of the lengths selected should be suitable for measuring short elements such as the length of a map scale. If necessary, longer scales should be acquired for measuring long elements such as the radius of curvature of a parallel of latitude. An appropriate selection might include, for example, four different scales: one a foot long, divided into inches and fractional parts of inches (tenths, fiftieths, hundredths); one a yard long, divided into inches and fractions; one 10 to 30 cm long, divided into millimeters or half-millimeters; and one a meter in length, divided into millimeters. In some cases, only the initial, major division of each scale is subdivided into the finer gradations.

Some scales have a flat cross section and from one to four sets of subdivisions, whereas others are triangular in cross section and have six sets of subdivisions. The decision as to whether to use a flat or a triangular scale is, to large extent, a matter

---

[2]For example: Staedtler Mars, J. S. Staedtler, Inc.; Kohinoor Rapidograph, Kohinoor, Inc.; Pelikan Graphos, available from Kratos/Keuffel & Esser Co.

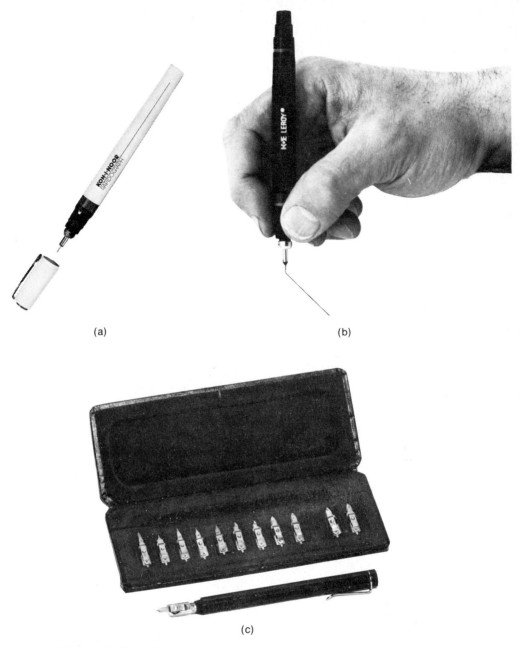

(a)

(b)

(c)

Figure 6.8 Three types of reservoir drawing pens. [(a) Courtesy of Koh-I-Noor Rapidograph, Inc.; (b) and (c) Courtesy of Kratos/Keuffel & Esser.]

of personal preference; it is obvious, however, that one triangular scale may take the place of two or more flat scales and may therefore be preferable if a number of scales are needed from time to time. Scales are for measuring purposes only and are not designed to be used as straightedges.

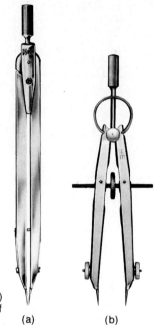

Figure 6.9   Two types of dividers: (a) Hairspring; (b) Bow. (Courtesy of Kratos/Keuffel & Esser.)

(a)   (b)

Dividers are two-legged instruments with a sharp point on each leg. They are used to lay off multiple units of the same length, to divide a line into equal parts, or to transfer measurements from a scale to a line or from one map element to another (Fig. 6.9). *Hairspring dividers* are adjusted by pulling the points apart or pushing them together, with the adjustment held by friction. *Bow dividers,* on the other hand, are adjusted by turning a knurled adjusting knob, and the adjustment is held by the adjusting screw.

Compasses are used to draw circles or arcs of circles [Fig. 6.10(a)]. The radius of the circle to be drawn is adjusted by moving the points closer together or farther apart. Compasses are essentially the same as dividers except that one of the points is replaced by a pencil lead or by a drafting pen. When the pen point is used, the width of the line is set by adjusting the space between its blades.

A *drop-bow compass* is used to draw a circle of very small radius [Fig. 6.10(b)]. This type of compass operates much like a regular bow compass except that the pen or pencil point revolves around a fixed pivot point.

A *beam compass* is used to draw a circle with a very large radius (Fig. 6.11). This compass consists of a pivot point (called a *dead center*) and a pen or pencil point (called a *live center*). Both points slide along a beam that can be extended to considerable length to achieve long radii. Approximate settings are made by moving the dead center; fine adjustments are made by turning a small setscrew that moves the live center.

Proportional dividers consist of a pair of legs that are pivoted on an adjustable

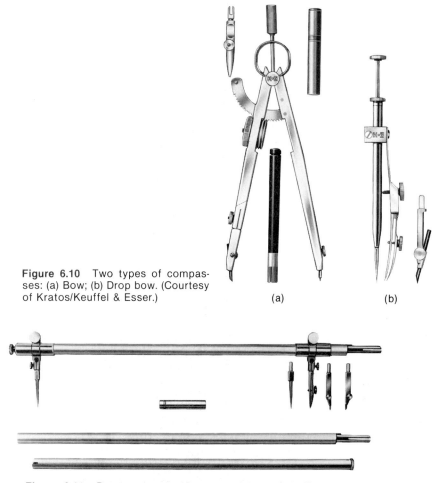

Figure 6.10 Two types of compasses: (a) Bow; (b) Drop bow. (Courtesy of Kratos/Keuffel & Esser.)   (a)   (b)

Figure 6.11 Beam compass. (Courtesy of Kratos/Keuffel & Esser.)

pivot point in the form of a letter X [Fig. 6.12(a)]. The location of the pivot point determines the proportion between the opening between the points at one end of the dividers and the opening between the points at the other end. One purpose of these dividers is to transfer distances from a drawing at one scale to a second drawing at another scale. The pivot point is first set to the ratio between the scales of the two drawings. Distances are then transferred directly: The measurement on the source map is taken with one pair of points and is transfered to the other map with the points at the other end of the dividers. This process eliminates the need to measure the distances with a scale and to compute and measure the converted distance. Other proportions, such as the ratio between the diameter and the circumference of a circle, are converted by using appropriate settings of the proportional scale.

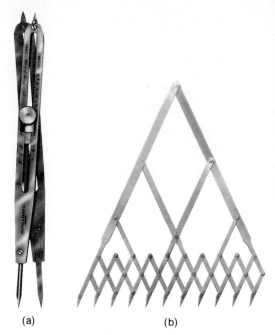

Figure 6.12 (a) Proportional dividers. (Courtesy of Kratos/Keuffel & Esser.) (b) Spacing dividers. (Courtesy of Charvoz-Carsen Corporation.)   (a)   (b)

Another useful type of divider is the *spacing divider;* it has 11 points, hinged together in accordionlike fashion [Fig. 6.12(b)]. This instrument is used to divide a line into anywhere from two to ten equal parts. The division is done by placing one point at the beginning of the line and another appropriate point at the other end. (If the line is to be divided into ten parts, for example, the first point is placed at the beginning and the eleventh point at the end.) The intermediate points, then, are automatically aligned at the required number of equal intervals.

Irregular curves (sometimes called *French curves*) are templates that are used to draw curved lines through points that are not part of a circle. The curves are available in a wide variety of sizes and shapes [Fig. 6.13(a)]. This type of curve is used so that the curved lines are drawn smoothly, which is not possible when working freehand.

Railroad curves, on the other hand, are fixed-radius curves. They are used to draw a portion of the arc of a circle when it is not convenient to use a beam compass [Fig. 6.13(b)]. This occurs, for example, when the drafting table is too small to accommodate a long beam. Railroad curves usually include a short straight section, or tangent, which is joined to the circle. The tangent on the template provides a smooth transition between the circle and any straight line that must be drawn tangent to it.

A variety of *plastic templates* is available to assist in the drawing of simple map symbols. These templates consist of cutouts of the symbols, including circles, squares, triangles, arrows, letters, and numbers (Fig. 6.14). A tubular pen is used to trace the outlines and draw the desired symbols. Although these templates are

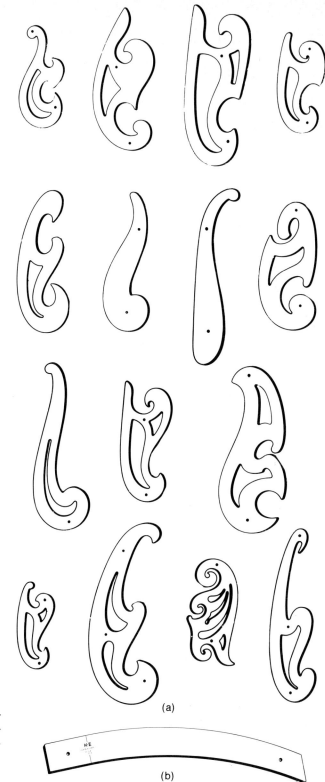

Figure 6.13 (a) Typical irregular curves. (b) Railroad curve, with tangent. (Courtesy of Kratos/Keuffel & Esser.)

(a)

(b)

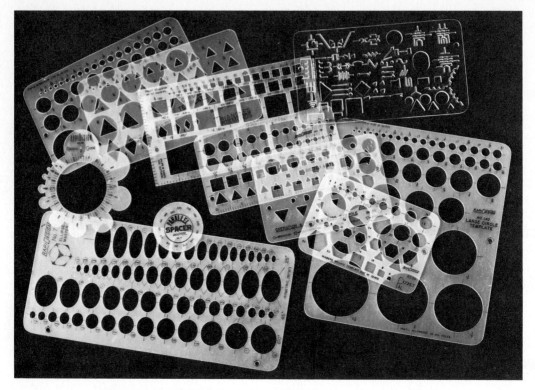

Figure 6.14 Typical symbol templates. (Courtesy of Kratos/Keuffel & Esser.)

sometimes useful for quick work or when a number of repetitive symbols are needed, they are often not suitable for use on finished maps because of the relatively crude quality of the symbols that are produced.

Other special tools are sometimes used. These include rolling rules, which are used to draw sets of parallel lines; flexible splines, which are used to provide a guide for lines of long, rather smooth curvature; and pantographs, which are used for mechanically enlarging or reducing drawings. All of these are in addition to the various types of lead holders, pencil sharpeners, brushes, scissors, erasers, and so forth, which are needed. The specific set of tools an individual uses is largely a matter of experience and preference. Some cartographers are incurable collectors who spend considerable amounts of money acquiring special tools for every conceivable task whereas others, who are equally skillful and successful, use only the sparest selection of tools.

Anyone working on the production of map drawings should strive from the beginning to develop habits of neatness and cleanliness in the drafting room. It is obvious that smudged or dirty drawings cannot produce the most effective results, nor do cluttered working conditions lead to the efficient production of high-quality drawings.

DRAFTED ORIGINAL

When the worksheet is completed, along with a specification sheet, the preparation of the final drawing begins. The worksheet is usually fastened to a light table so that it is easily traced. A sheet of drafting paper or plastic is then placed over the worksheet and is also fastened in place. No additional preparations are needed for creating a single-color map. The slightly more complex procedures involved when a multicolor map is being produced are explained in Chapter 8.

The first step in drafting is usually the preparation of the linework. Pens of the proper size are selected and each required line is drawn, following the specifications provided. Gaps are usually left in the lines at appropriate locations to allow for the later addition of lettering and symbols. One advantage of using colored symbols on the worksheet is that the tracing is more easily done. When the black ink lines are placed on the final drawing the translucent colored lines on the worksheet do not create a shadow effect; if the lines on the worksheet are black, the shadow they cast makes it difficult to judge the quality and opacity of the drafted line.

Straight horizontal lines are always drawn using a T square; straight vertical or slanting lines are drawn with the appropriate triangle or straightedge. Arcs of circles are drawn with compasses or railroad curves and smoothly curved lines utilize irregular curves or splines. Irregular lines, such as coastlines, are drawn freehand, but all regular lines, whether straight or curved, are drawn using an appropriate guide. The reason for these choices is simply the difference in appearance, on the final map, between lines drawn with and without mechanical assistance. A general rule is that lines representing man-made features (buildings, roads, canals, railroads, and fences) or imaginary lines (graticules, grids, and boundary lines) are drawn with mechanical assistance. Such features are usually regular and mechanical in appearance or layout and the use of mechanical aids produces a line of suitable character. Natural features, such as rivers or coastlines, are appropriately drawn freehand—the use of mechanical aids for such lines produces an unnaturally stiff and regular appearance.

After the linework is completed, the required symbols, patterns, and lettering are added. Descriptions of materials used for these purposes comprise the balance of this chapter.

TYPOGRAPHY

The considerations involved in type selection and positioning were described in the previous chapter. This section describes the materials and processes that are used to actually place the lettering on the map. Most of the discussion is based on commercially produced lettering materials and on the procedures related to using them. Mention is also made, however, of freehand lettering and of the mechanically assisted methods of hand lettering that are sometimes used.

Methods of Application

A variety of means are used to add typography to a map; the most common of these are briefly described here. Scribing requires specialized application procedures, and these are discussed in conjunction with the description of scribing in Chapter 7.

Pen-and-ink method   The most basic means of applying topography is to do the lettering by hand, either with or without mechanical aids.

Freehand lettering is theoretically the most flexible technique available. Unfortunately, unless done by an expert, it is not satisfactory for most purposes and is therefore seldom used.

A number of *mechanical aids* are available to assist in hand lettering.[3] The main advantage of these aids is that they produce lettering that is quite consistent in form. The aids usually utilize stencillike lettering guides which are available in a variety of styles. In general, these mechanical aids result in a relatively low-cost product that is readily available. Unfortunately, even the best of them do not provide lettering that equals the attractive appearance and variety available through the use of printed type in one of its various forms and they are also somewhat slow to use. Three examples of mechanical lettering devices are pictured in Fig. 6.15.

Letter-by-letter method   Commercially prepared sheets containing alphabets and numerals, printed in the standard type styles described above, are readily available. Two basic types of sheets are produced, either of which allows the cartographer to build up any required word or number, one letter or numeral at a time. Both types are easy to use and provide good results. The main difficulty in working letter by letter is in establishing the spacing between letters and aligning them properly. The process is also slower than using the typeset materials that will be described.

One type of alphabet sheet has letters which must be *individually cut out*.[4] The letters are printed on a thin, flexible, transparent plastic material. The back of the sheet is coated with an adhesive and the sheet is combined with a protective backing. To use this material, a cut is made around the desired letter, using a sharp knife, and the section of the translucent plastic base containing the letter is removed from the backing sheet (Fig. 6.16). The letter is then aligned at the desired location on the drawing, covered with a piece of thin paper to protect its surface, and rubbed firmly with a smooth wood or plastic burnisher. The pressure and friction from this rubbing fastens the letter firmly in place. Some types of adhesive are derived from beeswax and may be removed and replaced rather easily, whereas other types of adhesive are less easily adjusted. Because it melts, the beeswax adhesive should be

---

[3]For example: Leroy, Kratos/Keuffel & Esser Co.; Wrico, Wood-Regan Instrument Co.; Varigraph, Varigraph, Inc.

[4]For example: Artype, Artype, Inc.; Letraset, Letraset USA; Formatt, Graphic Products Corp.; Para-Type, Para-Tone Inc.

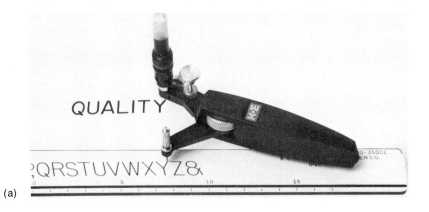

(a)

(b)

(c)

Figure 6.15 Lettering devices: (a) Leroy. (Courtesy of Kratos/Keuffel & Esser.) (b) Wrico. (Courtesy of Wood-Regan Instrument Co.) (c) Varigraph. (Courtesy of Varigraph Inc.)

(a)

(b)

Figure 6.16 Application of cut-out lettering: (a) Desired letter is cut from printed sheet. (b) Letter is lifted from sheet and placed in position. (c) Letter is burnished in place. (Courtesy of Artype, Inc.)

(c)

Figure 6.16 (*cont.*)

avoided when reproduction processes that involve heat, such as diazo or blueprinting, are to be used (see Chapter 7). The process is then repeated, using as many different letters as are required. Because the backing of each letter is transparent, the appearance that results is almost the same as if the letter were printed directly onto the drawing. There is, however, some reflection from the plastic material around the letter that is undesirable if the original is to be used for display purposes. If the drawing is to be photographed, this material is quite satisfactory.

The second type of alphabet sheet is a *pressure-sensitive* type containing letters and numerals that are fastened to the back of a translucent backing sheet.[5] In this case the individual letters are adhesive and the support material is not. To use this material, the entire alphabet sheet is aligned to bring the desired letter into place and the carrier sheet is firmly rubbed with a burnisher. The result is that the individual letter is transferred directly to the drawing, without any surrounding support material (Fig. 6.17). This type of sheet has the advantage that there is no reflection from the base material and the letter appears to be directly printed in place.

Typeset method Perhaps the ideal way to obtain typography for a map is to have the words and numbers needed for a particular map set to order by a typesetting firm. To accomplish this, the cartographer first prepares a list of all of the words, letters, and numbers that will appear on the final map. The list is organized so that

[5]For example: Trans-Artype; Artype, Inc.; Letraset, Letraset USA; Para-Type, Para-Tone, Inc., Prestype, Prestype, Inc.

223

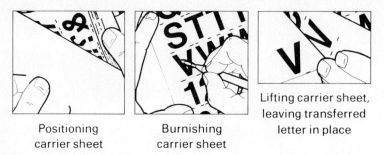

Positioning
carrier sheet

Burnishing
carrier sheet

Lifting carrier sheet,
leaving transferred
letter in place

Figure 6.17 Application of rub-on lettering. (Courtesy of Letraset USA Inc.)

all of the names of similar features are grouped together, and the size and style of type desired for each set of features is then specified. Any special spacing or layout that is required, such as for the organization of a legend, can also be requested. The list of specifications is then sent to a printing firm, which sets the type and prepares proofs on the desired material.

It may be difficult, under some circumstances, to arrange to have type specially set. First, the process may take several days from beginning to end because it is usually necessary to order the typesetting from an outside source, perhaps located some distance away. Second, the process is relatively expensive, especially as compared with hand lettering, although the amount of production time saved, compared with other forms of lettering, will offset this expense to some extent. When time and budget allow, custom-set lettering is generally favored because of the high quality of the results.

The simplest form of custom-set lettering is a *paper proof,* or *repro;* that is, once the type is set it is simply printed on a sheet of paper. The individual words or groups of words are then cut out and fastened in place on the drawing, using glue, rubber cement, or a layer of beeswax adhesive applied to the back of the paper.[6] Type is set in the traditional, straight-line format, so a small cut has to be made between letters if a curved arrangement is desired. Because whole words are cut out and fastened in place in one piece, the spacing and alignment of individual letters is automatically maintained—entire words, however, must still be carefully aligned.

Paper proofs are easy to obtain, but are not the most useful form. The main difficulty with a paper proof is that the cut-out piece of paper shows up rather noticeably. It also blocks out any lines that lie behind it, which sometimes makes placement difficult. When possible, it is preferable to have the custom-set lettering

---

[6]Beeswax adhesive is applied by using a coating machine. Machines that coat a full sheet of material at a time are available for large-scale operations. Small, hand-held machines are also available and are suitable for occasional use. As previously noted, beeswax adhesive is not suitable for reproduction processes involving heat.

proofed on a sheet of thin, *translucent material.* This material is then coated with a thin layer of beeswax adhesive and is used in the same way as the sheets of individual letters described above.

An alternative to traditional forms of typesetting is *phototypesetting.* Various types of phototypesetting machines are available, some of them simple and inexpensive enough to be purchased for a medium-size cartographic establishment. Instead of setting metal type, these devices directly produce photographic paper prints, or film positives or negatives, using standard type styles. The film positives may also be created on what is called *stripping film.* The emulsion layer of this film, which contains the image, is quite thin, but tough, and can be peeled away from the heavier backing material. It is then waxed and used in the same manner as other translucent backed, typeset materials. If stripping film is not available, regular film may be used, preferably a type with a thin base.

Photography can also be used to duplicate lettering done by any of the approaches described above. Indeed, if one is in desperate straits, lettering can be cut from almost any source and assembled as needed, as long as the lettering is black and is on a white background. The prepared copy is photographed to the proper size and contact positives are made. After development, the image is waxed and used as already described.

When a map is produced by a computer-driven plotter, lettering may be applied directly by the plotter (see Chapter 11). Modern plotters carry out this type of work rapidly and accurately and often have several lettering styles from which to choose. This approach is especially useful when the user can specify the desired location of the label prior to starting the plot, so that unwanted overlaps with other labels and map details are avoided.

PATTERNS AND SYMBOLS

Patterns of lines and dots and specialized map symbols are used by cartographers in many different applications. This section is limited to descriptions of the various forms in which these patterns and symbols are available and to explanations of how they are applied to the map. The considerations involved in the selection of patterns and symbols that are suitable, from the standpoint of either appearance or effectiveness, are discussed in Chapter 9.

The two basic types of materials on which patterns and symbols are available, pressure-sensitive and cut-out, are the same as those on which typography is available. Patterns, however, are most commonly available in the cut-out form. To use this material the desired portion of the pattern, or the desired symbol, is cut out with a knife. The cut-out portion is then removed from the sheet, placed in position on the map, and burnished into place.[7]

[7]For example: Artype, Artype, Inc.; Letratone, Letraset USA; Zip-a-Tone, Para-Tone, Inc.

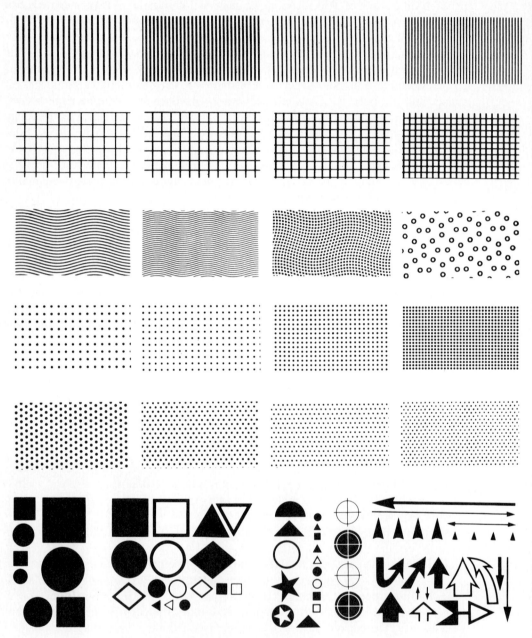

Figure 6.18 Typical variations in preprinted line, dot patterns, and symbols. (Courtesy of Letraset USA Inc.)

Variations in line patterns are available in many different line weights and spacings (Fig. 6.18). Dot patterns are available in a number of arrangements, either regular or irregular, and in a range of different dot sizes and shapes. A variety of different symbols, such as dots, circles, triangles, stars, squares, and arrows is also available.

When cut-out patterns, symbols, or type are used, the material must be burnished into place very firmly. This is especially true when the edges overlap linework or other material on the map. If there is anything less than perfect adhesion, either reflections or shadows will result. Reflections interfere with the image when the map is photographed, and weak spots result. Shadows, on the other hand, result in widened lines or unwanted images. When each separation is completed, it should be viewed so that light is reflected from its surface from a variety of directions. This will help to locate any areas that require additional burnishing.

COMPLETION

The completed line drawing, with linework, lettering, symbols, and patterns in place, is next checked for accuracy. This review includes examining the quality of the inking, the size, style, and placement of the lettering, the placement of the symbols, the angle at which the dot or line patterns are placed, and the overall quality and accuracy of the drawing. The worksheet is used as the primary reference material for this checking process, but any problems that are encountered are verified by referring to the original information sources, if necessary. Upon completion of the checking process, the drawing is ready for reproduction.

Suggested Readings

CRAIG, JAMES, *Production for the Graphic Designer*. New York: Watson-Guptill Publications, 1974.

HALEY, ALLAN, *Photo Typography: A Guide to In-House Typesetting & Design*. New York: Charles Scribner's Sons, 1980.

Pocket Pal: A Graphic Arts Production Handbook (11th ed.). New York: International Paper Co., 1974.

7

Map Reproduction: Monochrome

HIGH-CONTRAST PHOTOGRAPHY

When a map drawing is completed, the first step in the reproduction process is to photograph the original drawing. The chief requirement for *photographic reproduction* is that the drawing be the type of *high-contrast,* black-and-white drawing that was described in the previous chapter (there are exceptions to this requirement, as is explained in later sections). The entire reproduction process, including the materials and chemicals used, is based on this black-and-white contrast.

Many photographic and printing processes are, today, accomplished to a greater or lesser degree with the aid of specially designed machinery. Some cameras have computer-controlled exposure meters, for example, and exposed film and plates are fed into continuous processors that automatically handle the development, stop bath, fixing, and drying steps. The more traditional "hand" methods are described here because the processes are more easily grasped if the specifics of modern machinery are not allowed to complicate matters. Once the traditional methods are understood, the functions of the modern machines are easily appreciated when they are encountered.

Process Camera

The photographic step in reproduction involves the use of a large camera, called a *process camera.* Process cameras range in size from a small vertical model that fits into the smallest shop (Fig. 7.1) to immense machines that literally fill an entire room (Fig. 7.2). The camera size that is needed for a particular application is governed by the size of the drawing to be photographed and by the size of the film needed to record the drawing at reproduction size. The size of a process camera is specified in terms of the maximum size sheet of film which it can accommodate. Typical sizes range from 12 in. × 18 in. to 30 in. × 40 in., with some cameras capable of handling film as large as 60 in. × 80 in. Regardless of size, however, the components of the camera and the characteristics of the photographic process are essentially the same.

The three main components of a process camera are the copyboard; the lens, with its shutter, iris, and bellows; and the camera back, with its ground-glass screen and film holder. A lighting system, as well as controls for the movement of the lens and copyboard, are also provided. The components are kept in proper alignment

Figure 7.1 Vertical process camera. (Courtesy of nuArc Company, Inc.)

with one another by the camera frame and are arranged in either a vertical or a horizontal alignment. Vertical cameras, however, are usually limited to the smaller sizes.

A series of lights is arranged to provide bright, even illumination of the copy. The lights are usually placed in two vertical banks, one on each side of the lens. A timing control governs the length of the exposure of the film.

Figure 7.2 Horizontal process camera. (Courtesy of nuArc Company, Inc.)

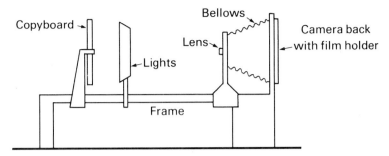

Figure 7.3 Typical arrangement of the components of a horizontal process camera.

The arrangement and operation of a typical horizontal copy camera (Fig. 7.3) will now be described.

Copyboard   A typical *copyboard* consists of a piece of stiff backing material on which the drawing (copy) is placed. The drawing is held in position by a glass cover. A hinged metal frame holds the glass and is latched in place over the drawing. Spring tension or vacuum pressure holds the drawing flat against the glass cover. The copyboard pivots into a horizontal position so that the drawing can be inserted, and into a vertical position, aligned with the lens, for the photographic operation.

The copyboard is mounted on the camera frame in such a way that it can be moved closer to the lens or farther away, depending upon the reduction or enlargement that is desired, and in order to focus the image.

Lens   The copy camera lens is an assemblage of several specially ground pieces of glass called a *process lens.* This type of lens focuses on the plane of the copyboard, rather than providing the depth of focus that is needed in the lens of a snapshot or a portrait camera. In particular, it is designed so that straight lines on the copy will not be distorted on the negative.

The amount of light that passes through the lens is controlled by the opening or closing of the *iris,* an *aperture* formed by a set of interleaved plates. The size of this opening is designated by the $f/$stop system. The $f/$stop is based upon the ratio between the diameter of the opening in the lens and the focal length of the lens. If, for example, the aperture in a 20 cm focal length lens is set to a 2.5 cm diameter, the $f/$stop is considered to be $f/8$. If the opening is reduced to 1.25 cm the $f/$stop is $f/16$, and the amount of light that passes through the lens is reduced to one-fourth of the amount that would pass through at $f/8$. The size of the opening of the iris is one of the factors the photographer adjusts in order to control the amount of light reaching the film; the other factor is the length of time the shutter is open. The relationship between these two factors in the determination of exposure is discussed in the section on film, below.

A *flexible bellows* is fitted between the lens and the film holder. The purpose of this bellows is simply to prevent stray light rays from striking the film. It must be flexible to allow the lens to move back and forth when the camera is focused.

A *shutter* is provided to control the passage of light from the copy, through the lens, to the film. It consists of a number of thin leaves that overlap one another and pivot open and closed. A *timer* is provided to open the shutter at the start of the exposure and to close it at the end of the specified exposure time. The determination of the required exposure time is discussed in the section on film, below.

Camera back The *camera back* provides a *film loader* and a *ground-glass screen,* either of which can be swung into place when needed.

The film holder is a flat board that pivots into place at the rear of the camera, holding the film in the correct focal plane behind the lens. The holder is usually perforated or slotted and is provided with a vacuum pump that draws air through the openings. When a sheet of film is put on the holder and the pump is turned on, the vacuum created between the film and the back of the holder presses the film firmly in place and holds it flat. This arrangement holds the film without having a glass plate over its surface and therefore reduces the problems with dust that the glass would introduce. The holder, with the film secured, is then pivoted into place so that the film is positioned behind the lens in a plane that is exactly parallel to the plane of the copyboard.

A translucent ground-glass screen can be swung into position in place of the film holder. When the lights are turned on and the shutter is opened, the camera operator can view the image of the copy on this ground glass. This allows the image size, position, and focus to be checked before an exposure is made.

Size The relationship between the distance from the copyboard to the lens and the distance from the lens to the focal plane of the camera determines the size of negative that is obtained when a drawing is photographed (Fig. 7.4). When the distance between the center of the lens and the film is twice the focal length of the lens and is equal to the distance between the center of the lens and the copy, the camera produces an image the same size as the original copy. When the lens-to-copy distance is increased and the lens-to-film distance is decreased, the image size is re-

Figure 7.4 Relationship between film, lens, and copy, for same-size photograph.

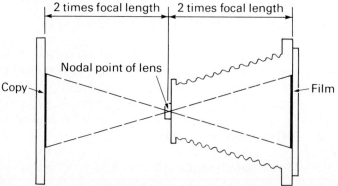

duced. When the lens-to-copy distance is decreased and the lens-to-film distance is increased, the image is enlarged.

Typical cameras accommodate a reduction to one-fifth of the size of the original at one extreme, and an enlargement to five times the size of the original at the other. Greater reductions or enlargements are achieved by using supplementary lenses.

Film

The photographic process results in a film negative. Because the lines drawn on the original copy are black, very little light is reflected from them through the camera lens and onto the film. When the exposure and development process is completed, the images of the original black lines appear on the negative as transparent lines and the areas of white paper are a full opaque black. This reversal of the image leads to the use of the term *negative,* to describe the result of the photographic process.

Lithographic, *orthochromatic film* is most frequently used for process photography.[1] It consists of a sheet of transparent plastic material coated with an *emulsion layer*. The emulsion is made up of *light-sensitive silver halide crystals* in *colloidal suspension* in a *gelatin* compound. The film also has an *antihalation backing* that prevents the reflection of stray light within the film, and an *overcoating layer* that protects the fragile emulsion (Fig. 7.5). Both acetate-base films (which are not particularly stable) and stable-base films are available. The stable-base type is more suitable for most cartographic applications.

In photography, light passes through the lens and strikes the film in the camera. This causes a structural change in the silver halide crystals in the film, forming what is called a *latent image.* When the exposed film is placed in a developer solution, the crystals that form the latent image turn to black metallic silver. The crystals that were not struck by light are also affected by the developer but they change so slowly that, for the normal processing period, it is possible to consider that they do not develop. The speed with which the development process takes place depends upon the sensitivity of the film, as well as upon the amount of light reaching the film and the type of developer which is used. When film is properly exposed, the various factors affecting development are regulated so that the negative has fully developed, opaque black areas but retains clear open areas. In order to accomplish this, a standard exposure and development sequence is established.

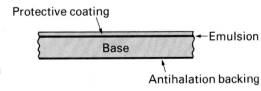

Figure 7.5 Cross section through lithographic film.

---

[1]For example: Kodalith Ortho, Type 3, Estar base, Eastman Kodak Co.; Cronar films, E. I. DuPont deNemours Co.

The variables involved in determining the proper exposure for a piece of film are the sensitivity of the film emulsion, the intensity of the light reflected from the copy and through the lens, the size of the lens opening, the length of time the shutter is open, the length of time the film is in the developer, and the temperature and strength of the developer. In order to produce a satisfactory negative for a particular type of film in a given camera, most of these variables are standardized, leaving only two that are manipulated by the camera operator. First, the strength of the developer and its temperature, as well as the amount of time the film is allowed to remain in contact with the developer, are all standardized according to manufacturer's instructions. These instructions are established so that, on properly exposed film, the black areas are fully developed but the clear areas remain undeveloped. Second, the amount of light reflected from the copy is standardized because the same set of bulbs and reflectors are used for each exposure and the same distance between the reflectors and the copy is maintained. Although line-voltage variation and the age of the bulbs affects light output, the variation is slight enough that, for purposes of general understanding, it can be ignored.

With the intensity of the light source and the development process standardized, the remaining variables are the lens opening and the time of exposure, both of which are controlled by the camera operator. Typically, a series of test exposures is made, with the camera adjusted to produce a negative that is the same size as the original copy. Each exposure uses the same lens opening, but different exposure times are used for each one.

The films used for the test exposures are developed, using the standard development time and temperature. After the required time in the developer, they are placed in a *stop bath*, which halts the development process. They are then transferred to a *fixer,* which dissolves away the undeveloped silver halide crystals, the antihalation backing, and the protective overcoating. After they are washed and dried, the test negatives that have been produced are carefully examined to find the one that has the desired balance of exposure and development. The settings used to produce this negative are then established as the standard for same-size negatives, on the particular film emulsion, shot on the particular camera.

Once a standard exposure is established for same-size negatives, appropriate adjustments are made for enlarged or reduced negatives. In enlargement, a given amount of light is spread over a greater film area, with the result that the amount of light per square inch is decreased. If a 20 cm × 25 cm image area is doubled in size, to 40 cm × 50 cm, for example, the lens opening must be increased (or the exposure time lengthened, or some combination of both) to allow not just twice as much light to pass through, but four times as much. This is because the area of the film has been increased by a factor of four (20 cm × 25 cm = 500 cm^2 versus 40 cm × 50 cm = 2000 cm^2). The same principle applies to reductions, except that the amount of light passing through the lens is decreased in order to maintain the correct exposure.

The copy used in the photographic process must be black and white in order to produce a sharp negative. If, for example, a line on the drawing is drawn with watery ink, or is partially erased, so that it is gray rather than black, more light is reflected from it than is reflected from a dense black line. This means that the emulsion is affected to some extent, and some of the silver halide crystals in the area of the line, which ordinarily would not be developed, turn black. The resulting open area representing the line is narrow and weak, so that the final image is not as satisfactory as it would have been with a strong black original. Most drawings are done on paper or plastic that is at least partially translucent. A sheet of white paper is usually placed behind the drawing when it is placed in the copyboard in order to assure a clean, white background that yields a solid black negative.

Because a high-contrast negative is desired for printing purposes, orthochromatic lithographic film is used to photograph the black-and-white line drawings. The emulsion of this film is appropriate because, when it is exposed and developed, a sharp jump from low to high density occurs at a certain exposure level and a high-contrast negative results. The high-contrast nature of the film is reflected in its *characteristic curve*. The characteristic curve is a graph showing the density of the negative that will be produced by the film under standardized conditions plotted against the logarithm of the exposure that will produce it [Fig. 7.6(a)]. A logarithmic scale is used for the exposure so that a given horizontal distance on the graph always indicates an increase in exposure of the same ratio. High-contrast films have a steeply sloping characteristic curve.

Orthochromatic film is relatively sensitive to the green and blue wavelengths but is insensitive to the red, as is shown in the sensitivity spectrum [Fig. 7.6(b)]. This characteristic allows the film to be handled in a darkroom that is illuminated by a low level of red light. Panchromatic films, on the other hand, require complete

Figure 7.6 (a) Relationship between log exposure and density of negative. (b) Sensitivity spectrum of orthochromatic film. (Data courtesy of Eastman Kodak Co.)

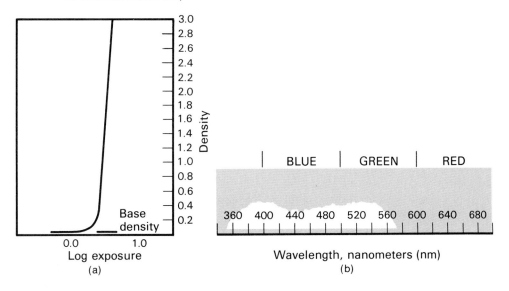

darkness because they are sensitive to all wavelengths in the visible spectrum and, as a result, are more difficult to handle.

The differing reactions of orthochromatic film to blues and reds are useful. Lines drawn on the original in light blue are "seen" by the film as though they were white and are not visible on the negative. This is helpful because it means that light blue guidelines on the drawing will drop out when it is photographed. If any areas or lines on the original are drawn in dark red, however, the film reacts as though they are black. This characteristic is useful because various adhesive materials are available in a translucent or transparent red. These materials have special applications that are explained in Chapter 8.

LITHOGRAPHY

Artists have long depended on the truth of the age-old adage that oil and water do not mix. They use this principle for the type of work that gives the word *lithography* its literal meaning—drawing on stone (the word is derived from the Greek *lithos,* which means stone, and *graphein,* which means to write or draw).

The lithographic artist draws an image on a smooth, flat, moisture-absorbent stone surface, using a greasy pencil. Because the final image is the reverse of the image on the stone, the artist takes the reversal into account when doing the drawing. When the drawing is complete, the surface of the stone is dampened with water, which is repelled from the greasy image surface but absorbed by the stone. Ink is then applied to the surface of the stone with a roller. The ink adheres to the greasy image areas but does not adhere to the damp, nonimage areas. Finally, a piece of paper is placed over the stone and pressure is applied, resulting in a transfer of the ink from the image on the stone to the paper.

Today, most maps are reproduced by photo-offset lithography, which is a modern, high-speed, mechanized derivative of the artist's process of drawing on stone. Although the specific materials and methods used in the two processes are different, the basic concepts are essentially the same.

In the simplest type of photo-offset lithography, the drawing is done in black ink on a paper or plastic surface, and is then photographed, as has been described. The resulting negative is used to create a printing plate, which is the equivalent of the stone, and the image is transferred to paper using a lithographic press. The following paragraphs describe in more detail the processes involved in creating the printing plate and printing the final product.

Film Stripping

After the negative is photographed and developed, it is prepared for use in the production of the printing plate. The first step in this process is to place a sheet of special *masking material* on a light table. The material used for this purpose is usually a yellow-colored paper, called *goldenrod,* which is an actinically opaque material. The term *actinically opaque* means that it holds back the blue to ultraviolet wavelengths. The light that reaches the film, after passing through the goldenrod, is in the yellow-red range and has a minimal effect on the normal orthochromatic emulsions (the closer the color is to red the more effective it is in holding back unwanted exposures). If greater dimensional stability is required, an orange-colored, vinyl masking sheet is used instead of paper.[2]

The negative is placed face down on the masking sheet and is positioned so that the image will be in the desired location on the final printed sheet. Printed *guidelines* on the mask assist in this process, or, if the appropriate guidelines are not provided, the *stripper* (the lithographic technician who positions the negative on the mask) draws them in. The location of the image on the plate takes into account the required margins around the image on the printed sheet, including the space at the edge of the paper that is gripped by the feed device on the printing press. This *gripper edge* cannot receive any printed image. Also, the mask is usually larger than the plate so that no light will leak around its edges and produce an unwanted image on the plate.

The negative is then fastened into position using thin, adhesive plastic tape. The mask is next turned over, a razor blade or sharp knife is used to cut around the desired image area, and the actinically opaque material over the image is removed. Care must be taken at this stage to avoid cutting through both the masking material and the negative.

Small "pinholes" may occur in the negative because of dust specks on the film, or unwanted spots may occur because of marks on the drawing or on the glass cover of the copyboard. These blemishes will be printed as unwanted specks if they are left untreated, so the mask is once again turned face down on the light table. Any pinholes or marks within the image area are readily visible because of the light shining through the negative. These spots are removed by brushing a small amount of a water-soluble *opaquing material* over the spot, on the emulsion side of the negative. This material blocks the light and prevents the specks from appearing on the plate.

The completed masking sheet, with the negative in place, is called a *flat.*

Platemaking

Various types of material, including metal, paper, and plastic, are used for *lithographic printing plates,* but aluminum plates are probably the most commonly used. Although there are differences in the processes involved in making and using the various types of plates, the basic principles are the same and, for our purposes, the details are not important.

All types of plates are coated with a light-sensitive emulsion. This emulsion is less sensitive than the emulsion used for film and may be handled in subdued room light. If metal plates are used, their surface is grained or roughened before the emulsion is applied. The coating is applied in the printing shop just prior to use, or presensitized plates are obtained directly from the manufacturer.

The sensitized plate is placed in a *vacuum frame,* a glass-covered frame that has a rubber pressure blanket behind it (Fig. 7.7). The plate is placed in position

---

[2]For example, Maskrite, Direct Reproduction Corp.

Figure 7.7 Vacuum frame. (Courtesy of nuArc Company, Inc.)

with its emulsion side facing up. The flat containing the negative is then placed over the sensitized plate, with the emulsion of the negative in contact with the emulsion of the plate. This arrangement results in a right-reading image on the plate. A right-reading image is required because, unlike the artist's litho stone process, the offset litho process has an intermediate (offset) step. This step reverses the image prior to printing the final, right-reading image (Fig. 7.8).

The glass cover of the vacuum frame is lowered into place and the air is evacuated from behind the glass, bringing the negative and plate into close contact with one another. A timed exposure is then made, using a bright light that contains a large proportion of rays in the ultraviolet range of the spectrum. The light rays pass through the open areas on the negative and strike the corresponding areas on the plate, creating a latent image in the plate's coating. The plate is then removed from the vacuum frame and is developed.

When the plate is developed, the exposed areas, which form the image to be printed, are hardened and remain on the plate, whereas the unexposed areas are removed. The developed plate is washed to remove the remaining chemicals and is dried. Finally, a protective coating is applied and the plate is ready for use.

The plate that has been described is a *negative-acting planimetric plate;* that is, the positive image is obtained from a photographic negative and the image is flush with the surface of the plate. Other types of plates, including positive-acting and deep-etch plates, are also commonly used. In the case of a deep-etch plate, the image area is treated through a chemical etching process so that the image is de-

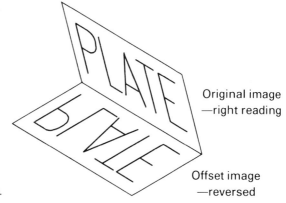

Original image
—right reading

Offset image
—reversed

Figure 7.8   Reversal of offset image.

pressed below the nonprinting areas. The result is a plate that is used for longer production runs, because the image does not wear away as rapidly as the planimetric image. A major difference, in terms of processing, is that a deep-etch plate is made from a film positive rather than from a negative.

Lithographic Press (Single-Color)

The completed lithographic plate is mounted on a press. The simplest type of *one-color, offset lithographic press* consists of a system of *three cylinders* that, along with mechanisms for transporting the paper, transfer the image from the printing plate to a sheet of paper (Fig. 7.9).

Figure 7.9   One-color, offset lithographic press. (Courtesy of Heidelberg U.S.A.)

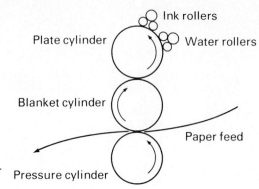

Figure 7.10 Arrangement of cylinders in one-color lithographic press.

In the press, the plate is fastened to a cylinder that, when it rotates, brings the plate into contact, in sequence, with two sets of rollers (Fig. 7.10). The first set of rollers applies a thin coating of water to the plate. The water adheres to the plate surface (nonimage areas) but does not adhere to the image areas. The second set of rollers applies ink of the desired color to the image areas of the plate. The ink does not adhere to the moistened, nonimage areas.

The inked plate is next brought into contact with a dense rubber blanket that is wrapped around the second cylinder. This is done because paper is abrasive and would wear out the image on the printing plate very rapidly if the two were allowed to come into direct contact. The inked image is then transferred (offset) to the rubber blanket as a wrong-reading image. It is this intermediate transfer process that gives the name *offset* to this method of printing. The offset image is finally transferred to the sheet of paper as a right-reading image when the paper passes between the offset cylinder and the impression cylinder.

The printing processes described here are also used in conjunction with color printing, which is described in Chapter 8.

DIRECT NEGATIVE LINEWORK (SCRIBING)

A process called *scribing* is used extensively in modern cartographic work. This process bypasses many of the previously described drawing and photographic steps and directly produces the equivalent of a line photographic negative. This substitution of a scribed original for a photographic negative usually results in quality improvements and cost savings. Quality improvements are obtained because accurate line weights and sharp lines are produced. Cost savings come about, in part, because even a relatively inexperienced worker can often produce an excellent scribed sheet much more rapidly and easily than an experienced worker can produce an equivalent pen-and-ink drawing. Cost savings are also obtained because of the elimination of a considerable amount of photographic work, especially when corrections or changes are needed. The advantages of scribing are described in more detail as part of the following discussion of the materials, tools, and processes that are used.

Materials

The most basic material in the scribing process is the film on which the scribing is done. This material is a stable-base, plastic film that is coated with an *actinically opaque, scribable material*.[3] The scribable layer, which is usually red or orange in color, is selectively removed by using appropriate tools; it is this removal of the coating that is called *scribing*. After the actinically opaque coating is removed from the film base, light passes through the open areas in exactly the same way that light passes through the open areas of a photographic negative. One important characteristic of scribing is that, when properly done, the removal of the material creates a very sharp edge in contrast to the relatively ragged edge of a drafted line (Fig. 7.11). This results in a crisp-appearing printed image.

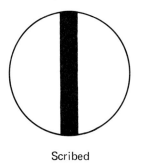 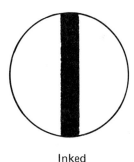

Figure 7.11 Unretouched photographs of scribed and inked lines, showing comparative line quality. The original lines are enlarged four times.

Scribed   Inked

Tools

Several specialized tools are used for scribing. These consist of both needle and blade scribing points, mounted in either swivel or rigid holders. The selection of a needle or a blade, and of a particular type of holder, depends upon the nature of the line to be scribed. Tools for cutting dots and rectangular symbols are also available.[4]

Needles *Needles* are the simplest of the scribing tools. They consist of a round shank that tapers to a point of the desired diameter. The needle is held in a two-legged holder so that it is perpendicular to the surface of the scribing film [Fig. 7.12(a)]. To use the scriber, one moves the holder, with the needle in place, across the surface of the scribing film, using a moderate amount of vertical pressure on the needle. This causes the point of the needle to penetrate the surface of the scribe coating and to scrape the coating away from the clear plastic base material. Care must be taken, however, to avoid applying so much pressure that the needle gouges

[3]For example: Stabilene Scribe Coat, Keuffel & Esser Co.; Scriberite, Direct Reproduction Corp.

[4]The details of these tools vary, so only general descriptions are provided here. Specific details are available from the manufacturers, for example: Direct Reproduction Corp. (Astrascribe tools); Keuffel & Esser Co.

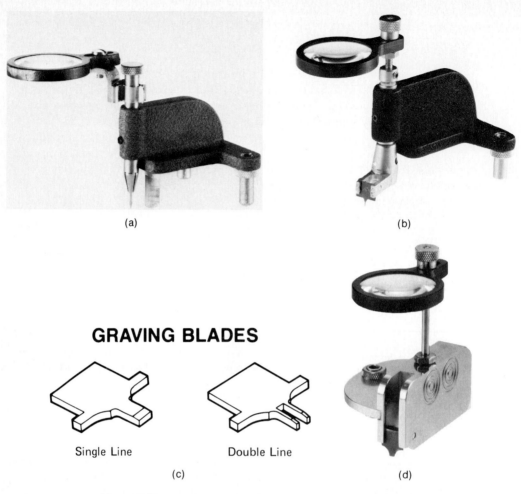

GRAVING BLADES

Single Line   Double Line

(c)

(a)

(b)

(d)

Figure 7.12 (a) Rigid needle holder; (b) Swivel holder; (c) Single-line and double-line scribing blades; (d) Rigid blade holder. (Courtesy of Kratos/Keuffel & Esser.)

into the base layer. Gouging results in an unsatisfactory negative because the path of the light through the image area is scattered by the damaged plastic.

Needles are used for the scribing of fine to medium-weight lines (0.05–0.635 mm or 0.002–0.025 in.). Because the tip of the needle has a circular cross section, the width of the scribed line remains the same regardless of the direction the needle is moved. This makes the needle scriber especially useful for irregular lines such as coastlines or rivers. It also makes it possible for the person doing the scribing to maintain accurate line weights with far less difficulty than is encountered in most conventional drafting. Needle scribers are also used against straightedges, such as T squares or triangles, or against French curves or railroad curves, when straight or smoothly curved lines are scribed.

Because the scribable coating is rather abrasive, the point of an ordinary steel needle wears down with continued use. Special needles made of a hard alloy or tipped with sapphire reduce the wear problem considerably.

Swivel cutters   *Swivel-type scribers* use *chisel-shaped tools* or special needles. The tools are held vertically with the cutting edge at right angles to the direction of movement of the scriber [Fig. 7.12(b)]. Swivel cutters, therefore, are moved in one direction. They are used for fine to wide line weights (up to 3.8 mm or 0.15 in.).

Special cutters are also available with two cutting surfaces [Fig. 7.12(c)]. Each of the cutting surfaces, as well as the spacing between them, can be obtained in various widths, thus permitting the scribing of multiple lines, with constant line weights and spacings between lines. This result is achieved much more easily, and with better appearance, than is generally accomplished in even an expertly done pen-and-ink drawing.

Chisel-shaped cutters are held in a *fixed holder* when they are used against a straightedge or a curved template [Fig. 7.12(d)]. This allows them to be used for smooth, regular lines, such as lines of latitude or longitude, borders, and neatlines. The cutters are used in swivel holders for the freehand scribing of irregular lines, such as coastlines, rivers, contours, paths, and some boundaries.

Special tools   Three types of special scribing tools are described here although others undoubtedly have been designed for particular applications. These are the *hand-held needle,* the dot scriber, and the building scriber.

A scribing needle may be mounted in a holder similar to that used for holding pen points [Fig. 7.13(a)]. This combination is used for the selective removal of the scribable coating when touch-up work is required. It is also used to scribe short lines but is not normally used for extensive linework.

In a *dot scriber,* the scribing point is mounted in a special holder that spins it about a vertical axis (sometimes a small electric motor is used to impart the spin). This device is used like a small drill press. When the rotating point is lowered into contact with the scribable coating, a small hole is cut in the surface, thus creating a dot symbol in the desired location.

A special *building scriber* is designed to allow a scribing blade to be moved a specified distance each time it is used [Fig. 7.13(b)]. This tool consists of a block

Figure 7.13 (a) Freehand holder; (b) Building scriber. (Courtesy of Kratos/Keuffel & Esser.)

(a)   (b)

in which the blade slides; the length of the movement is controlled by an adjustable stop at the end of the block. With this tool the line that is scribed is the width of the blade and is limited to the desired length. The result is a square or rectangular symbol, such as is often used on a map to represent a building.

Worksheet Preparation

When a map is produced using scribing techniques, a worksheet is usually required. The worksheet is either drawn at scribing size or it is drawn at a larger size and photographically reduced to the required size. Although the content is the same in both cases, the preparation of a worksheet for scribing differs somewhat from the preparation of a worksheet for a drafted map. This is especially true when provision must be made for the photographic reproduction of the worksheet, as is explained below.

Traced worksheet   It is perfectly possible to prepare a worksheet on a sheet of paper or plastic at scribing size. The worksheet is placed under a sheet of scribing film on a light table, and the appropriate scribing tools are used to scribe the necessary lines. One problem with this method is that the image of the worksheet is somewhat blurred because it is viewed through the scribe coating, and the exact tracing of the lines is rather difficult.

Photosensitive scribing film   A more suitable means of preparing a worksheet for scribing is to draw it in black ink on a sheet of drafting plastic, using regular drafting techniques. When this is done, the linework is symbolized so that features that are otherwise similar in appearance, for example, rivers and railroads, are distinguished from one another.

The worksheet is drawn at any convenient size, but it is preferable to make it somewhat larger than the final map size. Working at a larger size usually simplifies the compilation process because an appropriate amount of detail is more easily maintained. Also, it frequently allows the use of source maps that are not available at the required scale without the necessity of reducing them during the compilation process. The completed worksheet is photographed and a negative is produced at the final map size. The negative is then used to make a contact film positive, which is the basis for the next step in the process.

Scribing film is available with a *diazo coating* that is especially sensitive to light in the ultraviolet range. This material can be handled in subdued room lighting for short periods of time, and does not require a photographic darkroom. If pre-sensitized scribing film is not available, a wipe-on diazo coating may be applied by the user. The first step in using this material is to punch pin-register holes in a sheet of the sensitized scribing film and in the film positive of the worksheet. The film positive is then pin-registered over the scribing film and the two sheets are placed in a vacuum frame and exposed to a high-ultraviolet light source. This exposure bleaches away the diazo coating under the clear areas of the positive but the coating protected by the black image remains. After the exposure, the materials are removed from the vacuum frame and the scribing film is passed through the development chamber of a diazo printmaking machine. In the chamber, the remaining diazo coating is exposed to *ammonia fumes* which turn it black or dark blue, thus creating a duplicate of the original film positive image on the surface of the scribing film.

Scribing Process

The end product of the above process is a scribable separation that contains a positive image of the map worksheet at reproduction size. As previously described, the desired portion of the image is then scribed, using the appropriate tools, in order to produce the equivalent of a line negative of the image.

Line symbols, such as dashed lines, are usually produced by first scribing a solid line and then selectively masking it. An effective way to do this is to interrupt the scribed line by drawing masking lines on the back of the scribing film, using an appropriate opaquing fluid. The width and spacing of the masking lines determines the length and spacing of the dashes.

The completed scribed separation has the same characteristics as the photographic negative of a drafted original, and is used in the same way for making printing plates, film positives, and proofs.

Scribing is done so that either a *right-reading* or a *wrong-reading* image is produced when the separation is viewed with its emulsion up. A wrong-reading image is sometimes preferred because the emulsion side of the scribed separation is then in contact with the emulsion of the sensitized material when prints, positives, proofs, or plates are made. If a right-reading image is scribed, on the other hand, the light used to make the exposure has to pass through the thickness of the scribe film before it reaches the emulsion of the sensitized material; the result can be a widening of the image, which is especially noticeable if very fine line weights are involved. This concern is greatest in platemaking because the light sources used in platemakers are spread out rather than shining from a single point, which can result in additional line spread problems. When film and paper positives are made, however, a *pinpoint light source* is usually used, so spread is less likely to take place.

The circumstances of the particular project, including any pertinent previous experience with similar projects, will influence the final decision as to whether to scribe right- or wrong-reading separations. The particular reproduction techniques involved are taken into consideration. If, for example, the type of plates being used require film positive intermediates, the scribed separation is not used directly in the platemaking. Finally, the convenience of working with a right-reading image often offsets concern for the possible deterioration of the scribed image, especially if testing shows that image quality is maintained at satisfactory levels.

Corrections and revisions   If an error is made during the scribing process, it is usually relatively easy to correct it. An *opaquing material,* which consists of a liquid or crayon similar to the original scribe coating, is brushed or rubbed over the portion of the scribed image to be deleted. This material blocks light so that, when a printing plate or other product is produced, the opaqued area is not reproduced. Corrected lines are scribed in the opaqued material as required.

Minor revisions that are required at a later time are handled in the same way as corrections. If more extensive revisions are required, it is possible to mask out the unwanted portions of the old separation and to prepare a new scribed separation containing the new portions of the image. These two separations are then combined to produce a complete image on the printing plate (see the section on double-burns in Chapter 8).

Another approach, which is especially useful when extensive revisions are necessary but a great deal of complex work is to be retained, is to produce a duplicate scribed separation. This has the advantage of limiting the number of separations. A duplicate separation is made by masking out the unwanted linework on the original scribed separation. The masked separation is then exposed to a special scribable material that has a photosensitive emulsion layer over the scribable coating.[5] When this material is developed, a new image results that duplicates the unmasked portion of the original scribing. Additional linework is scribed on the duplicate separation, as needed.

Making corrections and revisions to scribed separations is generally simpler than making equivalent changes on drafted separations. This is because it is usually necessary to rephotograph a revised separation drawing in order to obtain a new negative. The scale of the negative of the revision must match the original exactly, which is difficult to accomplish, and the process of stripping and opaquing must be repeated.

Symbols and Typography

It is possible to scribe dots, squares, rectangles, and even lettering by using special tools. There are limitations to this approach, however, so adhesive letters and symbols are frequently used in conjunction with scribed separations (see Chapter 6). The most common practice is to place a transparent, dimensionally stable plastic overlay over the scribed separation, using the pin-register system. The typography and symbols, which must be on a transparent or translucent base, are then fastened into position on the overlay. A contact film negative is made from the type and symbol overlay. This negative is combined with the scribed linework, when a printing plate or other product is to be produced, by making two separate exposures (see Chapter 8).

OTHER REPRODUCTION METHODS

Several techniques are available for quick reproduction of one-color or, in some cases, multicolor drawings. These techniques are relatively low in cost, so long as a limited number of copies is needed. This is because they do not require all the

---

[5]For example: Reproscribe Film, Keuffel & Esser Co.

steps involved in lithography or other printing processes. Although the quality of the results obtained from these methods is usually not as good as is obtained using photographic and printing processes, it is satisfactory for many purposes.

Additional techniques are described in the section on proofing in Chapter 8.

Photostat

A *photostat* machine is essentially a copy camera that uses a sensitized paper instead of film. It is used for the production of black-and-white negatives from black-and-white originals. Color originals can also be photostated if a black-and-white copy is satisfactory. Some colors do not reproduce well, however, so it is necessary to test color originals to see if the results in a particular case are usable.

Because the machine incorporates a special prism, photostats are right-reading images. This means that they are useful as copy for compilation or other applications in which a wrong-reading image would be inconvenient. Photostat copies can be at the same size as the original, or they may be enlarged or reduced. The original does not have to be on translucent material.

If a positive image is required, a photostat negative is photostated and the result is a right-reading positive image. This may also be a reduced or enlarged image, so that a two-step process provides a much greater range of enlargement or reduction than would ordinarily be available. *Direct-positive paper,* which produces positive images in one step, is sometimes available.

Because photostat development is a wet process, and the paper is not dimensionally stable, the image is subject to stretching or shrinking.

Xerography

Xerography, a process used in many office duplicating machines, reproduces line drawings. This is a dry process that produces a positive copy from a positive original, using ordinary paper. Most xerography machines produce copies that are the same size as the original, although limited enlargement or reduction, usually within a range from 50 to 200 percent of the original size, is possible on some machines. The maximum size of originals is usually 11 in. × 17 in., and final copy size is usually limited to about 8½ in. × 14 in. Machines with much greater capacity are now available for use with large drawings, however. Originals as large as 36 in. wide and several feet long can be accommodated by one model, which produces prints up to 24 in. wide. The original can also be reduced to 45 percent of its original size or enlarged to 141 percent, within the stated size limits.

In the usual office model machine, the original to be reproduced is placed face down on a glass-covered opening, either directly by the operator or by an automatic feed mechanism. There is usually some type of pressure plate to hold the original flat against the glass. An automatically timed lighting system provides the exposure. The image of the original passes through a lens that focuses it onto a plate with a positive charge of *static electricity.* When the light from the white areas on the original image strikes the plate, the positive charge is discharged. Because there is no light reflected by the black lines or areas on the original, the static charge remains in the areas that correspond to the image.

The plate is then brought into contact with a supply of negatively charged *black powder.* Because of the attraction between objects with unlike electrical charges, the powder adheres to the positively charged image areas on the plate but is not attracted to the nonimage areas, thus creating a wrong-reading image. The next step in the process is to bring a positively charged sheet of paper into contact with the negatively charged powder image on the plate. The powder, because of the opposite charges, transfers to the paper as a right-reading image. The paper, with the powder image in place, is then passed over a source of heat, which melts the powder and *fuses* it to the paper. The end result is a permanent, positive copy of the original image.

One major advantage of xerography is the fact that it is readily available in many offices. The speed of production is also quite rapid when only small quantities are needed. The original does not have to be on translucent material and the quality of the copies is reasonably good, especially if the lines in the original are sharp and black. Multicolor originals and originals with screening can be copied, but the results are variable. One disadvantage of xerography is that large areas of tone tend to wash out in the middle, so that an area that is a uniform tone in the original may have a variation of tone in the copy. Also, not all office copiers use the xerographic process. Many machines use a sensitized paper that develops with the application of heat or a developing agent. It is recommended, therefore, that test exposures be made to see whether or not an acceptable copy can be obtained.

Diazo Processes

Diazo processes allow the same-size reproduction of line originals. The process is positive-working, which means that a positive original is needed to produce a positive copy. Paper coated with a light-sensitive diazo material is required.

In order to utilize diazo processes, the original must have strong dark lines on a translucent or transparent material. A pencil drawing on tracing paper is a satisfactory original, although inked lines produce sharper copies. A film positive is also a satisfactory original. When a film positive is used, the best results are obtained when the film is right-reading with the emulsion down; otherwise, light leaking around the lines will weaken them.

Various qualities of diazo-sensitized paper are available; for cartographic purposes, it is best to obtain the type with the smoothest finish. When this is done, and when film positive originals are used, diazo processes can reproduce fine linework and even allow the reproduction of screens (see Chapter 8).

In use, the coated paper is held emulsion side up and the original is placed over it in the right-reading position. This does not have to be done in a darkroom because the sensitized paper can be handled in subdued room lighting for brief periods of time. The two pieces are held together and fed into the light chamber portion of a diazo machine (Fig. 7.14). In the machine, a light source high in ultraviolet

Figure 7.14 Diazo machine. (Courtesy of Teledyne Rotolite.)

light is located in the middle of a transparent tube. Light from this source passes through the original and strikes the sensitized paper. When the light strikes the paper, the emulsion is bleached away except in the areas protected by the linework in the original.

Because the sensitized paper and the original are fed through the machine on moving tapes and are wrapped around a transparent tube, there may be some slippage which can affect the size of the image and the strength of the lines. If this proves to be a problem, the exposure may be made in a vacuum frame, using a carbon arc lamp, pulsed-xenon lamp, or other high-ultraviolet light source. This approach also allows overlays to be held in register with the original, using pin register, if desired. This provides flexibility because one drawing is used as a base, and different overlays provide the details for a variety of topics.

The exposure is adjusted to suit the particular project. It will usually take some experimentation to determine the exact exposure that is suitable for the transparency of the original, the strength of the lines, and the type of sensitized paper that is selected. The goal is to bleach out the background but to retain readable lines and tones. Exposure is varied on the diazo machine by varying the speed with which the drum turns, which governs the length of time that the material is exposed to the light. When a vacuum frame is used, the length of the exposure is varied directly, as required.

After the exposure, the original and the sensitized paper are separated. The sensitized paper is then passed through the development chamber where it is exposed to ammonia fumes. When the ammonia fumes reach the unbleached coating it is turned dark and the image becomes visible.

Rub-on lettering or patterns are used on the originals as needed. It is necessary, however, to be sure that the materials are resistant to the heat encountered in the exposure chamber. Wax-based materials are unsuitable and may slide around or come off completely during the exposure process. They may even adhere to the exposure tube, creating problems for the operator and ill will toward the map maker. Materials with heat-resistant adhesive backing are available for use in diazo processes.

A diazo image is not stable and fades with time. It is bleached away by exposure to sunlight or even by prolonged exposure to room lighting. The process can handle large originals because the sensitized material is available in rolls 48 in. or more wide and many yards long. The limiting factor on size is usually the width of material that the available machinery can accommodate.

Transparent material in several colors is available with a diazo coating. This material is useful for producing map overlays. For example, if a drawing of a base map is reproduced on paper, using black lines, separate drawings of various topics may be reproduced on different colored transparent overlays. When the overlays are placed over the base, either singly or in combinations, an effective and flexible display is created. A pin-register system makes this overlay system particularly flexible.

The diazo process also produces intermediate reproduction materials. These intermediates provide a means of using one original drawing as a base for a variety of final drawings. The use of intermediates involves a translucent diazo-coated material that creates a sepia-colored image. This image is modified and used in the same manner as an original to produce diazo prints. Pencil or ink drawing, or rub-on lettering or patterns, is used to add information to the sepia intermediate. Portions of the sepia image are removed by bleaching if they are not needed. Final prints are made from the modified intermediate in the usual way.

The user must determine whether or not these techniques are suitable for the purpose at hand, considering the number of copies required and the quality of product that is produced. They may, for example, be usable for review of a proposed map or for display purposes, but not for final reproduction originals or for a large number of copies.

Diffusion Transfer

The use of *diffusion transfer* for the reproduction of both line and continuous-tone originals, is becoming popular because of its speed and relative simplicity. There is a variety of diffusion transfer materials, some of which are used in process cameras and others in contact work. The general types and applications of these materials are mentioned here—brochures describing the full range of applications and providing details about the materials and processing techniques are available from the manufacturers.[6]

The basic diffusion transfer process, using a process camera, starts with an exposure that is made in the same manner as when photographic film is used; the copy is placed in the copy holder, a light-sensitive paper is placed in the film holder, and an exposure is made for the required time. The image is enlarged, reduced, or kept the same size, as desired. The exposed light-sensitive material is then combined with a receiver material and the two sheets are fed through a developing processor that contains the appropriate liquid activator chemicals. The *developing processor* has a set of rollers that first separate the materials from one another, then move them through the activator at the required speed, and finally squeeze the emulsions of the two moistened materials together. The result of this step is a sandwich consisting of a *paper negative* in intimate contact with the *receiver material.* In the presence of the *activator,* the negative allows the formation of a positive image on

[6]For example: Kodak PMT, Eastman Kodak Company, Graphics Markets Division; and Copy-proof (or, in color, Copychrome) Agfa-Gevaert, Inc.

the receiver material. The negative is then peeled away from the receiver material and discarded. The receiver material may be washed to improve its permanency or, if desired, may be used almost immediately.

If the final image is to be the same size as the original, a *reflex light-sensitive material* may be used. This procedure requires a vacuum frame and a light source, instead of a camera. The original is placed in the vacuum frame, emulsion up, and the light-sensitive material is placed over it, emulsion down. An exposure is then made with the light passing through the light-sensitive material. Where there is an image on the original the light is absorbed and where there is no image it is reflected. As a result, a latent image forms in the areas where light is reflected from the original. The light-sensitive material is then combined with the desired receiver material and the image is processed in the same manner as the image resulting from the use of a camera.

Receiver materials available for either the camera or contact processes include opaque paper, transparent film, and paper or metal lithographic plates. The light-sensitive paper is either negative-working, as described above, or reversing, which results in a negative image on the receiver material. Special contact screens are used if a halftone image is desired.

Blueprint

Blueprinting allows the same-size reproduction of originals that are on translucent materials. Large drawings can be reproduced because the sensitized paper comes in wide rolls.

In a blueprint machine, the original is held firmly against the sensitized paper while a bright light source is used to make the exposure. In traditional blueprinting, which is a negative-working process, a pencil or ink original is reproduced as a white line image on a blue background or, with a different type of paper, a brown background. A paper is also available that produces a positive, black line image on a white background.

After exposure the unexposed light-sensitive salts are washed away. The wet processing of the paper means that stretching and shrinking are to be expected, which may render the process unusable for some applications.

Suggested Readings

COGOLI, J. E., *Photo Offset Fundamentals* (2nd ed.). Bloomington, Ill.: McKnight Publishing Co., 1967. An easily understood technical manual regarding the basic photo offset techniques.

CRAIG, JAMES, *Production for the Graphic Designer.* New York: Watson-Guptill Publications, 1974. Describes preparation of materials for printing, as well as the printing processes. Although the focus is on artwork for advertising and other graphic arts applications, much of the material will assist in understanding similar aspects of cartography. Useful glossary of terms used in the printing trades.

FAUX, I., *Modern Lithography*. London: Macdonald & Evans Ltd., 1973.

HALEY, ALLAN, *Phototypography: A Guide to In-House Typesetting and Design*. New York: Charles Scribner's Sons, 1980.

MERTLE, J. S., and GORDON L. MONSEN, *Photomechanics and Printing*. Chicago: Mertle Publishing Co., 1957.

MOORE, LIONEL C., *Cartographic Scribing Materials, Instruments, and Techniques*, Technical Monograph No. CA-3 (2nd rev. ed.). Washington, D.C.: American Congress on Surveying and Mapping, Cartography Division, 1975.

Pocket Pal: A Graphic Arts Production Handbook (11th ed.). New York: International Paper Co., 1974.

8

Map Production:
Multicolor (Multitone)
Maps

Many maps involve the use of more than one color, or of darker or lighter tones of a single color. Printing multitone and multicolor maps uses basically the same processes as printing single-color, single-tone maps. Additional considerations are taken into account, however, and these matters are emphasized in this chapter. The next chapter discusses the use of tone and color as elements in map design.

PRODUCTION

As with a monochrome map, the first step in the production of a map that contains more than one tone or one color is the preparation of a worksheet showing all the information that will appear on the final printed map. For a monochrome map, the worksheet must indicate the symbols that are to be used for each of the various points, lines, and areas to be distinguished on the final map. For a multiple tone or color map the worksheet must indicate the tone or color as well as the symbolization to be used on the final map.

Separations

The reproduction of multiple tones or colors usually involves the use of several components instead of a single drawing. These components may be drawings, scribed sheets, or windows (which are described in this chapter). The determination of which separation each line, symbol, or pattern will be placed on is based on the reproduction requirements and is designated on the worksheet. Each component is called a *separation*, and each separation contains only those items that will appear in one particular color on the final map. Items that will appear in a second color are placed on a second separation, and so on.

There are normally at least as many separations as there are colors on the final map. In fact, because variations in the tone of each color may require additional separations, it is more accurate to say that normally there is one separation for each tone of each color that appears on the final map. (As is explained later in this chapter, this general rule does not hold true when colors are obtained by the use of process color techniques.) The shorelines, for example, may be dark blue whereas the water areas may be light blue. As described later, it is possible to create the light blue by using a screened tone of the darker blue instead of by printing it in a separate, light blue color. In either case, one separation is produced for the coastlines and a second for the water-tone areas.

In the case of a complex, multicolor map, as many as a dozen or more separations may be required. In order to maintain flexibility, additional separations may be used. It is possible, for example, that the same materials will be used later to produce a single-color map, or some other modifications may be desired. In such cases, it is frequently easier and less expensive to modify a map that consists of more separations than were absolutely necessary for the initial application.

As has been intimated, there are means other than the use of separations by which final tones and colors are produced. In cartography, however, separations are the most straightforward and most frequently used method. Although other methods that may be encountered are not described, they will be more easily appreciated after this basic method is understood.

The use of separations requires that each component be maintained in exact alignment, or *register,* with each of the other components. During the reproduction process, the various elements must be brought together, in the correct relationship to one another, to make the complete map. The endpapers of this book illustrate the flow of typical production sequences from worksheet to printed map; procedures for drafted maps are shown in the front endpaper and procedures for scribed maps are presented in the back endpaper.

Stable-base materials   Stable-base materials do not change size appreciably as temperature and humidity conditions change. Stable-base drafting and scribing plastics, and films, are used when separations are required. The use of these stable-base materials helps to maintain the alignment of the separations. The process of establishing and maintaining precise alignment throughout the production and printing process requires the use of both pin-register systems and register marks.

Register pins and register marks   *Pin-register* systems are frequently used to hold separations in alignment with one another. For drafting, a typical system involves punching a pair of 1/4 in. diameter holes into the worksheet, using a specially designed punch that maintains a fixed spacing between the holes [Fig. 8.1(a)]. The holes are usually placed at the top of the sheet, outside the image area of the map (Fig. 8.2). Register pins fit into the punched holes [Fig. 8.1(b)]. A typical register pin is a flat metal plate with a short round metal stud projecting vertically from it. In some systems, other sizes and shapes of pins are used and the punches are placed in other locations, but the end result is essentially the same.

Every sheet of drafting material used in the preparation of the map is punched in the same manner as the worksheet. This makes it possible to place the drafting sheets on the register pins with the worksheet still in place. When this is done, the pins hold the sheets in a fixed alignment in relation to one another. The required linework is inked on the drafting sheet, using the worksheet as a guide. Working on a light table makes it a simple matter to trace the desired lines from the worksheet.

Another advantage of pin register is that the various separations can be placed

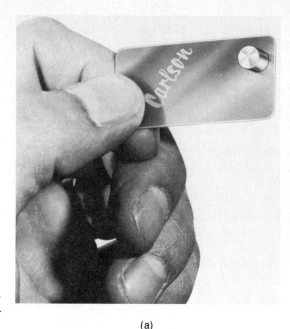

Figure 8.1 (a) Register pin; (b) register punch. (Courtesy of Chesley F. Carlson Co.)

(a)

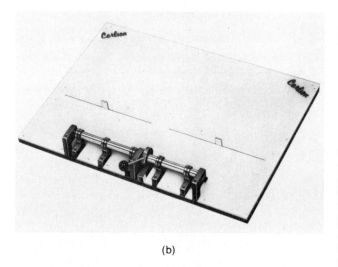

(b)

over one another in any convenient sequence. This allows the alignment of any portion of any separation to be checked against the others to make certain there are no overlaps or other alignment errors.

Register marks are required on separation drawings even though pin register is used. Register marks are small, cross-shaped marks that are drawn on each separation (Fig. 8.2). The marks are precisely aligned over one another on each sheet. They are usually placed outside the map image so they can be trimmed away when the printing is completed. (Another common practice is to use the corners of the map

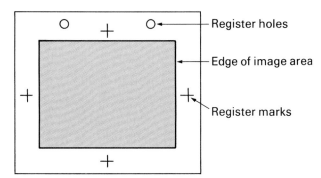

Figure 8.2 Typical arrangement of register holes and register marks.

neatline as register points.) When the separations are photographed, the register marks are included in the film image, along with the drawing of the map itself. Aligning the marks after the separations have been photographed places the negatives in the correct relationship to one another. This is discussed further in the sections on multiple plates and multiple burns, below.

Register marks are sometimes used instead of register pins to align separations with one another during the drafting stage. This is quite satisfactory when a fairly simple map is involved. Because the use of register marks requires careful visual alignment each time a different combination of separations is desired, however, it is quite easy for slight differences in alignment to occur from one time to the next. These differences may cause some portions of the images to be misaligned. If the map is at all complex, and many alignments are required, the pin-register system is much more accurate, simpler, and more flexible.

Line Separations

Line separations contain linear features such as rivers, coastlines, railroads, and roads, as well as neatlines, borders, grid lines, and scales. The linework is produced by drafting or by using scribing techniques, as already described. The line separations may include symbols and typography, or those elements may be placed on additional separations.

When scribing is involved, the image of the worksheet is usually photographically transferred to the required number of scribe-coats, using pin register. The lines needed on each separation are then selectively scribed.

Windows (Area Separations)

Areas of different tones or colors are commonly used on maps to designate certain features. A green area, for example, may indicate a woodland, or a water body may be distinguished from the rest of the map by printing a light blue on its surface. *Windows* are used to create such areas of color or tone. A window, in the parlance of the printing trade, is a clear, open area in a negative. An opening such as this, when exposed to a printing plate, creates an image that can be printed in any desired color. A window is also frequently used to expose tonal areas on printing plates. This is done by combining the window with a screen, as described below.

Although windows are created in a number of different ways, the processes all involve the preparation of a suitable separation negative or its equivalent. The following methods are commonly used to create windows for use in map production.

Drafted windows   When drafting techniques are used to create a window, the area that will be in color or tone on the final map is outlined in ink on a separate drawing. The drafting plastic on which the color separation is to be drawn is placed over the particular linework separation that contains the boundaries of the desired area. If a water area is involved, for example, the coastline is used as a guide. The outline of the water area is carefully traced and the entire area within the outline is painted black, using India ink or black opaque. The edge of this black area must exactly match the line that outlines the area. The result of this process is a black image corresponding to the desired tone area.

At times, portions of the outline of the desired window appear on more than one separation. The outline of a water area, for example, may include the coastline and part of the map neatline, and these two components may be drawn on different overlays. When this occurs, the separations are put in place sequentially, and each part of the outline is traced from the appropriate separation. As already noted, this ability to interchange separations is one of the advantages of using a pin-register system.

When the completed separation is photographed, all of the black areas become clear areas (windows) on the negative. The window is left open if a solid color is to be printed. It is combined with a screen at the platemaking stage if a tone is desired, as is described in the section on flat tint process colors.

The procedure just described is a straightforward but cumbersome way to create a window. Regardless of how much care is taken, the tracing process is seldom completely accurate because it is very difficult to produce a drawing that exactly matches the twists and turns of a complex line. Almost inevitably there are slight deviations resulting in a window that overlaps the edge of the desired area or falls short of the edge (Fig. 8.3). The process is also time-consuming because the entire area must be carefully outlined and painted, which is rather slow and potentially messy. Finally, the image does not always photograph well because it is difficult to make it completely black and any slightly gray areas will show on the negative. For these reasons, other techniques are favored.

Peelable materials   Special materials are used to produce windows, in lieu of the inking process just described. *Peelable material,* which is dark red in color, may be substituted for black ink, for example.[1] This can be done because dark red photographs on orthochromatic film as though it were opaque black. The window ob-

---

[1]For example: Peelrite-M, Direct Reproduction Corp.; Cut'N'Strip, Keuffel & Esser Co.; Para-Paque, Para-Tone Inc.; Letramask Film, Letraset USA.

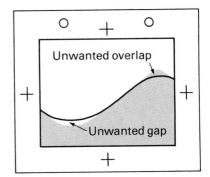

Figure 8.3 Problems with irregularity of window edge.

tained by using this material is usually sharper and clearer than that produced by using a pen-and-ink drawing because of the even density of the red material. Another advantage of this approach is that it is not as slow and messy as painting with ink or opaque.

A sheet of this peelable material is registered over the appropriate separation drawing or drawings. Because the material is translucent, the drawing shows through quite clearly. A sharp knife is used to cut carefully through the red layer, along the outlines of the areas to be screened. This cut is made along the middle of the bounding lines, for the same reasons as described for drafted windows. The red coating is then peeled away from the areas outside the window and is left in place within the window area. Finally, register marks are put in place and the separation is photographed. The resulting negative is handled in exactly the same way as negatives made from drafted separations.

The cutting and peeling process just described is quite slow and relatively inaccurate, although it usually is quicker than a pen-and-ink drawing.[2]

Reproduction-Size Windows

Windows are often created at reproduction size. This approach eliminates a camera step that is necessary if larger originals are drafted and then photographed to final size. If photoprocessing techniques are used, it has the additional benefit of much greater speed and accuracy.

Hand techniques   If the window is directly created, using hand techniques, the negative containing the outline of the desired window is stripped into place in a flat. This flat is then overlaid with a register-punched sheet of the same type of strippable material described in the preceding section. The overlay and the flat are held in the correct relationship to one another by register pins. A cut is then made through the strippable layer, following the appropriate lines on the negative. If various portions

[2]If the drawing is on a translucent material, an intermediate contact negative can be prepared from it. This negative is used to make a peelable negative image of the type discussed in the section on photoprocess reproduction-size windows, which follows. This negative is selectively peeled, with no cutting required, and is used as a camera-ready original.

of the outline are on separate negatives, the negatives are put in place one at a time, and the pertinent portion of the outline is cut with the proper negative in place. When the cutting of the outline is completed, the red coating is selectively stripped away, leaving a transparent window in the required location.

The cutting required for these materials is not completely satisfactory because it is time-consuming. If the linework is complex it is especially difficult, because the work is being done at final size, to maintain a satisfactory level of accuracy within the smaller working area. The result is that gaps and overlaps are common when hand cutting techniques are used. Because of the slow speed and relative inaccuracy of hand techniques, the creation of windows through the use of photoprocessing has come into increasing use.

Photoprocess Materials are available that allow the preparation of windows at reproduction scale, with the added advantage of the greater speed and accuracy of photoprocessing.[3] These materials use a red, strippable material similar to that described above except there is also a photosensitive emulsion over the strippable layer (Fig. 8.4). When the negative of the linework has been fastened into its proper location on the flat, a sheet of the sensitized peelable material is register-punched and placed in a vacuum frame in combination with the flat. An exposure is then made and the peelable material is developed. If parts of the required outline appear on separate negatives, successive exposures are made before the image is developed.

Processing this material involves *reversal*. That is, instead of a line positive, another line negative results. In this process, the emulsion exposed to the light is removed from the surface of the peelable material by the developer. What was an open line on the negative becomes a duplicate open line on the emulsion of the peelable material. An *etching solution* is next spread over the surface of the peelable material and the negative image acts as a stencil. The etching solution penetrates the open areas on the stencil and dissolves away the red, actinically opaque material in the exposed areas. The emulsion, and the red material, is left in place in the areas that were not exposed to light.

The sheet of film that results is identical to the original negative, except that the image is created in the strippable red material instead of in a firmly attached black emulsion. The desired portions of the red material are then peeled away and the required window is created. The peeling is very quickly accomplished because the etching process is the equivalent of the cutting that formerly had to be done by hand; in this case, however, the linework, no matter how intricate, is identically reproduced on the peelable material through the photographic process. This results in a completely accurate window without the problems of gaps and overlaps that may accompany the hand-cut or drawn processes.

The lines that surround an area on a peelcoat may themselves be printed on the final map. If they are printed as screened gray tones, or in color, it is necessary to keep them from being overprinted by the tone area created by the peelcoat window. This is accomplished in one of two ways. The simplest way is to brush masking

[3]For example: Striprite, Direct Reproduction Corp.; Peel Coat, Keuffel & Esser Co.

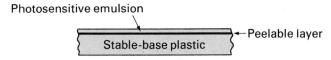

Figure 8.4   Cross section through photosensitive peelable film.

fluid over the linework on the peelcoat before the windows are peeled. This means that the lines themselves are filled in and are not exposed when the window is used. Another way is to produce a film mask by making a contact film positive from the line negative. Placing this positive in pin register with the peelcoat masks the linework when any exposures are made.

Any of the materials used for reproduction-size windows can be used in two ways. They can be used as negatives if the area corresponding to the window is peeled, or as positives if the areas outside the desired window are peeled.

MULTIPLE TONES

As is evident from the earlier description of the lithographic printing process, additional printing plates are needed when more than one color is printed on a map. One plate is utilized for each pass through the press, or for each unit of the press if a multicolor press is available. In the standard situation, each plate is the end product of an individual separation that is stripped into a flat and burned to the plate.

The lithographic process involves transferring ink of a particular color from a reservoir, through a system of rollers, onto a printing plate, then onto an offset blanket, and finally onto the paper. Because the types of film and plates used in this process are high-contrast materials, the color of the ink placed in the reservoir is the color that is finally printed on the paper. Assume, then, that two tones of blue are to be used on a map, the coastlines a dark blue and the water areas a light blue. If no special steps are taken, it is necessary to make a separate press run, using a separate plate and a different tone of blue ink on the press, for each tone printed on the map. In many cases, however, flat tint screens provide a more economical means of printing two or more tones of the same color on a map. Using screens reduces the number of printing plates and colors of ink, as well as the number of press runs required.

Flat Tint Screens

Although a given printing plate may be based on a single separation, it is also possible to create a plate that combines multiple tones of one color. This is done by combining properly prepared separations onto a single printing plate and by using flat tint screens.

A *flat tint screen* is a sheet of film with a multitude of small, approximately

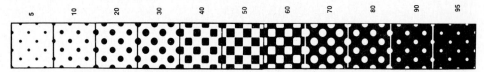

Figure 8.5 Enlarged sample of flat tint screens with varying sizes of black or open dots.

circular, clear openings, arranged in evenly spaced columns and rows in an opaque black matrix (or, the reverse—black dots on a clear background) (Fig. 8.5). These openings break an image into a series of dots, the size of which is varied to produce different tones. Some special screens create lines, or patterns, but most of the discussion here is limited to dot screens because they are more commonly encountered.

Screens are defined on the basis of two factors. The spacing between the dots, expressed in terms of the number of lines of *dots per inch,* is the first factor. The individual dots are visible in the coarser spacings, such as 55 to 85 lines per inch, when they are viewed from close up. When viewed at a distance, however, the dots blend together to give the impression of a tone of a particular color. If the individual dots are more closely spaced, and smaller, they are more difficult to distinguish and give a smoother impression of tone. These wider spacings are used for applications, such as newspapers, where the surface of the paper is relatively rough and the quality of resolution is poor. The finer spacings, up to 150 lines per inch or more, are used for lithographic work with high resolution, on smooth-surfaced paper.

As an illustration of the use of a flat tint screen, assume that a map is to be printed in black ink on white paper and that a particular area is to be printed in a gray tone. First, a window is prepared for the gray-tone area, using any of the techniques previously described. When the printing plate is made, the desired screen is sandwiched between the window negative and the plate. The result is that an array of regularly sized and spaced dots appears on the printing plate in the area beneath the window.

When the printed image is viewed, the dots, each of which is black, are seen against the white background provided by the paper. The visual merging of the white paper and the black dots gives the viewer the impression of an area of a particular tone of gray. The lightness or darkness of the gray tone depends upon the size of the dots relative to the amount of white paper background (Fig. 8.6). The relative size of the dots, expressed as the amount of clear area in the screen as a *percentage* of the total area, is the second factor used to specify a particular screen. A 10 percent screen, for example, used as a negative, has very small openings. These result in a printed image that, ideally, has 10 percent of the surface area of the paper inked. Similarly, a 50 percent screen ideally results in 50 percent of the surface area being inked, and an 80 percent screen in 80 percent being inked. In practice, ink spread makes a perfect match unlikely—it is usually necessary to measure printed samples in order to determine the actual tone obtained with a particular screen.

Notice that the nominal percentage tones shown in Fig. 8.6 do not give an

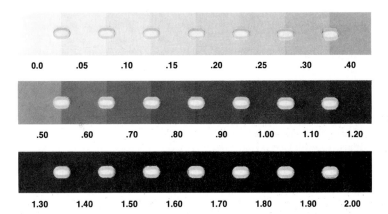

Figure 8.6 Twenty-four step reflection density guide. (Courtesy of Eastman Kodak Co.)

accurate indication of the apparent gray tone of each patch. This aspect was discussed in Chapter 5.

Multiple burns   Although a separate printing plate is required for each color, various tones of the same color may be combined onto one plate through the use of multiple exposures. This process, which is usually called *double-burning,* is not, however, limited to only two exposures.

Double-burning begins by aligning the first flat over the plate and making the necessary exposure. This flat is then removed, the second flat is put in place, and a second exposure is made. Screens of the desired tones are used with the appropriate negatives. This process is continued until all the flats to be printed in the given color have been exposed to the plate. Only then is the plate removed and developed. The result is a single plate that contains the image of all the negatives that have been exposed to it.

Halftone Screening

The previous discussion has dealt with maps that have flat gray tones, or color tones, in selected areas (although a variety of such tones may be included). In some situations, however, certain map elements are best represented by a continuously changing range of tones; hill shading is an example (see Chapter 10). To produce such *continuous-tone* elements, a *halftone screen* is introduced during the photographic process. This is because, as already discussed, the lithographic process cannot directly print gray tones. The halftone screen breaks the image into a multitude of dots, each of which is printed in a solid color. The dots, as with flat tint screens, create an impression of gray tones. In this case, however, the size of the dots produced by the screen varies in relation to the different tones that occur at different locations on the original continuous-tone drawing.

There are two principal types of halftone screen; glass and film. For our purposes, a description of the commonly used *magenta screen*, which is a film screen, is sufficient. A magenta screen consists of a network of open dots that are spaced at regular intervals on a sheet of film. The spacing is defined in terms of the number of lines of dots per inch, in the same manner as flat tint screens are defined. Instead of being a solid black, the emulsion of the halftone screen is dyed with a magenta color that varies in density; the center of each dot is essentially clear and the density of the magenta color reaches a maximum midway between the dots (Fig. 8.7).

In use, the magenta screen is placed on the camera back so that its emulsion is in contact with the emulsion of the unexposed film. The screen overlaps the film and is held in place by the same vacuum that holds the film. With this arrangement, the light from the copy passes through the screen before it reaches the film and is, therefore, differentially held back by the magenta dye in the screen.

The result of using a magenta screen, in conjunction with continuous-tone copy, is that there is a variation in the amount of light that reaches the film and forms a latent image. An area on the copy that is comparatively light reflects a large amount of the light focused onto the appropriate area on the film. This light penetrates even the darker portions of the magenta screen and forms a relatively large, latent dot image. Those areas that are dark on the copy reflect little or no light to penetrate the screen and reach the film. In these areas, then, only a small latent dot image is formed. In areas of intermediate tone, the amount of light that penetrates

Figure 8.7 Enlargement of magenta halftone screen. (Courtesy of Eastman Kodak Co.)

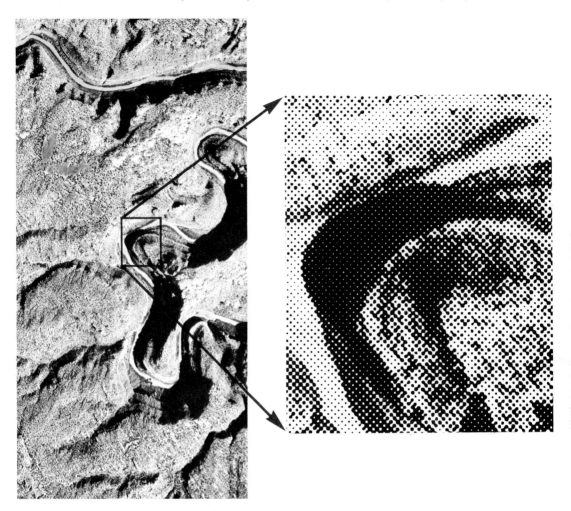

Figure 8.8 Range of values in a halftone image.

the screen and reaches the film depends upon how light or dark the copy is; the lighter the area the greater the amount of light that reaches the film and the larger the dot image that is formed.[4] The result, then, is a negative composed of a vast number of individual dots of varying sizes (Fig. 8.8).

As with flat tint screens, the spacing between the lines of halftone screens generally ranges from 55 to 150 or more lines per inch. When the halftone image is printed, the individual dots merge into a more or less smooth tonal gradation. The screen that is selected depends on the requirements of the particular printing

[4]Actual practice calls for a supplementary exposure, called a flash exposure. This detail, along with information regarding the use of glass screens and such aspects as the determination of exposure and the processing of the film, is omitted here for the sake of simplicity.

Figure 8.9 Comparison of coarse-line (left) and fine-line (right) halftone screens.

process being used. In general, however, the finer screens give more pleasing results (Fig. 8.9).

When a printing plate is made from a halftone negative, the continuous tones of the original separation are represented by larger or smaller percentages of ink. Large black dots on the negative, which correspond to the light areas on the original, hold back the light from the plate and result in a relatively small inked area which is seen as a light tone. The smaller dots of the dark areas on the original hold back light from less area and the result is a relatively large amount of inked area which is seen as a darker tone.

Masking When preparing a continuous-tone drawing, it is very difficult to match the edge of the tone exactly with any bounding lines. When relief shading is being used, for example, the terrain representation should not overlap the coastline. It is possible, when doing the drawing, to place a mask along the coastline, or to opaque out any tone that overlaps the coastline with white paint. Both methods are awkward and inaccurate, however, so it is more usual simply to continue the tone across the bounding lines. When the halftone negative of the drawing is prepared, halftone dots appear beyond the bounding lines if no other steps are taken. The overlapping dots can be opaqued out of the negative, but it is often quicker and more effective to use a *photographic mask* instead.

Assume, for example, that a halftone representation of relief is to appear on a map and that a flat tint tone—either gray or color—is to appear in the water areas. If this is so, a window is prepared for the water tone area. In order to produce a mask, this window is used as a negative and a contact film positive is made, using pin register. This positive is solid black in the areas that are to contain the water tone and is an open window in the area that is to be shown in shaded relief. The positive is then combined with the halftone negative of the shaded relief. When this is done, the positive acts as a mask so that only the halftone dots that appear within the land area show through, and the shaded relief image will terminate accurately at the coastline.

It may be desired to exclude the halftone image from other areas, such as the land areas outside of a particular region. In this case, when the mask is made, the windows for all such areas are exposed to the film before it is developed. The resulting mask is solid black wherever the halftone image is not wanted. This process is particularly useful if the outline of the area involved is complex.

Reversals and Other Techniques

If the background is dark enough to permit it, it is possible to have any linework, symbol, or lettering appear in white against a dark background [Fig. 8.10(a)]. The background may be black, gray, or a color, but it must be dark enough so that a white image will be visible against it. An image of this type is called a drop-out, or a *reversal*.

In order to produce a reversal, a contact film positive is prepared, using the negative on which the images of the items to be reversed appear. This positive is combined with the window containing the image of the background tone area, using pin register. When a printing plate, film positive, paper print, or other product is made, the positive image protects the emulsion so that a blank area appears where the reversed image is desired. The result is that the tone or color surrounds a white image.

It is also possible to use the original negative of the reversed image in other ways. A normal exposure could be made on the appropriate plate, for example, so that the symbol that was dropped out by the reversal step is printed within the drop-

Figure 8.10 Reversals and spread images: (a) Reversal; (b) Positive image within spread window; (c) Method of producing spread mask.

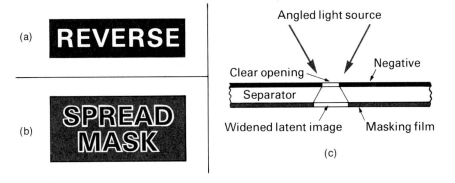

out area in a color or tone that contrasts with its background [Fig. 8.10(c)]. Because of the accuracy of register required, printing an image in this manner is difficult, so a white area around the image is often preferred.

If there is to be a white surround, a *spread positive mask* is needed. This is produced by placing a transparent separator between the negative and the film on which the mask is being made, during the exposure. The extra gap that is created results in a spread of the light coming in contact with the film. The light source may also be placed off center and rotated during the exposure. This results in a wider and more uniform spread in all directions. The degree to which these methods are used depends upon the width of spread required. The resulting mask is wider than the original image, producing the white surround that is desired [Fig. 8.10(b)].

Many other combinations of masks, spreads, and chokes (intermediates with a narrower image than the original) are possible. Such manipulations yield a variety of results that is too extensive to explain here. Suffice it to say that an ingenious worker can create special effects that may improve the quality of the map.

COLOR

It is helpful to point out some basic aspects of color perception and definition, before discussing how colors are printed. The techniques involved in printing multiple colors are the subject of the next section of this chapter. The considerations involved in the use of color as a design element were discussed in Chapter 5.

Physically, color is an aspect of the *electromagnetic spectrum*. This spectrum consists of radiant energy in wave form, ranging from the very short wavelengths of the gamma rays through the long radio waves (Fig. 8.11). A narrow portion of this spectrum, from about 400 to 700 nm,[5] is visible to us as light. This range lies between the relatively short ultraviolet and the relatively long infrared portions of the spectrum.

Light waves emitted by the sun include all of the visible frequencies and are seen as white light. The composition of white light is demonstrated by directing a

Figure 8.11 Visible light within the electromagnetic spectrum.

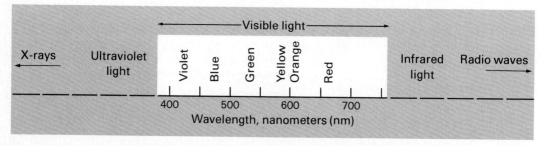

[5]A nanometer (nm) is equal to one-billionth of a meter.

beam of sunlight through a prism, which separates it into the well-known *visible spectrum* of the rainbow (Plate 3). The colors of the spectrum are perceived through the action of the different frequency light waves as they are focused on the retina of the eye. We seldom see colors that are the pure colors of the spectrum, however; most colors are the result of a mixture of wavelengths with differing intensities.

Additive Mixing

Additive color mixing consists of combining rays of light of different frequencies— the process can be visualized as the equivalent of reassembling parts of the rainbow. In practical terms, additive mixing involves three *primary colors.* Although other combinations can be used, the usual *additive primaries* are blue, green, and red. By mixing these colors in the proper proportion, virtually all of the other colors are formed, as occurs on the screen of a television set.

The additive mixing of primaries is demonstrated by shining three lamps onto a white surface. If each of the lamps is equipped with a filter of one of the primary colors, it will throw a spot of light of that color. This occurs because the other wavelengths are blocked by the filter and only the wavelengths of its particular color are transmitted. When the lights from the lamps overlap one another, additional colors are created in the areas of overlap (Plate 4). A combination (adding together) of blue and red is seen as magenta, a combination of blue and green is seen as cyan (blue-green), and a combination of red and green is seen as yellow. The combination of all three of the primaries results in white, whereas the unilluminated areas are black.

The preparation of color separations for the reproduction of full-colored originals involves additive color mixing. These concepts, therefore, are referred to when process color separation is described.

Subtractive Mixing

An opaque object, or a pigment, that is illuminated by a light source absorbs some of the wavelengths of the light and reflects others.[6] The effect of the reflected wavelengths gives the object its particular color. Pigments of some colors are mixed together to obtain other colors. Because the colors are the result of the absorption (subtraction) of certain wavelengths, the process of mixing pigments is called *subtractive mixing.*

The *primary colors* used for subtractive color mixing are magenta, cyan, and yellow. A mixture of magenta and yellow results in red, cyan and yellow yield green, and magenta and cyan combine to make blue (Plate 5). If magenta, yellow, and cyan are mixed, the result is a very dark color approaching black.

Because the actual printing of colors involves subtractive mixing, this subject is emphasized when process color and flat color printing processes are discussed.

---

[6]The color of the light source affects the perceived color of the object. For simplicity, this discussion assumes a white light.

Color Identification

One of the most widely used systems for the definition of color is the *Munsell system*.[7] This system is based on how colors appear to an observer with normal color vision, rather than on an analysis of the wavelengths of light that make up a particular color.

In the Munsell system, colors are designated on the basis of three essential dimensions. These dimensions are as follows:

1. *Hue* is the name of the color; for example, red, orange, yellow, blue, or green. Hue is based on the dominant wavelengths of the light waves that produce the particular color.
2. *Value* is the lightness or darkness of a particular hue; for example, light red (pink) as contrasted with dark red (maroon). In the absence of color, value is the equivalent of a gray scale, ranging from white through the light grays and dark grays to black.
3. *Chroma* is the strength or intensity of the color, or its degree of saturation; for example, weak blue versus strong blue. Chroma may be visualized as the extent to which a color differs from a gray of the same value.

For our purposes, there are two main virtues of the Munsell system. First, it provides a means of designating a particular color. By using a full Munsell designation, anyone who has access to Munsell color samples can refer to an exact sample of the desired color. This is a very real advantage in comparison to a designation based purely on descriptive names, such as medium blue or light orange. Second, the system provides a basic vocabulary for the discussion of color attributes. Hue, value, and chroma are one set of standard descriptive terms, although other terms are frequently encountered for the same concepts.

The Munsell system represents the three color dimensions, in diagrammatic form, as three directions along which measurements are taken (Fig. 8.12). Arranging colors in an orderly manner along these directions creates a distinctive color chart. This chart is used as the basis of a numerical coding that provides a standard reference for each patch of color on the chart (Plate 6).

Munsell coding designates hue, value, and chroma, written as an ordered combination of letters and numbers, such as 5R 5/5. The first group (5R) represents the hue, the number before the slash (5/) stands for the value, and the number after the slash (/5) identifies the chroma. The ranges of the numbers and the meanings of the designations are as follows.

Hue   The designations of hue are arranged in a circle around the central axis of the diagram. The simple hues occur in sequence and are separated by intermediate hues, which are obtained by mixing the adjacent simple hues. Reading clockwise,

[7]Munsell Color, Baltimore, Md. 21218.

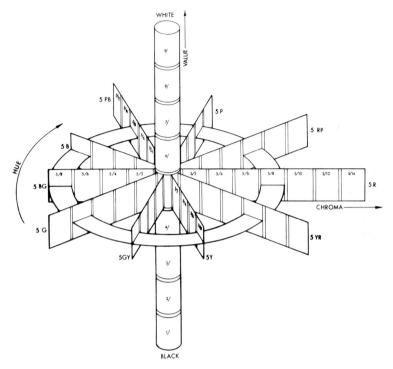

Figure 8.12 Relationships between hue, value, and chroma. (Courtesy of Munsell Color, Baltimore, Md. 21218.)

this ten-color sequence of hues and intermediate hues is red (R), yellow-red (YR), yellow (Y), green-yellow (GY), green (G), blue-green (BG), blue (B), purple-blue (PB), purple (P), red-purple (RP), and back to red. Further subdivisions are based on a numerical system, as indicated in Fig. 8.13. The hue identified as 5R is pure red, for example, and the intermediate hue identified as 5YR is yellow-red. The use of decimal numbers provides as fine a gradation of hues as is required to distinguish between very similar hues.

Value   Value is accommodated on the vertical axis of the diagram. Values range from 0/, representing pure black, to 10/, representing pure white. The steps in between represent equal-appearing value intervals, so that 5/ represents a middle gray. By definition, black and white values are achromatic, which means that they do not involve color distinctions. For that reason, the darkest color value in the Munsell system is indicated by a value of 1/ and the lightest color is indicated by a value of 9/. On this scale, a pink color is a light value of the hue red, and is designated by a notation like 5R 7/, whereas a maroon color is a dark value of the same hue and is designated by a notation like 5R 2/. Again, decimal values are used to designate very small differences in value.

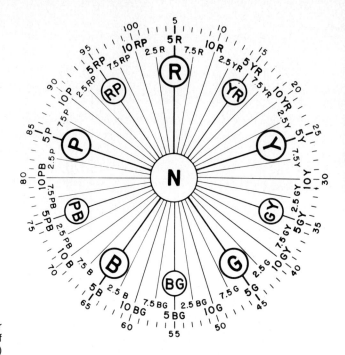

Figure 8.13 Hue symbols and their relation to one another. (Courtesy of Munsell Color, Baltimore, Md. 21218.)

Chroma Chroma is designated in the diagram in terms of distance from the central axis. The strength of a color, and therefore its chroma value, increases away from the axis, so a value of /1 is found closest to the gray value. Not all colors have the same range of chroma. The maximum length of the chroma scale, and the values assigned to it, varies from hue to hue. This means that some hues reach a chroma value of /10 or more at the outer limits of the diagram, whereas others reach a maximum chroma at /5.

MULTICOLOR PRINTING

Multiple colors are obtained most directly by individually printing each plate with ink that has been mixed to the desired color. In this approach, each color is applied directly to the paper, using the appropriate printing plate, in a sequence of passes through a monochrome press—red on one pass, blue on a second, green on a third, and so on. This approach is called *simple color*. Simple colors are obtained by using premixed inks or, if necessary, inks of different colors are mixed to obtain the desired color in the same way that any pigments are mixed.[8]

---

[8]Another system that is widely used in the printing trades is the Pantone (TM) system, available through Letraset USA.

Some lithographic presses have the capability of printing multiple colors with only one pass of the paper through the press. This is accomplished, in effect, by combining a series of two, three, four, or more individual presses into one machine (Fig. 8.14). Paper fed into the first section of this type of press is imprinted with the image for the first color. Without interruption, the paper is then fed directly into the second section where the image for the second color is printed in register with the first. This process continues, with each section of the press printing each successive color, until all the colors are printed and the sheet of paper containing the completed multicolor image is stacked at the end of the press. A *multicolor press,* therefore, provides a rapid and efficient means of printing multiple colors.

A multicolor press generally provides good register among the various colors. Even so, the paper stretches as it passes through the press because of the moisture it picks up from the blanket. Adjustments must be made during the printing process to keep the various images aligned.

Prevailing atmospheric conditions do not change during the very short period of time the paper is in a multicolor press. Conditions often change, however, between the separate runs involved in printing multiple colors on a single-color press— runs which could be carried out hours or days apart. The problem with such changes is that the paper stretches or shrinks as the atmospheric conditions change, making it difficult if not impossible to achieve adequate alignment of the separate colors. Modern printing plants, especially paper storage areas, are air-conditioned so that the paper is subjected to as little variation in temperature and humidity as possible. Air conditioning is helpful whether the printing is done on a single-color or a multicolor press.

Maintaining accurate register is particularly important in multicolor printing. This is because the effectiveness of delicate linework and of careful symbol design and color selection can easily be lost if the various elements are misregistered.

Figure 8.14   Four-color lithographic press. (Courtesy of Heidelberg U.S.A.)

Process Color

There are two methods of color reproduction that involve *process-color* techniques. One method is used for the reproduction of full-color originals. This method is not common in mapping applications, but there are instances, such as the reproduction of full-color terrain renderings, when it is used. The second method, which involves the overprinting of screened values of various colors, is very common. Brief descriptions of the procedures involved in each method are provided here.

Photographic separations Although various methods are used in making process-color separations, the steps involved in the relatively simple, direct method are described here. The original full-color artwork is photographed four separate times using a halftone screen and panchromatic film (that is, film that is sensitive to approximately the full range of visible colors). A differently colored filter is introduced between the artwork and the film for each separate exposure, producing what are called color separation negatives.

The apparent colors contained in the full-color original change greatly when they are viewed through the colored filters used in the color separation process. This is because each filter transmits light of its own color and absorbs its complementary color. A red filter, for example, transmits the red reflections from the original and absorbs green and blue (cyan) light. A negative produced using such a filter receives most light, and becomes most opaque, in the red areas of the original. It receives least light, and becomes least opaque, in green and blue areas of the original. A negative made with a red filter, then, is used to create the printing plate that is printed in cyan—the least opaque, green and blue areas of the original are the areas that are printed in cyan ink. A blue filter similarly transmits blue light and absorbs green and red (yellow) light. The negative produced with a blue filter is used to print yellow ink. Finally, a green filter transmits green light and absorbs blue and red (magenta) light and the negative that is produced is used to print magenta ink.

In addition to the three color negatives, a black negative is produced for process-color printing. A special filter, or combination of filters, is used to produce this negative. Black provides definition, reduces intermediate gray values, and strengthens certain colors.

The halftone screen is rotated each time one of the separation negatives is shot. If this is not done the dots will form distracting patterns, called *moiré* [Fig. 8.15(a)]. The standard pattern is to set the yellow printer dot pattern at 90° (that is, vertically and horizontally), and the black printer at 45°. The magenta printer is then angled 30 degrees to one side of the black printer, and the cyan printer is angled 30 degrees in the other direction [Fig. 8.15(b)].

Some *color correction* is usually done, using one of several available techniques, before the negatives are finally used for printing. Color correction involves chemically treating the film so that the individual dots in certain areas of the film are increased or decreased in size. This is required because the filters, films, and

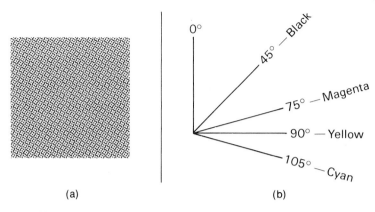

(a)   (b)

Figure 8.15 (a) Moiré. (b) Screen angles for process colors.

inks that are used do not have completely pure color characteristics and the uncorrected separations would not accurately reproduce the colors of the original.

Process-color printing is usually done in a sequence that lays down the yellow ink first, the magenta second, the cyan third, and the black last. The sequence may be varied, however, depending upon the circumstances involved in a particular job. The result of combining the four separated colors is a composite that closely represents the full-color original—the eye blends the individual dots so that intermediate hues are seen. Some colors cannot be exactly duplicated in this manner, but the results are generally effective (Plate 7).

Process color using flat tint screens Varying the size of the dots with which any color of ink is printed changes its apparent value. Furthermore, the production of a wide variety of colors is made possible through the printing of different screen values of various colors in combination with one another; where colors overlap, hues other than those of the inks themselves are produced. By printing a screened value of magenta over a background of solid yellow, for example, a red hue is obtained and, by varying the proportions of each color, other colors are produced. If the magenta is printed using a high-percentage screen (large dots), the red that is produced is reddish orange. If, on the other hand, the magenta is printed using a low-percentage screen (small dots), the result is yellowish orange.

Windows are used to determine where each screen value of each hue is printed and, therefore, what colors will result. The required windows are created by any of the techniques described above. A decision must be made, however, regarding what areas to include on each window; there are two approaches to be considered. In the *final color approach,* a window is prepared for each of the colors that will ultimately be printed on the map. In the *component tone approach,* a window is prepared for each screen value of each of the ink colors which will be used on the press.

The differences between the two approaches to creating windows can be appreciated by considering a simple example. Suppose that a combination of 40 per-

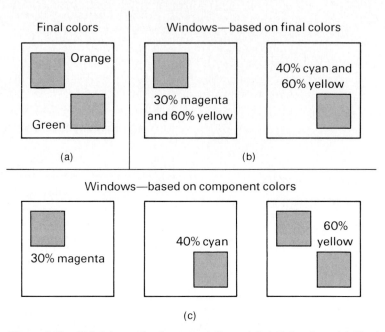

Figure 8.16   Obtaining color by overprinting of flat tint colors: (a) Final colors; (b) Window for each final color; (c) Window for each component color.

cent cyan and 60 percent yellow is being used to obtain the desired shade of green. Similarly, a combination of 30 percent magenta and 60 percent yellow is being used to obtain red [Fig. 8.16(a)]. In the first approach, the windows are prepared on the basis of the final colors: one for the green area and another for the red area [Fig. 8.16(b)]. When the printing plates are made, two exposures are made using the "green" window: one to the cyan plate, using a 40 percent screen, and the other to the yellow plate, using a 60 percent screen. Two similar exposures are made using the "red" window: one of the magenta plate, using a 30 percent screen, and the other (a double-burn) to the yellow plate, using a 60 percent screen. In the second approach, the windows are prepared on the basis of the values to be printed: one for 40 percent cyan, one for 30 percent magenta, and one for 60 percent yellow [Fig. 8.16(c)]. Three exposures are then required, one to each of the plates.

The production differences between the two approaches are significant, even in this simple example. When the windows are produced on the basis of the final colors, two windows and four exposures are required. When the windows are produced on the basis of the component colors, on the other hand, three windows and three exposures are required. Separation by component colors tends to be simpler and more efficient at the printing plant. Separation by final colors, on the other hand, is much more flexible. If it is decided that the colors must be changed, which happens fairly frequently after proofs are evaluated, the green can be changed to a combination of 40 percent cyan and 50 percent yellow, for example, without affecting the combination of screens for the red. If the second approach is used, the yellow component of both the red and the green must be the same: If one is changed, both are affected. If a change is required, the only way to overcome this difficulty is to revise the windows involved. The decision as to which color separation approach to use can only be made after considering the specific situation and must take the relative costs of time and materials into account, along with the expected need for production flexibility.[9] If the map is likely to be revised or printed in different versions, it is usually best to have each type of feature on its own separation.

Depending upon the number of screen values that are used with each hue, a very large number of color combinations can be produced by the overprinting method.[10] When using this technique, samples, called *color charts,* are obtained from the printer who is going to print the finished product. These samples indicate the range of colors obtained by printing various combinations of inks, screened to different values (Plate 8). The particular final color that is desired is then indicated to the printer by specifying the hues and percentage screens to be used for each of the final colors. Although the usual primary colors are most commonly used to obtain combination colors, other colors of ink are sometimes used to produce distinctive combinations.

PROOFING

A *proof* is simply a sample produced to show what the final product will look like and to provide a means of checking for errors. For all but the simplest printing jobs, a proof is necessary to provide an opportunity for making corrections or adjustments prior to making the final printing plates and inking up the press for the production run.

Press Proofs

When it is especially important to assess the quality of the final product, it may be desirable to produce a *press proof*. This is, in all essentials, the same as producing a limited quantity of the finished product. It is sometimes possible to reduce costs by using a special proofing press, which is less expensive to operate than a full-sized production press.

---

[9]See William G. Loy, "State Atlas Creation," *The American Cartographer,* 7, no. 2 (October 1980), 105–21, for a discussion of these considerations.

[10]Another approach to producing color separations is provided by Hans J. Stolle, "Notes on the Single Peelcoat Method for Color Separation of Textbook Maps," *The Canadian Cartographer,* 9, no. 2 (December 1972), 141–45.

Photographic Processes

Several techniques based on photographic processes are used to produce proofs without resorting to a printing press. Some of the more important of these processes, which are less costly than press proofs, will now be described. Throughout this section, the term *intermediate* is used to include line negatives, windows, and scribed separations.

Photo prints High-contrast *photographic prints* are produced using the intermediates that will later be used to make the printing plates. These prints are in black and white or in color, depending upon the type of paper and processing that is used. Because of the greater cost of color proofing processes, it is not unusual for a map that is eventually to be multicolor to be proofed in black and white. In this case, different percentage screens are often used to distinquish between portions that will appear in different colors on the final product. Using this approach, it is still possible to check for problems such as missing symbols, unwanted overprints, and misalignments, even though the colors are not present.

To make a photographic proof, the paper is placed in a vacuum frame with the first negative held in place by pin register. After the vacuum is established, an exposure is made through the negative. Multiple burns are made, using other negatives, and screens are introduced as required. When all the desired exposures have been made, the print is developed, washed, and dried.

Vandyke prints *Vandyke prints* are low-cost line prints. They are similar to the photoprints discussed above, but use less expensive paper and simpler processing. The emulsion is not as sensitive to light, so a darkroom is not required.

A Vandyke is produced in a manner very similar to photoprints, using the negatives, windows, and screens that will be used to make the printing plate. In this case, however, the exposure is made using a light source that is high in the ultraviolet portion of the spectrum.

Development consists of placing the paper in a chemical solution that turns the exposed lines a dark brown color. The paper is then washed to remove the excess chemicals and hung to dry. Similar processes are used to create inexpensive blueprint, silverprint, or brownprint proofs.

Wipe-on proofs *Wipe-on proofs* use colored dyes to represent the colored inks of the final printed product.[11] These dyes are sequentially applied and developed as follows: The first step involves wiping one of the dyes over the entire base sheet, which is usually a thin sheet of white plastic. When the dye has dried, the appropriate intermediate is placed over the base sheet, using the pin-register system. The base sheet and the intermediate are then placed in a vacuum frame and an exposure is made, using a light source that is high in the ultraviolet portion of the spectrum. This exposure hardens the dye in the image areas. Multiple exposures are made, if needed, and screens are used for different values.

[11]For example, Kwik-Proof, Direct Reproduction Corp.

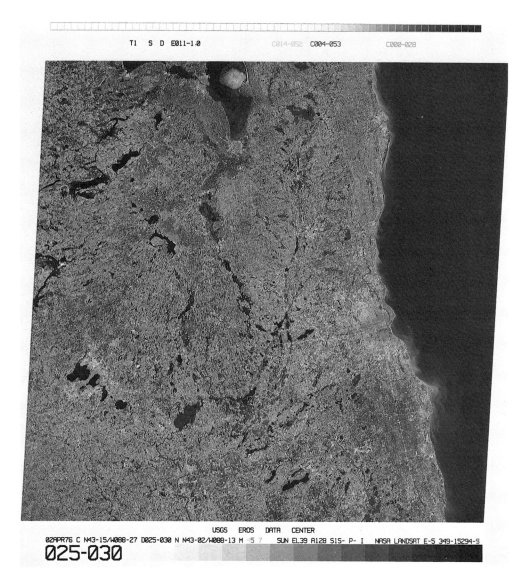

Plate 1 False color Landsat image of Milwaukee, Wisconsin, and vicinity, April 2, 1976. (USGS EROS Data Center.)

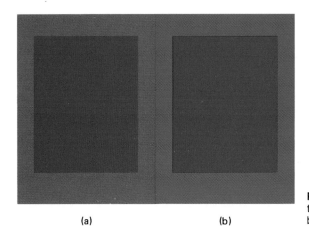

(a)   (b)

Plate 2 Effect of simultaneous contrast. The central color is the same in both (a) and (b).

Plate 3 White light projected through a prism is separated into the colors of the visible spectrum. (Photo by David Drewek.)

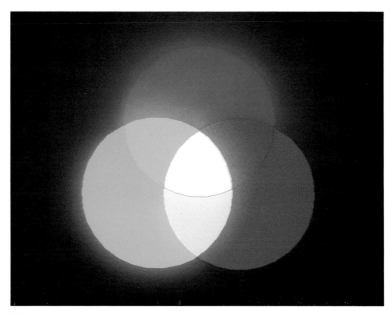

Plate 4 Computer simulation of colors obtained by mixing the additive primaries. (Courtesy of Madison Academic Computing Center, University of Wisconsin, Madison.)

Plate 5 Computer simulation of colors obtained by mixing the subtractive primaries. (Courtesy of Madison Academic Computing Center, University of Wisconsin, Madison.)

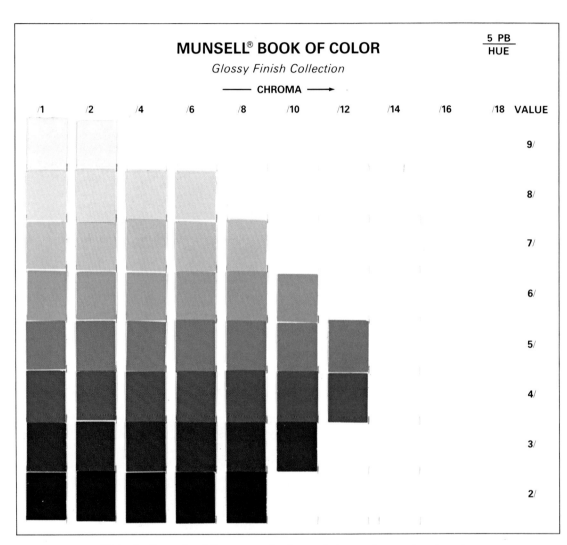

Plate 6 Example of the range of value and chroma for one hue (purple-blue). (Courtesy of Munsell Color, Baltimore, Md. 21218.)

Plate 7 Example of process-color printing. (Photo courtesy of Aero-Metric Engineering, Inc.)

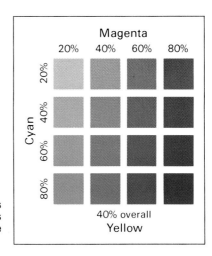

Plate 8 Example of process colors obtained by using flat tint screens and overprinting the subtractive primaries.

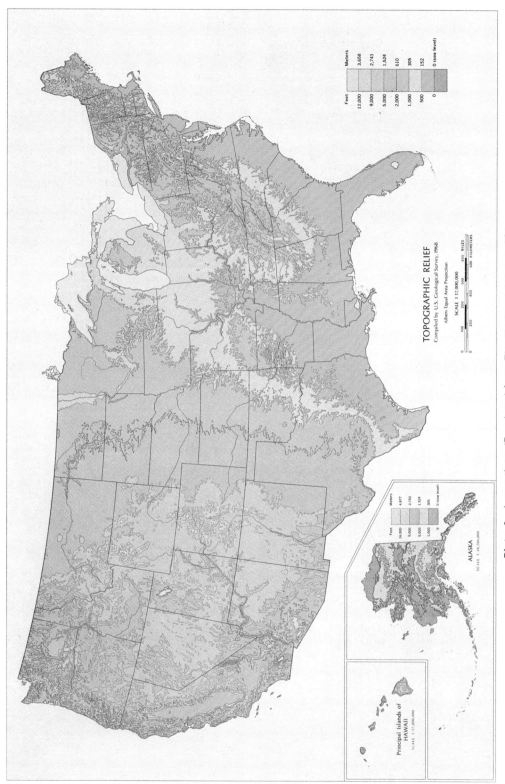

Plate 9 Layer tints. (Reprinted from *The National Atlas*, p. 59.)

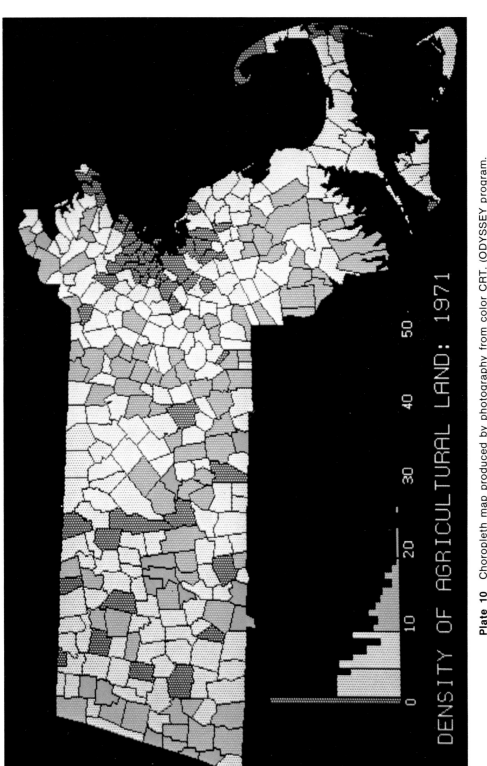

DENSITY OF AGRICULTURAL LAND: 1971

Plate 10 Choropleth map produced by photography from color CRT. (ODYSSEY program. Courtesy Laboratory for Computer Graphics & Spatial Analysis, Harvard Graduate School of Design.)

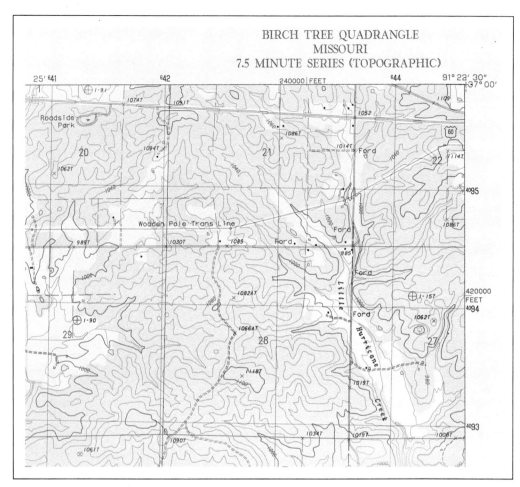

BIRCH TREE QUADRANGLE
MISSOURI
7.5 MINUTE SERIES (TOPOGRAPHIC)

Plate 11 Portion of 1:24,000 scale topographic map, Birch Tree, Missouri quadrangle. (USGS, Provisional Edition, 1982.) This is the first computer-generated topographic map produced by the USGS.

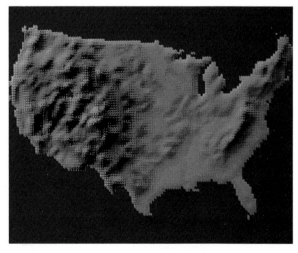

Plate 12 Relief representation produced by photography from color CRT. [Source: Geoffrey Dutton, "Land Alive," *Perspectives in Computing,* 2, no. 1 (March 1982), 26–39, copyright 1982 by IBM Corporation. With permission of the author, the Laboratory for Computer Graphics & Spatial Analysis, Harvard Graduate School of Design, and the editor of *Perspectives in Computing.*]

After the exposure of the first set of negatives is completed, the dye in the image areas has been hardened. The dye in the nonimage areas, which remains soluble, is then washed off. After the sheet is dried, the dye for the second color is wiped over the entire sheet and allowed to dry. The exposure process is repeated, using the appropriate intermediates, and the sheet is again washed and dried. This process is continued until all the desired colors are in place.

The proof that results from the wipe-on process bears a close resemblance to a printed product. The chief difference arises from the fact that the base is plastic rather than paper, and this affects the visual quality of the image slightly. Another consideration is that the color shades and densities of the dyes are not always exact duplicates of the colors and densities of the inks used in the printing press. This may result in a slight difference in appearance which must be taken into account in evaluating the proof. For purposes of checking for missing type or symbols, unwanted overprinting or gaps, and for evaluating the general appearance of the map, wipe-on proofs are very effective.

Because wipe-on proofs are produced one at a time, the process is relatively expensive, especially if more than one proof is needed. If a revision is needed, an entirely new proof must usually be created to check the effect of the change.

Colored overlays   Another proofing method involves combining a series of separate, *precolored, transparent-base overlays,* one for each hue.[12] The overlays are produced by using the intermediates that will be used to produce the printing plates. The completed overlays are registered over each other, on a white background, to give the effect of a full-color reproduction. The procedure used to produce this type of proof is as follows.

A sheet of precolored material is selected from a wide variety of colors to match the desired final hue as closely as possible. The sheet consists of a colored emulsion coated on a very thin sheet of transparent stable-based plastic. The coated material is placed in a vacuum frame, using pin register, and exposed to an ultraviolet light source. Multiple exposures are made, as required, using additional intermediates with or without screens. The exposure hardens the emulsion so that, when the material is developed, the nonimage areas are removed and the image areas remain as a colored image.

Details of the processing of these materials vary, depending upon the particular product being used. After a development step, the variously colored overlays are dried and combined with one another for viewing, using a white paper background. Because the overlay base material is transparent, the end result is a multicolor proof.

Because the overlays are plastic, they tend to be somewhat reflective; thus the final appearance of the proof is not quite the same as it would be if the image were printed on paper. If a correction is needed in one or more of the overlays, it is a

---

[12]For example: 3M Color Key, Minnesota Mining and Manufacturing Co.; Color-Guide, General Photo Products.

simple matter to redo the particular overlay, using corrected intermediates, and to replace the incorrect overlay with the corrected one.

Laminated overlays   Color proofs are also produced through the use of *adhesive-backed,* sensitized, transparent materials.[13] These materials are either precolored, or are given the appropriate color during the processing.

Processing begins by fastening the first sensitized overlay to a translucent white plastic base. This requires the use of a special roller device that applies even pressure over the surface of the material so that wrinkles do not develop. Using the appropriate intermediates, and pin register, the sensitized material is then exposed to a light source that is high in the ultraviolet frequencies.

The details of processing vary, depending upon the particular material which is being used. Some processes use a negative and others use a positive intermediate, for example; in some cases a colorant must be added. After development, an appropriately colored image remains. Additional colors are obtained by adding additional layers, each of which is exposed and developed in the same manner as the initial color until the proof is completed.

The resulting image is quite similar in appearance to a printed map but has the advantage that printing plates are not required and press proofing is avoided. A disadvantage of the method is that, if a portion of the proof requires correction, the entire proofing process ordinarily has to be repeated.

Suggested Readings

BILLMEYER, FRED W., JR., and MAX SALTZMAN, *Principles of Color Technology.* New York: Interscience Publishers, a division of John Wiley & Sons, 1966. Chapters 1–3 discuss many aspects of the characteristics of color and of color measurement systems.

BIRREN, FABER, *A Grammar of Color: A Basic Treatise on the Color System of Albert H. Munsell.* New York: Van Nostrand Reinhold Co., 1969.

COGOLI, J. E., *Photo Offset Fundamentals* (2nd ed.). Bloomington, Ill.: McKnight Publishing Co., 1967. Halftone photography is described in Chapter 9, and color reproduction is covered in Chapter 10.

CRAIG, JAMES, *Production for the Graphic Designer.* New York: Watson-Guptill Publications, 1974. A summary of color printing techniques is included (pp. 99–113).

MUNSELL, A. H., *A Color Notation* (11th ed.). Baltimore: Munsell Color Co., Inc., 1961. A classic approach to the description and classification of color.

Pocket Pal: A Graphic Arts Production Handbook (11th ed.). New York: Internatonal Paper Co., 1974.

---

[13]For example: Cromalin, E. I. DuPont deNemours and Co.; Transfer-Key, Minnesota Mining and Manufacturing.

9

Mapping Spatial Variations: Points, Lines, and Areas

Virtually all aspects of the physical environment of the earth, or of the human activities and institutions distributed on its surface, are (or could be) the subject of maps. The list of mappable topics is vast and can be extended to include phenomena found on other planets and the moon, as well. Physical, economic, social, and political aspects—weather and related atmospheric topics, surface and subsurface geology, soils, vegetation, animal types, economic systems, income patterns, population, nationality, religion, agriculture, and urban activities, to name a few of the broadest categories—are included. The unifying factor within this list, and its only real limitation, is that the topics differ from place to place in type, intensity, or both; without such variation maps are not needed (or, if produced, would be exceedingly dull).

VARIABLES

Any phenomenon that is mapped is defined in terms of its *location* and its *magnitude* at that location. Location is usually expressed in terms of latitude and longitude but other locational systems, such as reference grids, are also used. The magnitude, on the other hand, is the measurement of the quantity or value of the phenomenon in terms of an absolute amount, average, ratio, or other measure and can therefore be expressed in any appropriate units.

Examples of values are as diverse as the categories that are mapped. The altitude of the terrain is a physical characteristic that is defined in a straightforward way—each location is measured in terms of its elevation above some datum. Similarly, the amount of rainfall at different points is measured in terms of the quantity of moisture that is captured, or the temperature is recorded in degrees on a thermometer. When other types of phenomena are involved, the values are often measured rather indirectly, and some are quite abstract—corn yields per hectare and average income levels, for example. Nevertheless, the whole range of information, from physical, directly measured phenomena to abstract, indirectly measured concepts, can be converted into map form.

This chapter and the next focus on the ways in which information about the location and magnitude of different variables is managed, symbolized, and presented.

Data Evaluation

Whenever information is mapped, it must be evaluated to determine its appropriateness for the purpose at hand. It is especially important to be certain that the information is sufficiently detailed and accurate to allow the construction of a meaningful map. Even if someone other than the cartographer makes the final decision regarding the suitability of data, the cartographer needs to be aware of the potential pitfalls of using inappropriate information and, if need be, to question its use.

The main concerns regarding the appropriateness of information are related to its accuracy and timeliness. Unfortunately, it is often not possible to directly evaluate the accuracy of information. It is usually necessary, instead, to consider such secondary matters as the identity and reputation of the producing agency and the methods by which the information was acquired (for example, the surveying or sampling techniques). Consideration of these factors provides some indication of the level of confidence that can be placed in a particular set of data. If significant doubts are raised about the data, it is better not to produce a map than to prepare one that perpetuates inaccurate or misleading information.

The information used on a map must be timely, in addition to being as accurate as possible. Because information is often published years after it is gathered, the date of publication must not be confused with the date of acquisition. Perhaps even more frequently, an analysis may be carried out using earlier information, such as census materials, as its basis. If care is not taken, the date of the analysis may be confused with the date on which the information was gathered. If the study is an historical one, the use of older material may be appropriate. On the other hand, if a more recent time period is involved, the proper information must be obtained or the map should not be produced.

The acronym *GIGO,* which is used in conjunction with computers, summarizes the concern that lies behind the evaluation of information. GIGO stands for "garbage in, garbage out," and the implication is clear; the cartographer must be sure, prior to the construction of a map, that the acronym will not apply.

Data Handling

A data set frequently contains a great deal of complex information. One of the main tasks of the cartographer, therefore, is to sort through the welter of detail to find effective ways to handle the particular message that is to be presented. This usually involves summarizing the data and dividing it into meaningful categories. Appropriate symbols with which to represent the data are also required. The goal is to provide the map user with an accurate, understandable, visual presentation of the information.

Levels of Measurement

Measurements are taken at different levels of differentiation. Recognition of these levels is important to the cartographer because they govern the type of presentation which is made. The levels are usually defined as nominal, ordinal, interval, and ratio.[1]

Nominal level   This simplest level of measurement separates phenomena into categories or types. All that is involved is recognition of the existence (or nonexistence) of a particular category at a particular location and, sometimes, a count of the number of occurrences as well. *Nominal* information might distinguish between agricultural and nonagricultural land, for example. This level of information does not indicate anything about the productivity or other measurable characteristics of the land, such as crop yields.

Ordinal level   Acquiring additional information allows the data to be differentiated into relatively high or low values, or levels in between. When a measure of relative magnitude is assigned to an observation, but not a specific numerical value, it is referred to as an *ordinal* measure. In the case of agricultural land, to continue the previous example, ordinal information makes it possible to assign each unit of land to a grouping, starting with the least productive and progressing to the most productive—that is, to put them in order. On the other hand, the exact number of kilograms produced per hectare, or similar measurements, is not specified.

Interval and ratio levels   The next two levels of measurement are treated together because, although there is a difference in definition, there is little difference in the cartographic techniques involved in their use.

Further information might be acquired about the agricultural land mentioned in the preceding paragraphs. Instead of merely specifying which tracts were more productive and which were less so, for example, the number of kilograms produced on each hectare (ha) of field could be measured. The scale of production, on this basis, would begin at zero, with no production, and range upward to the most productive, say 100 kg/ha. The measurement would be specified in units, kilograms per hectare in this case, that are of known and fixed magnitude. The scale of measurement that would result is referred to as a *ratio* scale.

The distinguishing characteristic of a ratio scale is that it has both a nonarbitrary starting point and a constant distance between increments. This means that meaningful comparisons can be computed on the basis of a ratio scale. In terms of agricultural production, for example, an output of 50 kg/ha is exactly one-half of an output of 100 kg/ha.

If the scale used for measurement has an arbitrary starting point, it is referred to as an *interval* scale. An arbitrary starting point is a zero value that does not mean the complete absence of whatever is being measured. An example of this is the Celsius temperature scale.

The zero value of the Celsius scale is set at the freezing point of water and the boiling point of water is given a value of 100. The scale between the freezing and boiling point values is uniformly subdivided into constant value units, called

[1]S. S. Stevens, "On the Theory of Scales of Measurement," *Science,* 103 (1946), 677–80.

degrees, which means that it is an interval scale. The reason that Celsius degrees do not constitute a ratio scale, however, is rather easily seen. The temperature 0° Celsius does not mean that there is "no temperature," nor does the temperature 100° Celsius indicate that there is "100 times as much heat" as when the temperature is 1° Celsius. Instead, all that can be said about the relationship between the two readings is that 0° Celsius indicates the presence of less heat than does the temperature 1° Celsius and that both of these indicate less heat than the temperature 100° Celsius. The amount of difference between these readings is measured in terms of the constant value degrees.

Fortunately, interval scales, other than temperature scales, are seldom encountered in map work. For this reason, only ratio scales are treated in this discussion. The distinction between the interval and ratio types should be borne in mind, however, so that nonsensical results can be avoided if a nonratio interval scale is encountered.

DATA SIMPLIFICATION

When a complex set of data is presented, there is often a need to summarize or to simplify it. When this is properly done, it helps the map user to understand the general nature of the information without being overwhelmed by detail. Two of the most common methods of accomplishing this are taking averages and grouping the data into classes. These methods are discussed next, prior to the consideration of the problems involved in mapping the results.

Averages

The most extreme simplification is to reduce a range of data to a single number— a number that, by itself, summarizes and represents the whole set of data. Such summarization is done by using one of three types of *average*.

Mean   The most common form of average is the *mean*. In fact, it is so common that the word *average* is frequently used when what is specifically meant is the mean. The mean is determined by adding together the values of all of the individual observations in a set of data and dividing the total by the number of observations [Table 9.1(a)].[2] Because of the data requirements, the mean can only be determined for interval or ratio data.

It is important to note that the composition of the data, including the presence or absence of extreme values, has a significant effect on the value of the mean. If the maximum observation (or any other value in the data) is increased, for example, the mean also increases [see Table 9.1(b)]. If the data contain one or more rather extreme values, or are relatively spread out, the mean may not be a very useful form of summary.

[2]The data in this table are arranged in order from low to high for convenience. This is not necessary for determining the mean.

Table 9.1   DETERMINATION OF MEAN AND MEDIAN VALUES

Observation	a. Value		b. Value
1.	8		8
2.	13		13
3.	17		17
4.	49		49
5.	61		61
6.	65	—Median—	65
7.	82		82
8.	83		83
9.	90		90
10.	93		93
11.	99		594
Total	660		1155
Mean (total ÷ number of observations)	60		105
Median (sixth observation)	65		65

Median   The *median* is the value that is located in the middle of a range of observations. Unlike the mean, the median can be determined for ordinal data as well as for interval or ratio data.

The median is determined by arranging the data in order from low or high (or from high to low) and locating the midpoint. In Table 9.1, 65 is the median value in both sets of data. If there is an odd number of observations, the actual middle observation is the median value. In Table 9.2(a), for example, there are seven observations, so the median value is the fourth, counting from either end. If there is an even number of observations, however, there is no actual middle observation. In this case, the median value is arbitrarily determined by dividing the data into two groups, with an equal number of observations on the high and low sides of the range. The median is then assumed to lie halfway between the values that are adjacent to the dividing point. If there are six observations, as in Table 9.2(b) for

Table 9.2   DETERMINATION OF MEDIAN VALUE

	Number of Occurrences			
	a. Odd		b. Even	
1.	8		1.	8
2.	17		2.	17
3.	61		3.	61
4.	85	—Median—		73*
5.	90		4.	85
6.	93		5.	90
7.	99		6.	93

*Computed value (61 + 85) ÷ 2 = 73

example, the median value is between the third and fourth observations in the range and its value is calculated by averaging the two adjacent observations.

The median, unlike the mean, is not sensitive to extreme values. Even if all of the values in a data set change, the median often remains unchanged or changes only slightly. This occurs so long as none of the values move to the opposite side of the median value, and so long as the values on either side of an interpolated median, or the median value itself, do not change. Most importantly, if the extreme data values change, even by a large amount, the value of the median remains unchanged [Table 9.1(b)]. The median, therefore, is often a more useful statistic than the mean for summarizing data that include some rather extreme values.

Mode   The *mode* is simply the most frequently occurring value in a series of observations. It is found by recording the number of times each value appears in the data set; the value with the highest frequency count is the mode. Unlike the mean and the median, the modal value may be determined for a set of data at any level of measurement.

There are frequently some difficulties with the mode. For one thing, the data may be so spread out that no value occurs more than once so there is, in fact, no mode. On the other hand, the data may be arranged so that two or more values occur an equal number of times, so there are several modes. Because of its unpredictable nature, the mode is usually used only when the mean or median cannot be computed.

Grouping

Data are often simplified by combining them into relatively few *groups* or *classes*. This means that the level of detail of the data is reduced, thus making it easier for the user to see the general characteristics of the data distribution. Although the discussion of this process is often limited to maps of areas, the problems and procedures involved apply equally to point, line, and surface symbols.

The number of groups required is based on a judgment as to what is appropriate in a given case, as well as on the number that can be symbolized. The usual practice is to use somewhere between four and seven groups (see Chapter 5). The decision regarding how many classes to use depends in part on how the *class limits* of the groups are determined and how the *symbolization* is accomplished. This involves balancing the desire to differentiate more categories against the desire to avoid the confusion introduced by having too many categories. It is undoubtedly better to have a readable map with less detail than a detailed but unreadable product.

A *histogram* is a diagram that indicates how many times each value occurs in a set of data. The distribution of the data, as revealed in the histogram, is of considerable assistance in deciding how to divide a data set into a number of groups or classes. A set of sample data is shown in Table 9.3 and will be used as the basis for many of the examples shown in the remainder of this chapter. The histogram in Fig. 9.1(a) is based on these data.

Table 9.3   **POPULATION, AREA, AND POPULATION DENSITY**
STATE OF INDIANA 1980

County	Population	Area (km²)	Pop. Density (persons/km²)	Rank
Marion	765,233	1,026	745.8	1
Lake	522,965	1,297	403.2	2
Vanderburgh	167,515	611	274.2	3
St. Joseph	241,617	1,189	203.2	4
Allen	294,335	1,706	172.5	5
Floyd	61,169	388	157.7	6
Delaware	128,587	1,015	126.7	7
Madison	139,336	1,173	118.8	8
Howard	86,896	759	114.5	9
Elkhart	137,330	1,207	113.8	10
Porter	119,816	1,084	110.5	11
Vigo	112,385	1,049	107.1	12
Monroe	98,785	996	99.2	13
Tippecanoe	121,702	1,299	93.7	14
Johnson	77,240	832	92.8	15
Clark	88,838	974	91.2	16
Hamilton	82,027	1,032	79.5	17
Grant	80,934	1,075	75.3	18
Wayne	76,058	1,046	72.7	19
La Porte	108,632	1,555	69.9	20
Hendricks	69,804	1,059	65.9	21
Bartholomew	65,088	1,059	61.5	22
Hancock	43,939	795	55.3	23
Henry	53,336	1,022	52.2	24
Fayette	28,272	558	50.7	25
Morgan	51,999	1,060	49.1	26
Dearborn	34,291	796	43.1	27
Kosciusko	59,555	1,398	42.6	28
Miami	39,820	956	41.7	29
Scott	20,422	406	41.2	30
Warrick	41,474	1,013	40.9	31
Cass	40,936	1,073	38.2	32
Huntington	35,596	948	37.5	33
Shelby	39,887	1,068	37.3	34
Blackford	15,570	429	36.3	35
Lawrence	42,472	1,171	36.3	36
De Kalb	33,606	942	35.7	37
Wabash	36,640	1,032	35.5	38
Marshall	39,155	1,151	34.0	39
Adams	29,619	880	33.7	40
Boone	36,446	1,097	33.2	41
Noble	35,443	1,069	33.2	42
Jefferson	30,419	939	32.4	43
Knox	41,838	1,346	31.1	44
Steuben	24,694	798	30.9	45
Dubois	34,238	1,112	30.8	46

County	Population	Area (km²)	Pop. Density (persons/km²)	Rank
Clinton	31,545	1,049	30.1	47
Whitley	26,215	870	30.1	48
Jackson	36,523	1,330	27.5	49
Starke	21,997	801	27.5	50
Montgomery	35,501	1,308	27.1	51
Vermillion	18,229	674	27.0	52
Clay	24,862	933	26.6	53
Wells	25,401	959	26.5	54
Gibson	33,156	1,268	26.1	55
Lagrange	25,550	984	26.0	56
Randolph	29,997	1,175	25.5	57
Daviess	27,836	1,120	24.9	58
Posey	26,414	1,061	24.9	59
Tipton	16,819	675	24.9	60
Decatur	23,841	965	24.7	61
Jay	23,239	995	23.4	62
Putnam	29,163	1,248	23.4	63
Jennings	22,854	980	23.3	64
Ohio	5,114	226	22.6	65
Harrison	27,276	1,259	21.7	66
Greene	30,416	1,414	21.5	67
Ripley	24,398	1,158	21.1	68
Carroll	19,722	964	20.5	69
Fulton	19,335	956	20.2	70
Franklin	19,612	998	19.7	71
Perry	19,346	988	19.6	72
Spencer	19,361	1,036	18.7	73
Fountain	19,033	1,031	18.5	74
Rush	19,604	1,057	18.5	75
White	23,867	1,311	18.2	76
Jasper	26,138	1,454	18.0	77
Sullivan	21,107	1,171	18.0	78
Orange	18,677	1,057	17.7	79
Washington	21,932	1,336	16.4	80
Union	6,860	421	16.3	81
Owen	15,841	1,001	15.8	82
Brown	12,377	807	15.3	83
Pike	13,465	883	15.2	84
Newton	14,844	1,038	14.3	85
Parke	16,372	1,149	14.2	86
Martin	11,001	877	12.5	87
Crawford	9,820	794	12.4	88
Switzerland	7,153	579	12.4	89
Pulaski	13,258	1,126	11.8	90
Benton	10,218	1,053	9.7	91
Warren	8,976	949	9.5	92

Source: 1980 Census of Population, Vol. 1, *Characteristics of the Population,* Chapter A, Number of Inhabitants, Part 16, Indiana (U.S. Department of Commerce, Bureau of the Census, 1982), PC80-1-A16.

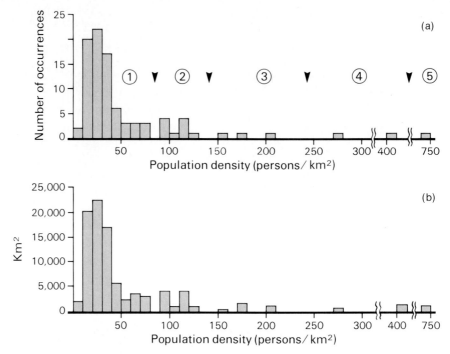

Figure 9.1 Histograms plotted from data in Table 9.3. (a) Vertical scale based on number of units with each value. (b) Vertical scale based on area of units with each value.

If the size of the units for which the data are provided varies considerably, the usefulness of the histogram is improved by taking area into account. This is done by making the length of the vertical bars proportional to the area of the units involved, instead of simply scaling them according to the number of units of each value [Fig. 9.1(b)].[3]

If the histogram assumes a *bell shape,* the data can be assumed to be what is termed *normally distributed* [Fig. 9.2(a)]. A normal distribution has most occurrences near the middle of the observation range and fewer occurrences toward the higher and lower ends of the range. If, however, the most frequent occurrences are not in the middle of the range but are toward one end or the other of it, the distribution is *skewed* [Fig. 9.2(b)]. Other shapes occur, such as a relatively flat (rectangular) curve, which indicates that there is no particular peak in the data [Fig. 9.2(c)], or a multi-modal distribution, which has more than one peak [Fig. 9.2(d)]. Although these characteristics can be measured and described statistically, the purpose here is simply to use the general shape of the curve as a means of selecting the

[3] J. Ross Mackay, "An Analysis of Isopleth and Choropleth Class Intervals," *Economic Geography,* 31, no. 1 (January 1955), 71–81.

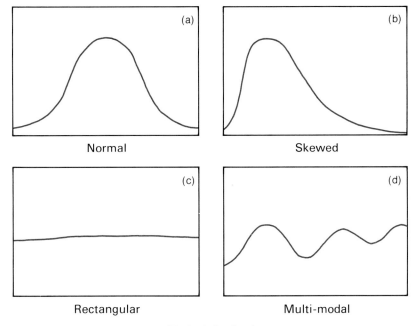

Figure 9.2 Typical distribution patterns.

appropriate system for assigning class values. More detailed analysis of this and other statistical matters is available in any introductory statistics text.

A few of the methods used for grouping data are described next, in order to provide some insight into the problems involved. Because each method results in a different representation of the data, all the approaches cannot be equally valid in a given situation. Unfortunately, it is often difficult to decide which method best reveals the ''truth'' about a particular set of data; the final decision in each case must be based on an analysis of the characteristics of the actual data set.[4]

The examples that are worked in the following sections are based on the data in Table 9.3. These same data are used later as the basis for sample choropleth maps.

Equal steps   The equal-steps method requires arranging the data from high to low (or from low to high). The *range* of the data is determined by subtracting the low value from the high value. In the case of the Indiana population density, the range

[4]The suggestions in the following sections are based on the work of Ian S. Evans, ''The Selection of Class Intervals,'' *Transactions, Institute of British Geographers,* 2 (new series), no. 1 (1977), 98–124. This article provides an extensive discussion, and classification into 16 types, of the methods available for establishing class intervals, as well as the considerations involved in deciding on the appropriate method in a given situation. In addition, George F. Jenks and Fred C. Caspall, ''Error on Choroplethic Maps: Definition, Meaurement, Reduction,'' *Annals of the Association of American Geographers,* 61, no. 2 (1971), 217–44, provides a listing and evaluation of 12 approaches to grouping and suggests a means of testing to determine the most suitable approach in a given situation.

Table 9.4   **EXAMPLES OF DATA GROUPINGS (BASED ON TABLE 9.3)**

	Equal Steps	Equal Steps (rounded)	Quintiles	Mean and Standard Deviation	Natural Breaks
Group 1	9.5–156.8	0–150	9.5– 18.5	below 11.25	9.5– 79.5
Group 2	156.9–304.1	151–300	18.7– 26.0	11.25– 57.50	91.2–126.7
Group 3	304.2–451.4	301–450	26.1– 35.5	57.50–103.75	157.7–203.2
Group 4	451.5–598.7	451–600	35.7– 72.7	103.75–196.25	274.2–403.2
Group 5	598.8–745.8	601–750	75.3–745.8	above 196.25	745.8

is 736.3 (745.8 − 9.5). This range is divided by the desired number of steps, in this case five, in order to determine the *step value* (736.3 ÷ 5 = 147.3). Beginning at the low end of the data range, the step value is added sequentially to determine the range of each group for the required number of steps; the starting point and the range are often adjusted to give rounded, easily used value ranges (Table 9.4).

Depending upon the distribution of the data, any number of observations, or none, may fall into each of the data classes when the equal-steps approach is used. In this example, there are many counties with population densities that are very low relative to the one county with an extremely high value. As a result, 86 counties fall into Group 1, 4 into Group 2, 1 into Group 3, none into Group 4, and only 1 into Group 5. This is obviously a very inadequate grouping method for a distribution that contains only a few values at one or the other extreme.

It would be more satisfactory in such a case to establish a separate category for the very high values and then to subdivide the rest of the values by computing new steps, based on the narrower remaining range. Marion and Lake counties, for example, could be placed in a group covering the range from 400 to 750. The remaining range would be 264.7 (from 274.2 to 9.5); when divided into four steps, rounded to 70 units each, the remaining groups would be 0–70, 71–140, 141–210, and 211–280. There would still be 72 counties in the first group, and small numbers of counties in the other groups, but the representation would be somewhat improved.

In summary, the equal-steps method is best suited to a rectangular distribution—one with a relatively equal number of occurrences of each value.

Quantiles   In the *quantile*[5] approach, the data are arranged in sequence from low to high values and the number of individual observations is counted. The observations are then separated into the desired number of groups so that each group contains the same number of observations. In this case there are five groups (*quintiles*), so one-fifth of the total observations are included in each. Because, as in this example, the number of observations cannot always be equally divided into the required number of classes, the number of observations assigned to each class may

[5]The general term, *quantile* is used to indicate division into an indefinite number of groups, with each group containing an equal number of observations. Because this example involves five groups, the term *quintile* is used. Other terms include the following: 4 groups—*quartile;* 10 groups—*decile;* 100 groups—*percentile;* and so on.

vary slightly. In this example, the 19 lowest-ranked counties are assigned to Group 1, the next 18 are assigned to Group 2, and so on. This grouping is more suitable for this particular data set than the previous one because it avoids having a very large number of cases in one group with very few (or even none) in the other groups. On the other hand, this grouping does mask the fact that there are a few densely settled counties that differ markedly from the rest.

The dividing lines between groups may come at rather irregular intervals when the quantile approach is used (Table 9.4) because the data may be bunched up or spread out in different portions of the range. For this reason, this approach is best suited to situations in which the data are in a rather uniformly spread-out, rectangular distribution.

Mean and standard deviation When the mean and standard deviation technique is used, the data are arranged in order and the mean is computed and established as the central point of the distribution. The *standard deviation,* a measure that describes the spread of the data around the mean, is then used to determine the interval between the categories. It is not necessary to use full standard deviation steps, which would normally result in establishing six classes, three on each side of the mean. Other ranges are often used, based on fractional portions of the standard deviation.

An examination of how the standard deviation is calculated brings out its characteristics.[6] The operations described here are shown in Table 9.5, which is based on the sample data from Table 9.1. The first step is to determine the mean of the data. The difference between the mean and each of the observations in the set is then obtained by subtracting the mean from each. Some of the observations are above the mean, so their *deviations* are postitive, and some are below the mean, so their deviations are negative.

Because the standard deviation is designed to respond to deviations on both sides of the mean, it would appear to be sensible, as a next step, to add the deviations together. If these positive and negative deviations are simply summed, however, the result is a value of zero. The effect of the negative signs on some of the deviations is removed, therefore, by squaring all of the values before adding them together. Squaring the deviations also places more weight on the larger deviation values.[7] The result of this calculation is called the *sum of the squared deviations.* This value, divided by the number of observations, yields the *mean squared deviation.* Taking the square root of the mean squared deviation eliminates the effect of the earlier squaring of the deviations and the resulting value is the standard deviation.

The statistical interpretation of the standard deviation is based on the existence of a normal distribution of the data. This technique is best suited, then, to situations

[6]The formula for the calculation of the standard deviation shown here is convenient for explanatory purposes. Other formulations, which are more convenient for purposes of calculation, are provided in standard statistics texts. Also, many pocket calculators and computer statistical packages are available to ease the calculation—these usually require simply entering the individual data values.

[7]See any standard statistics text for a further discussion of this and other characteristics of the standard deviation.

Table 9.5   DETERMINATION OF STANDARD DEVIATION

Observation	Value x	Deviation $(x - \bar{x})$	Squared Deviation $(x - \bar{x})^2$
1	8	− 52	2704
2	13	− 47	2209
3	17	− 43	1849
4	49	− 11	121
5	61	1	1
6	65	5	25
7	82	22	484
8	83	23	529
9	90	30	900
10	93	33	1089
11	99	39	1521

| Sum | 660 | 0 | 11432 | $=$ | $(x - \bar{x})^2$ |

Mean $\bar{x} = 60$

Standard deviation $= \sqrt{\dfrac{(x - \bar{x})^2}{n}} = 32.24$

where the histogram of the data exhibits a bell-shaped curve. Any number of observations may be included within each step when this method is used. If a normal distribution is involved, however, there will be a greater number of observations in the groups nearer the middle of the set; for this reason, some fraction of a standard deviation is often used instead of a full standard deviation to determine the width of each step.

One approach to using the mean and standard deviation technique to subdivide the data for Indiana is shown in Table 9.6 (the groupings are included, for comparative purposes, in Table 9.4). In this case, as previously noted, the distribution contains one extremely large value. As a result, the mean (57.5) falls between the 22nd and 23rd counties and the standard deviation is quite large (92.5). In order to provide any distinction between the 70 counties that fall below the mean, a category one-half a standard deviation wide is established to divide them into two groups. Above the mean, full standard deviation units are used to establish two more groups. If this method were being used for an actual mapping project, consideration would be given to splitting off the extreme value (Marion County) as a separate group. The mean and standard deviation could then be recomputed for the remaining values and new class limits determined.

"Natural breaks"   The "natural breaks" approach involves a direct examination of the data plotted on the histogram; any "natural breaks" in the distribution are used as dividing points for the classes. *Natural breaks* are points where there are gaps in the distribution, or where there are significantly fewer observations. The selection of natural breaks is subjective, however, so there is no absolute definition as to where a break occurs or does not occur. This technique is most likely to be useful when the data have more than one modal value.

Table 9.6　**STANDARD DEVIATION CLASSES (BASED ON TABLE 9.3)**

Where: Σ – sum of individual county population densities
　　　　x – individual county population densities
　　　　$\bar{x}$ – mean of population densities = 57.5
　　　　n – number of counties = 92

Standard deviation = $\sqrt{\dfrac{\Sigma\,(x - \bar{x})^2}{n}}$

　　　　　　　　= 92.50

Groups 2 and 3 (Starting from mean)

Limits extend one-half standard deviation in the appropriate direction.

Group 2—starting from 57.50, minus 46.25 = 11.25

Group 3—starting from 57.50, plus 46.25 = 103.75

Groups 4 and 5 (Additional groups above mean)

Limits extend one-half standard deviation in the appropriate direction.

Group 4—starting from 103.75, plus 92.50 = 196.25

Group 5—starting from 196.25 (extended to maximum value)

Group 1 (Lowest group)

Limits extend from Group 2 to minimum value.

Group 1—below 11.25

One problem with the natural breaks approach is that the number of observations within each group can vary considerably. In addition, the widths of the data groups usually differ from one to another. The results of using this technique on the Indiana population density data are shown in Fig. 9.1(b) and Table 9.4. In this case, the technique has the definite advantage of isolating densely populated Marion County from the other groups.

If there is a large number of observations, the plotting of the histogram is sometimes done with groups of values rather than with ungrouped data. The problem with this approach is that the location of the breaks may be affected in an unpredictable manner, depending upon the number and value range of the groupings. Furthermore, the value range of the groupings is often decided without considering the effect of the grouping on the outcome. A second arbitrary grouping of the Indiana data, and the resulting natural breaks, is shown in Fig. 9.3; the class

Figure 9.3　Histogram plotted from grouped data in Table 9.4.

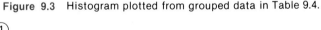
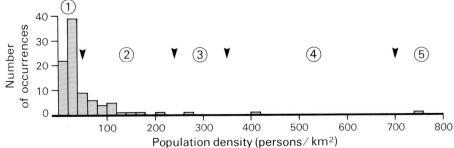

limits obtained from this grouping differ considerably from the class limits based on the original grouping. Because of the unpredictable effects of grouping, the selection of natural breaks is probably best done with ungrouped data.

SYMBOLS

Categories of Phenomena

Four categories of phenomena are symbolized on maps: those occurring at (1) points, (2) along lines, (3) over areas, and (4) on surfaces. The symbols used to represent these phenomena also conform to these categories. Each category is briefly described in this section and more detail is provided at appropriate points in the rest of this chapter and the next.

Points   Features considered to occur at a "point" in space are represented on maps by *point symbols*. Examples of such features include mines, buildings, historical sites, and benchmarks. Point symbols consist of dots, squares, circles, triangles, crosses, stars, and other shapes that are not true points [Fig. 9.4(a)]. For practical purposes, however, the distinction between small-sized symbols and dimensionless points does not cause any difficulty.

Whether or not a feature is suitably represented by a point symbol depends upon the scale of the map relative to the areal extent of the feature itself. Even a feature, such as a city, that occupies a considerable area on the earth's surface covers such a relatively small area on a small-scale map that it is conveniently represented by a dot. If a map is drawn in an extremely large scale, however, even a relatively small feature covers a significant area on the map, so that a point symbol might not be a suitable way to represent it.

Lines   *Linear symbols* represent map features that have length but do not have significant width. Items that fall into this category include roads, railroads, canals, pipelines, and power lines. These categories are distinguished from one another by lines of varying character (such as different combinations of dots, dashes, and crosses), lines of different colors, or both [Fig. 9.4(b)]. Line symbols are also used

Figure 9.4   Typical map symbols. See text for explanation.

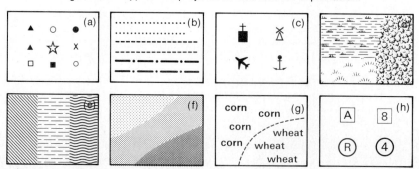

to designate volumes moved between points, or to indicate the capacity of a facility to carry a volume of cargo or traffic. The width of the line is varied to represent this type of information.

Areas   *Area symbols* represent phenomena of a type found within defined areas of the earth's surface. This includes categories such as crop types, religious denominations, climatic regions, income per capita, population per square mile, or other information reported on a per unit basis. They either actually apply or are assumed to apply uniformly over the area involved. Such data are reported for certain areas, such as countries, states, counties, or census tracts, or are summarized by such areal units.

Surfaces   A number of approaches are used to represent data that can be considered to be distributed on a *surface*. The physical surface of the earth is the most easily visualized example of this category. Other phenomena that vary from place to place within a region, such as quantity of rainfall, temperature, or total income, can also be considered as surfaces. The methods used to represent surfaces are discussed in the next chapter.

Symbol Design

Symbol designs range from realistic *pictorial* types to abstract *geometric* forms. The type selected varies depending on the sort of information that is being conveyed and the style and purpose of the map. There is no definite dividing line between pictorial and geometric symbols, but the range of differences is described below. In addition, typography is often used in conjunction with other symbols or by itself as a means of expanding the range of symbol types. Within each type of symbol, differences in appearance are typically used to differentiate nominal categories of information, whereas variations in size or gray value are used to symbolize quantity.

When they are available, colors provide a broader range of symbolization. Point, line, area, or surface symbols may be printed in different colors in order to distinguish between categories or quantities of phenomena. The most obvious use of color in this way involves conventions such as using blue type, symbols, and tones to identify water features, brown lines and lettering to represent physical features of the land, and black or red symbols to stand for cultural information. Care must be taken so that the colors are strong enough to be distinguished from one another yet not so strong as to produce a garish result.

Details regarding the use of specific types of symbols are discussed as the various categories of maps are explained.

Pictorial symbols   Pictorial symbols differentiate between categories by providing a recognizable picture of the features portrayed. Examples of this type of symbolization include using a drawing of a skier to indicate the location of a skiing facility, a pick and shovel to represent a mine, or an airplane to indicate a landing field. The chief advantage of such symbols is that they require a minimum of explanation and, once identified, are easily remembered. As a result, the map user seldom needs to refer to a legend in order to interpret them. The extent to which it is possible to design symbols that are easily recognized and interpreted varies with the topic.

Most examples of pictorial symbols are of the point symbol variety [Fig. 9.4(c)]. Pictorial line symbols can be prepared, such as a railroad locomotive set into a line to indicate a railroad alignment, but this is rather rare. Pictorial areal symbols are somewhat more common. Vegetation types, for example, are often indicated by a pattern of repeated symbols, such as sheaves of wheat, clumps of grass, or groves of trees [Fig. 9.4(d)].

Abstract Symbols

Some information is not suited to pictorial representation, or pictorial symbols may not be desired for a particular application. In either case, abstract geometric symbols such as circles, squares, dots, or triangles are used. Abstract symbols could literally represent anything until their meaning is defined by the legend on a particular map. If a specific type of dot is used to indicate the location of a health spa, for example, a legend is necessary to make the meaning clear.

There are cases, however, in which the use of a particular symbol is so conventional that the definition can simply be implied. This is often the case, for example, with the use of a dot, with name attached, to stand for a city. On the other hand, if the type of city (county seat, manufacturing center, or similar category) is being distinguished, a legend is usually required.

Abstract line symbols are frequently encountered. A variety of combinations of dots, dashes, crosses, and ticks are used to create distinctive line patterns. A legend is usually necessary to make the meaning of each such line clear, however, because there is nothing inherent in the appearance of a dashed line, for example, to indicate whether it represents a highway, a secondary road, a power line, or an intermittent stream.

Abstract symbols consisting of various patterns, colors, or tones are frequently used in order to differentiate areas with different characteristics from one another [Fig. 9.4(e)]. A line pattern might indicate, for example, either agricultural land, areas subject to flooding, or settled areas. Varying the tones applied to an area from dark to light, on the other hand, differentiates areas with relatively greater or lesser amounts of a particular variable [Fig. 9.4(f)]. A legend is needed to clarify the meaning of either type of symbol.

Typography as symbolization   Type styles are often used to differentiate between various categories of information. Italic lettering, for example, is often used to distinguish water bodies, verical serif styles may stand for physical features on the land, and vertical sans serif styles may indicate cultural features. The particular circumstances in each case influence whether or not a legend is needed

Another application of lettering is to use it as an areal symbol. In this case, a specific letter or word is chosen to represent each phenomenon. It is then repeated, as a pattern, over the appropriate area of the map. Areas devoted to particular crop types, for example, would be distinguished by a repeated use of the words *wheat* or *corn,* or the letters *W* or *C* [Fig. 9.4(g)]. Letters or numbers are also used as point symbols, often in combination with one of the geometric symbols—a letter inside a square, for example [Fig. 9.4(h)].

POINT FEATURES

The following discussion explains how point symbols are used to convey nominal, ordinal, or ratio information.

Nominal Data

Nominal data simply provide qualitative information; that is, they distinguish between different groupings. A great many types of nominal information are routinely mapped using point symbols, as we have noted. One way to make nominal distinctions is to use a specific symbol shape for each category of information: a dot to represent a city, a square for a manufacturing site, a triangle for a park, and so on. Different colors are also used, for example, to distinguish between subsets of major categories, such as green triangles for developed parks and red triangles for planned parks. The range and variety of such applications are virtually endless, but the common characteristic is that there is a recognizable difference between the symbol chosen for each cateogory of data.

Ordinal and Ratio Data

A variety of point symbols is used to represent ordinal or ratio data. The circle has been selected as the basis for the following discussion but the ideas expressed generally apply to other shapes as well.

Despite the fact that circles take up a considerable amount of map space, they are used to symbolize information that occurs at a specific point on the map and are therefore classified as point symbols. The center of the circle is usually placed at the point to which the information refers.[8]

Proportional sizes   A traditional approach to the use of circle symbols is to vary their size to reflect variations in the values they represent. The selection of suitable circle sizes is not necessarily a simple task.

The most basic method of sizing circle symbols is to make the area of each circle directly *proportional* to the value it represents. The calculation of this proportion is begun by taking the square root of each data value. The square root is then used as an *index value* for determining the size of the symbol (Table 9.7). After

---

[8]Circles are also used to represent data summarized for a particular area. In this case, the circle is located within the appropriate region on the map and its size is varied to indicate the value of the variable within that region. This discussion applies equally to circles used to represent point or areal data.

Table 9.7   **PROPORTIONAL CIRCLE RATIOS, SQUARE ROOT INDEX METHOD**

Data	Index (square root)	Constant (arbitrary)	Circle Radius (cm)	Area (cm²)*
4	2	2	4	16π
9	3	2	6	36π
16	4	2	8	64π
25	5	2	10	100π
36	6	2	12	144π

*Ratio to data stays constant with increasing data values. Note that, because π is a constant in the computation of the area of a circle, its value is ignored in calculating the index.

the index values are obtained, they are multiplied by an arbitrarily chosen *constant* in order to arrive at the radius of each circle.

Ideally, the value of the size constant is selected so that the largest circles fit into the available space on the map but, also, so that the smallest circles are large enough to be readable. As a practical matter, it is often difficult to select a value that accomplishes both of these goals. Depending upon the range of data values, choosing too large a constant results in large circles that take up too much space. Conversely, too small a constant produces circles at the lower end of the range that are so small that the map user cannot tell them apart (or, they cannot be properly drawn). The methods used to overcome this problem are discussed at the end of this section.

Assuming, then, that proportional circles are used, the question of appropriate scaling remains. Experiments indicate that map users do not necessarily interpret circular symbols in the purely mathematical ratio given by the square root method. Instead, they tend to underestimate the values represented by the larger circles.[9] A common solution to this problem is to adjust the size of the larger circles so their areas are progressively more than proportional to the data values they represent.

Table 9.8   **PROPORTIONAL CIRCLE RATIOS, PSYCHOLOGICAL INDEX METHOD**

Data	Index [N(0.5716)]	Constant (arbitrary)	Circle Radius (cm)	Area (cm²)*
4	2.21	2	4.2	17.6π
9	3.51	2	7.0	49.0π
16	4.88	2	9.8	96.0π
25	6.30	2	12.6	158.8π
36	7.76	2	15.5	240.3π

*Ratio to data increases with increasing data values.

[9]The selected references in the Symbol Size section of the Suggested Readings provide an introduction to the cartographic literature on this subject. The references themselves contain information about some of the related psychological research.

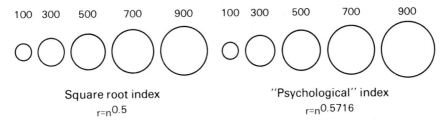

Figure 9.5   Comparison of circle sizes scaled by two different methods.

Table 9.8 indicates the type of change that results from using a power of 0.5716 for this purpose instead of taking the square root (which is the same as using a power of 0.5).[10] Fig. 9.5 provides a visual comparison of the results of the two methods.

Symbols on maps are found in various surroundings, including elements of the background map, names, patterns, colors, or tones of gray. They are also found in various combinations—their neighbors may be large, small, or a variety of sizes—which affects the apparent size of the symbol (Fig. 9.6). Ideally, the tests used to determine scaling ratios should take these complex situations into account, but this has proven to be very difficult to accomplish.

In test situations, the *underestimation* of the values associated with larger circles is frequently encountered. This indicates that the use of a ratio that increases

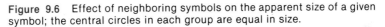

Figure 9.6   Effect of neighboring symbols on the apparent size of a given symbol; the central circles in each group are equal in size.

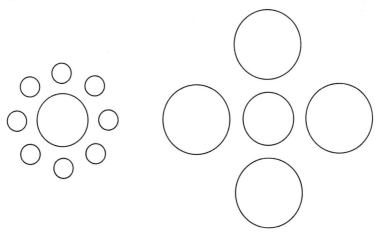

[10] James J. Flannery, "The Relative Effectiveness of Some Common Graduated Point Symbols in the Presentation of Quantitative Data," *The Canadian Cartographer*, 8, no. 2 (December 1971), 96–109. The use of logarithms allows this to be done quite readily—the log of the value multiplied by 0.5716 = X, the antilog of X is then the index value.

Figure 9.7 Sample legend for proportional circles. [Reprinted from *The National Atlas of the United States* (Washington, D.C.: U.S. Department of Interior, Geological Survey, 1970), p. 179.]

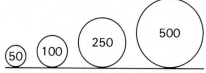

The area of each circle is proportional to the value it represents

the relative size of the symbol as the value increases should somewhat improve their interpretation. However, the ratio found to be appropriate varies from experiment to experiment.[11] This is partly because of the difficulty of devising an appropriate test, and partly because of the complex situations in which symbols actually occur. In the end it may prove to be more important to assist the map user in the interpretation of the symbols than to be concerned about the specific scaling ratio. It is suggested, therefore, that the square root method can be used to scale circular symbols, or one of the other ratios may be used if preferred.

Whatever scaling ratio is used, however, a suitable legend must be provided. The requirements of the legend are that it include at least three sample symbols, covering the range of symbol sizes. The value associated with each symbol should also be indicated. In addition, the wording of the legend ideally should indicate that the *area* of each symbol varies in relation to the value represented. Figure 9.7 shows one possible legend arrangement that follows these recommendations.

Large Data Ranges

Dealing with a very large range of data values is difficult. The simplest solution is to allow the symbols to overlap one another in the tighter areas [Fig. 9.8(a)]. This saves space but, depending upon the number of overlapping symbols, often becomes difficult to read. For this reason, two other approaches are sometimes used. First, dots, or graded circles, are substituted for proportional circles to represent the smaller values, or graded circles are used to represent all of the values [Fig. 9.8(b)]. Second, symbols that appear to be three-dimensional figures (spheres) are substituted for circles [Fig. 9.8(c)]. Both approaches are discussed further, below.

Graded sizes   Using proportional circle symbols requires ratio data. If only ordinal data are available, however, or if it is desired to simplify ratio data, a range of specific circle sizes is used. For example, a small circle may be used to represent small settlements (500–9999 population), a medium circle for settlements with a

[11]Some observers have found that this tendency is not uniformly encountered. See, for example, Kang-Tsung Chang, "Circle Size Judgment and Map Design," *The American Cartographer*, 7, no. 2, (October 1980), 155–62; Carleton W. Cox, "Anchor Effects and the Estimation of Graduated Circles and Squares," *The American Cartographer*, 3, no. 1 (April 1976), 65–74; and Hans-Joachim Meihoefer, "The Visual Perception of the Circle in Thematic Maps—Experimental Results," *The Canadian Cartographer*, 10, no. 1 (June 1973), 63–84.

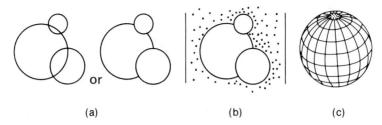

Figure 9.8 (a) Two methods of dealing with overlapping circles. (b) Circles combined with dots. (c) Spherical symbol.

larger population (10,000–99,999), and a large circle for places with the largest population (100,000 or more). The number of symbol size categories used is decided on a case-by-case basis.

Frequently, the sizes are arbitrarily selected so that there is simply a progression in size to represent the increasing values, particularly when smaller circle sizes are needed to relieve crowding. This is not encouraged, however, because the map reader will lose the sense of the proportionality of the symbols. A better way is to determine the median value for each size range and to use one of the scaling methods already described to proportion each symbol. Again, a legend must be provided to allow each symbol to be matched against a sample to determine its size category.

"Spherical" symbols It is tempting to use an apparently spherical symbol instead of a simple circle when the data to be represented have a very large range. This is done by taking the cube root of the data as the basis for the sizing. When the radius of each sphere is adjusted on this basis, its presumed volume is proportional to the value of the data it represents.

The result of using three-dimensional appearing symbols is that the range in size needed to represent a given set of values is greatly reduced. The advantage of this is that the symbols at the upper end of the range become much smaller and thus fit into the available space more easily. At the same time, it is easier to keep the symbols at the lower end of the range large enough to be visible.

Unfortunately, viewers looking at apparently spherical symbols interpret them in relation to their area, and not to their volume.[12] For this reason, their use is not recommended.

Other shapes It is a simple matter to draw squares, rectangles, or other shapes, so that their area is more or less proportional to a set of values. Although such symbols are often more interesting than simple circles, there is some question as to whether or not map users interpret their sizes accurately. For this reason, if they are used, an adequate legend is particularly important.

Cubes, or stacks of cubes, are drawn to appear as though they are three-dimensional; they bear the same relationship to squares as spheres do to circles.

---

[12]Robert L. Williams, *Statistical Symbols for Maps: Their Design and Relative Values* (New Haven, Conn.: Yale University Map Laboratory, 1956).

Cubes are sized by using the same basic scaling procedure as with spheres—that is, so that their volume is proportional to the data. Because of the perception problems involved with three-dimensional appearing symbols, the use of cubes is not recommended.

Subdivided symbols Proportional circle symbols are sometimes divided into subcategories in the same manner as a pie chart. When this is done, the size of the symbol is determined on the basis of the total of the data. Each sector of the pie is then drawn on the basis of its relationship to the total.

If, for example, the amount of lumber production at a number of centers, by type, is mapped, the total production at each center is used to scale the circle. Then, the amount of each type of lumber at each center is divided by the total production to obtain its percentage of the total (Fig. 9.9). Finally, the circle is subdivided on the basis of the percentage values—a category that constitutes 25 percent of the total, for example, is represented by a 90-degree sector (360 degrees × 0.25 = 90 degrees). A special protractor, which is subdivided directly in percentages, speeds this process.

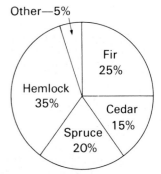

Figure 9.9 Subdivided circle.

The readability of a series of subdivided circles is improved if the plotting of the subdivisions is done consistently. The same sequence of categories should be used for each circle, and the starting point should be the same in each case.

The same general procedures are followed when symbols with other shapes are subdivided; the area representing each subcategory is made proportional to the percentage it represents of the total.

LINEAR FEATURES

Linear symbols are used to represent features that have length but essentially no width. There is a great multitude of such features, including different kinds of routes, such as railroads, roads, canals, pipelines, communication networks, and power lines, as well as other types of physical features, such as fence lines and rivers. There are also a number of more abstract pieces of information, such as boundaries or monetary exchanges, that are symbolized by linear symbols.

Nominal Data

A great many types of nominally differentiated linear features are routinely mapped. A typical highway map, for example, shows a variety of types of roads and highways, usually without presenting information regarding the volume of traffic or other quantitative aspects of the routes. Also, lines are used to represent boundaries, coastlines, paths, power lines, and so on. These various categories are differentiated from one another by using lines of different qualities, such as dots, dashes, and crossticks. At times these symbols may be used in combination with one another and may be combined with the use of different colors.

Ordinal and Ratio Data

Another use of linear symbols is to show flows or interactions between locations. The legend on this type of map indicates the value or volume of the flows that move through transportation facilities, or the capacity of such facilities to handle flows. These quantities are typically symbolized by variations in line width.

If ratio data are used, the width of the flow lines is made proportional to the value or quantity of the flow. The use of *proportional line widths* allows the volume of flow to be shown accurately (Fig. 9.10). This simply involves establishing a suitable linear scale, such as 1 mm per 100,000 units, and measuring the line widths according to the volume carried during a specified time period. The chief difficulty with this approach, usually, is in establishing a scale that is suitable for both large and small values. If the range is wide, and the space available on the map is limited, this method becomes difficult to use. When this occurs, the widths of the lines are often grouped into a series of steps, with each step representing a *range of values* (**Fig. 9.11**). Establishing the range of values represented by each width category involves the methods of grouping that were discussed earlier. Specific line widths are used to represent each relative value range if only ordinal data are available.

Often, especially when there is a wide range of data values, the lines that are needed to show low values become too small to differentiate easily. When this occurs, *symbolized lines* are used to show the smaller flows. A light dotted line, for example, may represent very small values, while a line of similar weight, but made up of short dashes, may indicate slightly larger values, and so on.

The path used to plot flow lines is determined in one of two ways. In one type of map, the actual route of the feature, such as a railroad track, a road alignment, or a pipeline right-of-way, is represented (Fig. 9.11). This treatment is particularly suitable when shipments of materials are shown. It is often difficult, however, because of crowding, to show the actual route of shipment accurately. Or there may simply be no single definable route involved, such as when monetary exchanges, telephone calls, or generalized population migrations are shown. When either of

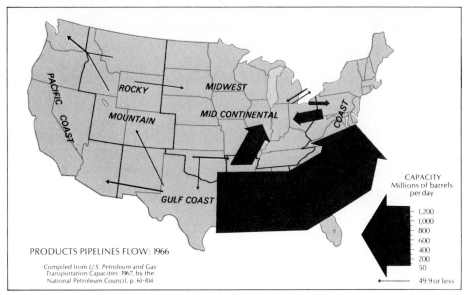

Figure 9.10 Flow map indicating connection, but not route, using proportional scaling. (Reprinted from *The National Atlas*, p. 235.)

these conditions exist, a convenient path is drawn as directly as possible simply to indicate that there is a connection between the two locations (Fig. 9.10).

AREAL DISTRIBUTIONS

Many phenomena are variably distributed over the earth's surface; in some locations they are concentrated, in others they are more dispersed. For example, a variety of crops is grown over land areas of greater or lesser extent, with different levels of productivity at different locations; people live in relatively concentrated population patterns that are separated from one another by less densely settled areas; and climatic characteristics change in relation to location. Information about such variations in concentration is presented on various types of distribution maps.

Dot Distribution Maps

Dot maps are often used to represent the distribution of areally distributed phenomena. On such maps, areas with relatively dense concentrations have a closely spaced array of dots, whereas areas with less dense distributions have a more scattered arrangement. The result of these differences in dot density is a visual impression of the distribution pattern of the actual phenomenon.

In the simplest type of dot distribution map, individual dots are placed on the map at suitable locations to represent each unit of the subject. If the distribution of human population is being mapped, for example, one dot is placed at the map

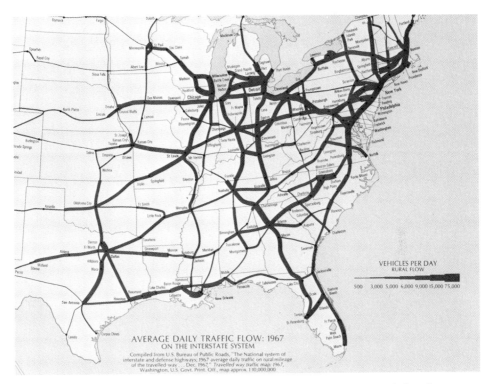

Figure 9.11   Flow map indicating connection and route, using graded scaling. (Reprinted from *The National Atlas*, p. 227.)

location, perhaps the residence, of each person. There are relatively few situations, however, in which this simple one-to-one relationship is used. It is more common to be faced with the need to represent the distribution of a population with hundreds or thousands of members. In such cases, a single dot usually represents many members of the population. Furthermore, that dot must be placed at a location that is as representative as possible of the location of the group for which it stands. Accomplishing this in an effective way requires the resolution of a number of problems.

A key decision in the design of a dot distribution map is how many members of the population to represent with each dot. (This is another way of saying how many dots will represent the total population.) The physical size of the dots must also be decided. Finally, it is necessary to decide where to place the dots so that the actual distribution of the population is well represented. These factors are interrelated. Given a specific map scale, the physical size of the area in which the dots must be placed is known. Then, when the number of dots to be used is determined, the dots cannot exceed a given size or the map will be simply an indecipherable mass of overlapping dots. Furthermore, because some areas have a more concentrated

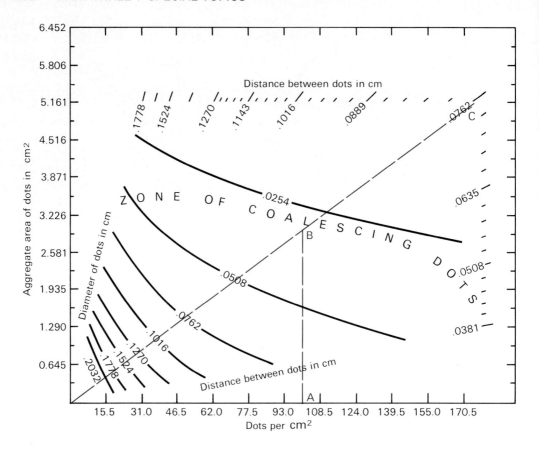

Figure 9.12 Nomograph for determining dot sizes. [Sources: J. Ross Mackay, "Dotting the Dot Map," *Surveying and Mapping,* IX (1949), 3–10, with permission.]

distribution than others, the number of dots that must fit into the denser areas is of greatest important. Fortunately, a *nomograph* is available to assist in the controlled testing of possible unit values and dot sizes (Fig. 9.12).

To use the nomograph, a decision is first made regarding the number of units each dot will represent. Because it is desirable to have the dots that are ultimately drawn almost coalesce with one another in the densest areas of the map, one such area is selected for test purposes. For example, one county on a state map may have the densest concentration of population per square kilometer. The portion of this county with the densest concentration of population is outlined and measured at the drawing scale of the map (that is, in square centimeters). The population of the test portion of the county is then divided by the unit dot value to determine the number of dots that are necessary to represent that population. Next, the number of dots is divided by the map area to obtain the number of dots per unit of area.

This value is located on the horizontal axis of the nomograph (for example, 100.0, at point *A*). A vertical line is drawn upward from point *A* until it almost touches the area labeled as the *Zone of Coalescing Dots* (point *B*). A diagonal line is then drawn from the origin of the nomograph until it intersects point *B*. This line is continued until it reaches the scale of dot sizes, which is located around the top and right edges of the nomograph (point *C*). The value indicated on the scale (0.07 cm) is a dot size suitable for testing.

The test of the selected dot size is carried out by using a pen that produces a dot as close to that size as is feasible.[13] When the proper pen size is determined, a piece of the material that will be used for the final drawing is placed over the test area on the map and the required number of dots are drawn within the area. It is a matter of judgment as to whether the result is satisfactory or whether the dot size should be increased or decreased. Ideally, the dots should almost coalesce, so that a maximum density is indicated but the impression of the dot distribution remains. If the test is not satisfactory, it is a simple matter to change the assigned dot value and to use the nomograph to determine the suitable dot size to accommodate the larger or smaller number of dots that are then required. The advantage of using the nomograph is that it provides a quick means of deciding on the practical dot sizes for the repeated tests that are often needed to determine the final, best combination. Examples of the effect of using different dot sizes and unit values are shown in Fig. 9.13.

The second matter of importance in the design of dot distribution maps is the placement of the dots themselves. The goal of the map is to provide a visual impression of the distribution of the actual phenomenon. This is difficult because the data that are used usually indicate information totals for relatively large regions. Within these regions, the dots should be more closely spaced in the areas of dense distribution and spaced farther apart in the sparse areas. Ideally, the spacing of the dots is not mechanical and regular but is varied to represent the transitions between dense and sparse areas in the actual distribution. This means the cartographer must have some knowledge of the distribution pattern, which may require some research prior to drawing the map. If the subject is a particular species of tree that tends to grow close to streams, for example, the stream pattern is taken into account when placing the dots. Although such placement is necessarily somewhat subjective, the result is far more satisfactory than simply randomly placing the dots throughout each mapping unit.

A more mechanical problem that is encountered when placing dots is the influence of the boundaries of the mapping units. Very few phenomena start or stop at the boundaries of the areas for which the data are provided. In most cases, therefore, the boundaries should not influence the placement of the dots. Any tendency

---

[13]Most pen manufacturers provide a table indicating the diameter of each pen point, or the points may be directly calibrated to a certain measure such as millimeters. If such specifications are not available, it is quite simple to produce and measure some sample dots—indeed, this is useful in any case because the dot size produced by a particular pen point varies from material to material.

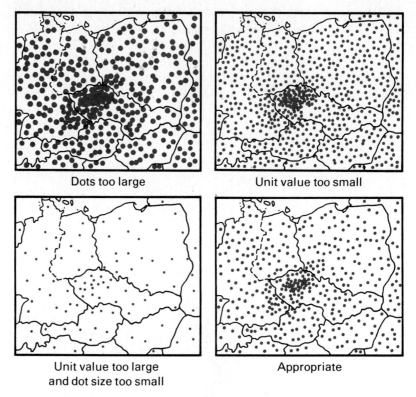

| Dots too large | Unit value too small |

| Unit value too large and dot size too small | Appropriate |

Figure 9.13 Effect of variations in dot values and sizes.

to avoid placing dots next to the boundaries should be avoided, in order to obtain realistic looking results.

The decision to draw a dot distribution map should not be taken lightly. There is a great deal of planning effort and research involved in the preparation of an effective map. In addition, the drafting problems encountered in creating the dots are significant. Tubular pens are often used, but they require a very steady hand; the dots tend to become more oval than round if the pen is not placed down and picked up accurately. The use of transfer or cut-out symbols to create the dots is also feasible. The latter, however, tend to pile up on one another because of the support base that surrounds each symbol. Probably the easiest and most accurate means of obtaining large numbers of perfectly round, consistently sized dot symbols is to use a dot-scribing tool (see Chapter 7). Whichever technique is selected, the time it will take to execute the drawing should not be underestimated.

Choropleth Maps

Information regarding distribution patterns is typically collected and organized on the basis of some existing system of areal units, such as political or administrative regions. Agricultural production, for example, is often reported on a county basis and population characteristics on a census tract basis. *Choropleth maps* use the boundaries of these reporting areas as the basis for mapping the information.

The first step in constructing a choropleth map is to determine the appropriate value to be associated with each area on the map. This is usually obtained from a source such as a census or, less frequently, a special study. Appropriate symbols are next selected to represent each of the categories. The symbolization may consist of different tones, patterns, colors, or a combination of all three. Finally, the map is drawn and the appropriate symbols are placed within the boundaries of each area on the map.

Types of data   Any of the three types of average may be derived for any suitably measured set of data, symbols of the appropriate design selected, and the result mapped.

The values shown on choropleth maps must be independent of the size of the area to which they apply. The total number of kilograms of wheat harvested by county, for example, is not an appropriate piece of information to put in choropleth form. This can be appreciated by considering the case of two counties, one large and the other small. If both counties have the same total output, they might both be represented by the same gray value. The result, however, would be a very misleading representation of the pattern of production; the two counties would appear to be equally productive, whereas the smaller county is much more productive, on a unit basis, than the larger one. Other types of maps, using proportional circles for example, are suitable for showing absolute values. It is necessary, therefore, to convert the information into a suitable form if a choropleth map is to be drawn.

The preparation of the sample data for choropleth mapping involves the computation of the average harvest per unit of area (kilograms per hectare, for example). The result is that the large county has a low output on a unit area basis, which is represented by a light gray value on the map. The small county, on the other hand, has a high output on a unit area basis, which is represented by a dark gray value. The resulting map conveys a more accurate impression of the relative productivity of the two areas.

Other values that are not related to the size of the area involved may be presented in choropleth form. Information such as per capita income, percentage of farms with tractors, the ratio of agricultural to nonagricultural land, and so on, can be mapped directly. This is because the interpretation of their value is not affected by the size of the mapping unit.

Nominal data   Nominal information is portrayed on a choropleth map simply by placing an appropriate symbol over the surface of each zone. In some cases, the categorization of each data zone is obvious. On a political map, for example, the different national territories are distinguished from one another on the basis of national sovereignty. The familiar maps with green for the one country, red for another, and so forth, are representative of this type of map. Other, less obvious, decisions must be made, however, when some types of nominal information are mapped. For example, if a map of forest types is being produced, data may be available regarding the number of hectares covered by each type of tree found in each county. In this case, the modal value (the largest category of tree types in each county) is calculated in order to determine the appropriate symbolization for that county.

Typically, patterns or colors of a similar value or intensity are used to symbolize different categories on a choropleth map of nominal data. It is not appropriate to distinguish such areas by the use of a gradation of gray values, for example, because there is no basis for determining which category should be given a light value and which a dark one—all of the categories are of equal importance. Care must be taken to keep readability in mind when selecting these symbols. Each symbol must be distinctive enough to be readable but, at the same time, garish or visually irritating combinations must be avoided.

Ordinal or ratio data   A range of gray values is often used to differentiate between areas on a choropleth map when ordinal or ratio data are represented. On such maps, the mean of the ratio data or the median of the ordinal data is calculated for each data zone. Then gray values are assigned so that the zone with the lowest average value has the lightest value symbol and the zone with the highest average value has the darkest value symbol.

It is an attractive idea to have a large number of levels in order to present more detail; the greater the number of levels the less generalization involved and the more realistic the representation. Theoretically, this sequence of values could even be continuous—that is, a 1 percent change in gray value could be associated with each 1 percent change in the numerical value being represented.[14] Generalization of the information, however, usually results in a more easily understood map. In practice, therefore, the most common approach is to divide the data into several categories and to assign a particular gray value to each. This process is subject to two main considerations: on one hand, how many categories to use and, on the other, what gray value to associate with each category.

The greater the number of levels the greater the difficulty in selecting gray values that can be distinguished from one another by the user. Even though the human eye can discern contrasts rather easily if two different gray values are placed next to one another, it has a limited ability to compare gray values that are separated from one another and surrounded by a variety of other values. Setting up a scale of gray values wherein each gray value represents a particular data value is therefore rather difficult. The shades of gray must differ from one another considerably in order to be distingishable on the map (see Chapter 8).

The use of differing patterns to indicate relative values is not encouraged. This is, in part, because there is no particular reason for a map reader to relate dots to low numerical values and cross-hatching to high values, for example. More importantly, however, when patterns are used, viewers seem to respond to the apparent gray value and not to the pattern. In essence, then, the use of varying patterns to indicate levels of density or importance is simply a means of obtaining varying gray

[14]See the section of the Suggested Readings entitled "Gray Values."

values. A pattern that reads as a dark value tends to be associated with a high incidence of the variable and one that yields a light value is associated with a low incidence—the pattern itself is of relatively little importance.

When color is available, it is used for the same purpose as gray values—that is, one color is assigned to each data category. This process is subject to some of the same problems as is the use of gray values, as well as to some additional ones.

Color provides a larger selection of easily distinguished hues, chroma and values, so that more data categories can be symbolized than by the use of gray values alone. The use of different hues is limited, however, by two considerations. First, aesthetic considerations provide a constraint. This is not easily defined, but there is no doubt that the use of differing hues for different categories can quickly result in a garish, patchwork appearance. Second, if two hues are used, red and green for example, there is no apparent rationale for selecting red to represent a smaller quantity and green to represent a larger quantity, or vice versa. It does, however, seem to make intuitive sense to use a range of values or chroma within a given hue to represent ordinal or interval quantities. Light blue or blue with low chroma, for example, may be used to indicate small annual rainfall amounts, whereas dark blue or blue with high chroma would indicate large amounts, and intermediate values or chroma would indicate intermediate amounts.

The use of two colors is sometimes permissible. For example, a range of blue values may be used to indicate precipitation above some transitional amount, and a range of browns to indicate smaller quantities. In this case, the darker blue is used to indicate greater moisture and lighter blue less moisture, whereas the brown values are made darker to indicate greater aridity. A similar approach is often taken when a single map shows areas where a given variable is positive, or increasing, and other areas where it is negative, or decreasing. Then, increasing values of one hue indicate greater positive quantities and increasing values of the other hue indicate greater negative quantities. Associations such as this, however, are the exception, and it is most common to limit a range of values to a single hue.

When different chroma of the same hue are used to represent differences in intensity there is a problem in determining the appropriate number of steps to use. This is because the range of chroma available for some colors is not as great as it is for others. When the stronger colors are used (red, for example), this problem is minimized; at the opposite extreme, however, even a strong chroma of yellow is difficult to distinguish. Attempting to break such a light color into a series of steps quickly results in differences that cannot be distinguished from one another.

The arrangement of colors on a map is often very complex; any given color can occur next to any or all of the other colors in different locations on the map. Depending on the colors that surround it, a patch of a given color changes in appearance (Plate 2). This effect, which is the result of simultaneous contrast, increases the difficulty of distinguishing one color from another, either on the map or in the legend. This means that the colors used for the various categories must be different enough to allow the viewer to distinguish between them regardless of their location. Color distinctions that are selected simply because they are subtle and attractive, therefore, are often not practical.

Data classes As was previously discussed, the selection of the break points between data classes is an important part of the design of any map that shows statistical information. The effect of the decision is particularly apparent on choropleth maps, as is shown in Fig. 9.14. This figure shows the same set of data discussed earlier, mapped on the basis of the four data divisions shown in Table 9.4. It is obvious that the very different appearance of each of these maps is simply the result of the classification system; the importance of giving careful consideration to the problem of establishing data classes is, therefore, clearly demonstrated.

Spatial averaging When a choropleth map is produced, the implicit assumption is made that the phenomenon being represented is uniformly distributed throughout each data zone. As was already mentioned, if a particular county produces so many kilograms of wheat on a given number of hectares of land, an average number of kilograms per hectare is calculated for use on a choropleth map. This approach does not recognize the variation in production within the county. There may be areas that are completely taken up with urban land uses, for example, and that produce no wheat at all. Similarly, some areas may be relatively poor agricultural land, whereas others may be productive wheatland. Despite these variations, all of the land within the county is treated on the choropleth map as though it is equally productive.

A major problem with choropleth maps, then, is that the spatial boundaries by which the data are reported are often arbitrary. Because they are set up for administrative or other purposes, they do not necessarily conform to the distribution of the natural or social phenomenon being mapped. In the example given in the previous paragraph, for example, there is no relationship between the boundaries of the county and the boundaries of the various land classifications.

The *spatial averaging* involved in choropleth mapping is acceptable in some circumstances and not in others. This is a function of the type of data involved, as well as of the scale of the map. The entire county may have very little variation in annual rainfall, for example, so that the use of an average value presents no particular problem. On the other hand, the pattern of wheat production may vary so markedly that the use of an average is not acceptable. In either case, however, the final determination of acceptability depends upon the scale of the map. Given sufficient information, a very large-scale map of the rainfall distribution could be drawn and relatively minor variations mapped. In that case, depending upon the purpose of the map, the use of a single average value is not likely to be acceptable. On the other hand, if the county is very small at the final scale, it could be perfectly satisfactory to use a single value, even for the wheat production. The final determination of the suitability of a choropleth map, then, is based on a balance between the variability of the phenomenon over space, and on the scale of the presentation. If the assumptions involved in a particular case are not acceptable, a different type of map, such as a dasymetric map, is required.

INDIANA: Number of Inhabitants per km², 1980

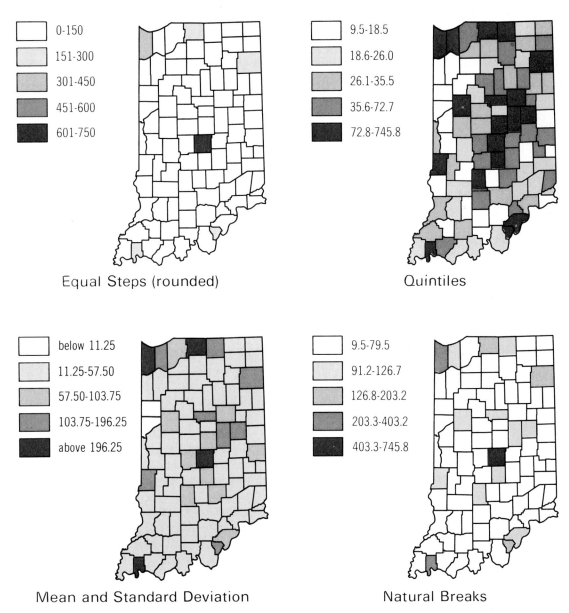

0-150	
151-300	
301-450	
451-600	
601-750	

Equal Steps (rounded)

9.5-18.5	
18.6-26.0	
26.1-35.5	
35.6-72.7	
72.8-745.8	

Quintiles

below 11.25	
11.25-57.50	
57.50-103.75	
103.75-196.25	
above 196.25	

Mean and Standard Deviation

9.5-79.5	
91.2-126.7	
126.8-203.2	
203.3-403.2	
403.3-745.8	

Natural Breaks

Figure 9.14 Choropleth maps based on differing class intervals. See text for explanation.

Dasymetric Maps

It is sometimes possible to obtain information regarding a particular distribution that goes beyond the statistical report. Such information can be used to provide a more realistic picture of a distribution than is shown on a choropleth map, through a process called *dasymetric mapping*.

Dasymetric maps are similar to choropleth maps to the extent that areas within the map are given symbols to indicate the average value of some phenomenon. They differ from choropleth maps, however, in that the areas mapped are not bounded solely by the artificial boundary lines of the data areas. Instead, "natural" boundaries are also taken into account and averages are calculated for each subdivision that is created.

Dasymetric maps are particularly suitable for showing a phenomenon that is not distributed in a uniform and continuously graded manner, but is characterized, instead, by sharp changes in intensity.[15] Population, for example, is frequently distributed in this manner. It is not unusual to find an area that has a high population density (apartments) located next to an area which has a very low density, or none at all (parkland). A choropleth map is not suited to displaying such a distribution because its areal averages do not take into account the variations from place to place within the overall areas (unless the boundaries happen to coincide with the changes in the distribution). At the same time, an isoline type of map is not particularly suitable, either, because it is misleading to portray zones of sharp change by the use of a series of contour lines that imply a gradation (see the section on isoline maps in Chapter 10).

To produce a dasymetric map, additional factors that influence the phenomenon being mapped are taken into account. Soil types, drainage, and surface slope, for example, affect the pattern of agricultural production. If information regarding these variables is available in addition to the agricultural production statistics, the pattern of distribution of each factor and its influence on agricultural production can be taken into account. When this is done, the agricultural patterns shown on the map are modified. Specifically, new spatial averages are computed for a variety of subunits within the original mapping unit. These subunits, and the new averages associated with them, are then mapped using the same techniques that are applied to the production of choropleth maps.

A simple example will clarify the process. Assume there is a county that has three areas within it, each with distinct characteristics related to agricultural production [Fig. 9.15(a)]. One of the areas is urbanized and has no agricultural activity, the second has relatively poor soil and only marginal production, and the third is very productive. The only agricultural production figure available is a total value of output for the county. Assuming this value is $5,000,000, and the county contains 10,000 ha, the average value of production is $500/ha. A choropleth map including

[15]J. K. Wright, "A Method of Mapping Densities of Population with Cape Cod as an Example," *Geographical Review,* 26, no. 1 (January 1936), 103–10.

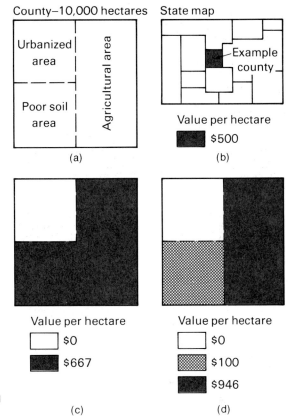

Figure 9.15 Increasing detail based on dasymetric mapping procedures.

this county would therefore show the entire area of the county with the symbol chosen to represent $500/ha [Fig. 9.15(b)].

It is obvious, however, that the figure for the average value of agricultural production in this example is misleading, because one-fourth of the area of the county is urbanized and does not contribute to the total value. It is reasonable, therefore, to divide the county into two parts representing the urban and agricultural areas. A suitable boundary line for this purpose can be obtained from land-use maps, aerial photographs, or a field reconnaissance of the area. The total value of production is then allocated to the agricultural area and a new average is computed. Because 2500 ha of the county is urban, the agricultural area is reduced to 7500 ha and the average value of production for this area is approximately $667/ha ($5,000,000 ÷ 7500 ha). The revised map then shows two areas: the urbanized area with a symbol indicating zero value of production, and the agricultural area with the symbol for $667/ha [Fig. 9.15(c)]. This map is an improvement on the original choropleth presentation.

The process described so far is not complete, however, because there is an area of 2500 ha that has poor soil. This area undoubtedly has a lower value of agricultural production per hectare, which is not yet taken into account. The determination of the value of output to assign to the poor soil area is based on whatever helpful additional information can be obtained. The local agricultural extension agent, for example, may be able to provide an estimate of the probable value of production per hectare in the poor soil area.

Taking the poor soil area into account necessitates an additional computation similar to that already undertaken. In this case, however, some production takes place in the poor soil area, so not all of the dollar value can be allocated to the better production area. The calculation of the new average production value per hectare, in the more productive area, is done by using the following formula:[16]

$$D_n = \frac{D - (D_m \times a_m)}{1 - a_m}$$

where

D = density of the overall region

D_m = estimated density of region m

a_m = fraction of total area in region m

$1 - a_m$ = fraction of total area in region n

D_n = density assigned to region n

The use of this formula removes the portion of the production that occurs in the low-production zone (based on the estimate). The output level in the high-production area is then determined. In this case, $D = \$667/ha$ (calculated for the agricultural area in step 1); $D_n = \$100/ha$ (based on information from the agricultural extension agent); $a_m = 0.33$ (2500 ha of poor soil ÷ 7500 ha of agricultural area). The result is $D_n = [667 - (100 \times 0.33)] \div (1 - 0.33) = 634 \div 0.67 =$ approximately \$946/ha.

The final dasymetric map, which is based on the foregoing computations, shows three areas. Each area is given an appropriate symbol for its value of production per hectare: Area 1, which is residential, \$0/ha; Area 2, which has poor soil, \$100/ha; and Area 3, which has good soil, \$946/ha [Fig. 9.15(d)]. This map could be refined further by obtaining estimates of the effect of additional variables and taking them into account. If this is done, the process of calculating the residual values is carried out in the same manner as in the above example. Each new limitation that is introduced requires assigning a value to the area involved and calculating a new average for the remaining area.

Provided sufficient information is available, the assignment technique described here results in a detailed and realistic product (Fig. 9.16). Personal judgment is involved in the use of this technique. If the work is carefully and responsibly done, however, the result is a more meaningful map than that produced by the simple choropleth mapping process.

Whenever one is examining a choropleth map, it will be helpful to keep Fig.

[16]Wright, "A Method of Mapping Densities."

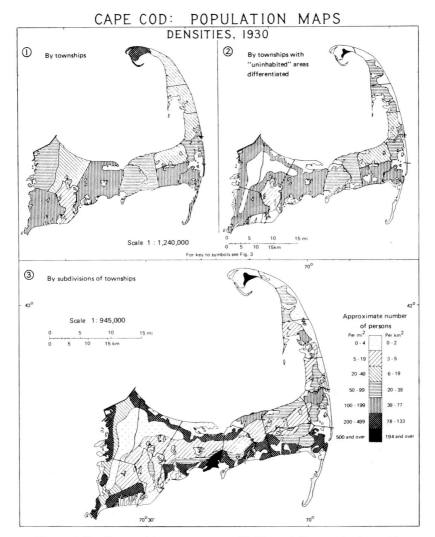

Figure 9.16 Dasymetric map process: (1) Choropleth map, by township; (2) Uninhabited areas differentiated; (3) Final dasymetric map. [Reprinted from J. K. Wright, "A Method of Mapping Densities of Population with Cape Cod as an Example," *Geographical Review,* 26, no. 1 (January 1936), 103–10, by courtesy of the American Geographical Society.]

9.16 in mind. There is a considerable contrast between the relatively realistic representation of the population distribution shown in the dasymetric map and the generalized picture shown in the choropleth map. This same type of generalization is involved, to a greater or lesser degree, in every choropleth map. Indeed, generalization is the hallmark of the choropleth method and, although it is a useful concept, the loss of information that necessarily occurs when it is used should not be overlooked.

Suggested Readings

General

BACHI, ROBERTO, *Graphical Rational Patterns: A New Approach to Graphical Presentation of Statistics.* New York: Israel Universities Press, 1968. Interesting suggestions for a graphic system that uses a progression of patterns to present statistical information.

BIRCH, T. W., *Maps: Topographical and Statistical* (2nd ed.). Oxford: The Clarendon Press, 1964. Part II discusses dot, density, isoline, and other statistical maps.

DICKINSON, GORDON CAWOOD, *Statistical Mapping and the Presentation of Statistics.* London: Edward Arnold; and New York: Crane, Russak & Co. Inc., 1973.

EVANS, IAN S., "The Selection of Class Intervals," *Transactions, Institute of British Geographers,* 2 (new series), no. 1 (1977), 98–124.

JENKS, GEORGE F., "Contemporary Statistical Maps—Evidence of Spatial and Graphic Ignorance," *The American Cartographer,* 3, no. 1 (1976), 11–19.

——, "Generalizations in Statistical Mapping," *Annals of the Association of American Geographers,* 53, no. 1 (March 1963), 15–26.

——, and FRED C. CASPALL, "Error on Choroplethic Maps: Definition, Measurement, Reduction," *Annals of the Association of American Geographers,* 61, no. 2 (June 1971), 217–44.

MCCLEARY, GEORGE F., JR., "How to Design an Effective Graphics Presentation," in *How to Design an Effective Graphics Presentation,* Harvard Library of Computer Graphics, 1981 Mapping Collection, vol. 17, 15–64. Cambridge, Mass.: Harvard University, Laboratory for Computer Graphics and Spatial Analysis, 1981. The topics treated in this chapter are discussed on pp. 34–48.

MACKAY, J. ROSS, "Dotting the Dot Map," *Surveying and Mapping*, 9, no. 1 (January-March 1949), 3–10.

MORRISON, JOEL J., *Method-Produced Error in Isarithmic Mapping,* Technical Monograph No. CA-5. Washington, D.C.: American Congress on Surveying and Mapping, Cartography Division, 1971.

MUEHRCKE, PHILLIP C., *Thematic Cartography.* Washington, D.C.: Association of American Geographers, Commission on College Geography, Resource Paper No. 19, 1972.

STEVENS, S. S., "On the Theory of Scales of Measurement," *Science,* 103 (1946), 677–80.

UNWIN, DAVID, *Introductory Spatial Analysis.* New York: Methuen Inc., University Paperback, 1981.

WRIGHT, J. K., "A Method of Mapping Densities of Population with Cape Cod as an Example," *Geographical Review,* 26, no. 1 (January 1936), 103–10.

Symbol Size

CHANG, KANG-TSUNG, "Circle Size Judgment and Map Design," *The American Cartographer,* 7, no. 2 (October 1980), 155–62.

———, "Visual Estimation of Graduated Circles," *The Canadian Cartographer,* 14, no. 2 (December 1977), 130–38.

COX, CARLETON, W., "Anchor Effects and the Estimation of Graduated Circles and Squares," *The American Cartographer,* 3, no. 1 (April 1976), 65–74.

———, "Adaptation-Level Theory as an Aid to the Understanding of Map Perception," *Proceedings,* American Congress on Surveying and Mapping, Washington, D. C. (1973), 334–59.

CRAWFORD, P. V., "The Perception of Graduated Squares as Cartographic Symbols," *The Cartographic Journal,* 10 (1973), 88.

DOBSON, MICHAEL W., "Refining Legend Values for Proportional Circle Maps," *The Canadian Cartographer,* 11, no. 1 (June 1974), 45–53.

FLANNERY, JAMES J., "The Relative Effectiveness of Some Common Graduated Point Symbols in the Presentation of Quantitative Data," *The Canadian Cartographer,* 8, no. 2 (December 1971), 96–109.

MEIHOEFER, HANS-JOACHIM, "The Visual Perception of the Circle in Thematic Maps—Experimental Results," *The Canadian Cartographer,* 10, no. 1 (June 1973), 63–84.

WILLAMS, ROBERT L., *Statistical Symbols for Maps: Their Design and Relative Values.* New Haven, Conn.: Yale University Map Laboratory, 1956.

Gray Values

CASTNER, H. W., and A. H. ROBINSON, *Dot Area Symbols in Cartography: The Influence of Pattern on Their Perception,* ACSM Monograph No. 4, 20–24. Washington, D. C.: American Congress on Surveying and Mapping, 1969.

CRAWFORD, P. V., "Perception of Grey-Tone Symbols," *Annals of the Association of American Geographers,* 61, (1971), 721–35.

DOBSON, MICHAEL W. "Choropleth Maps Without Class Intervals? A Comment," *Geographical Analysis,* V, no. 4 (October 1973), 358–60.

JENKS, GEORGE F., and DUANE S. KNOS, "The Use of Shading Patterns in Graded Series," *Annals of the Association of American Geographers,* 51, no. 3 (September 1961), 316–34.

KIMERLING, A. JON, "A Cartographic Study of Equal Value Gray Scales for Use with Screened Gray Areas," *The American Cartographer,* 2, no. 2 (October 1975), 119–27.

ROBINSON, ARTHUR H., "'The Curve of the Grey Spectrum,': A Review," *Annals of the Association of American Geographers,* 49, no. 4 (December 1959), 457–60.

SIBERT, JOHN L., "Continuous-Color Choropleth Maps," *Geo-Processing,* 1, no. 3 (November 1980), 207–16.

TOBLER, WALDO R., "Choropleth Maps without Class Intervals?" *Geographical Analysis,* V, no. 3 (July 1973), 262–65.

WILLIAMS, ROBERT L., "Map Symbols: Equal Appearing Intervals for Printed Screens," *Annals of the Association of American Geographers,* 48, no. 2 (June 1958), 132–39.

————, "Map Symbols: 'The Curve of the Grey Spectrum'—An Answer," *Annals of the Association of American Geographers,* 50, no. 4 (December 1960), 487–91.

10

Mapping Spatial Variations: Surfaces

Many phenomena are distributed in continually varying amounts over the earth; the most obvious example is the variation from place to place in the elevation of the surface of the earth itself. With a little reflection, it is apparent that other physical characteristics, which are not so directly observable, can also be represented as *surfaces*. Snow, for example, falls in varying amounts at different locations and accumulates to form an undulating surface; the shape of the surface is a direct reflection of the quantity of snow at various points. Similarly, the quantity of rain that falls is a measure of the surface that would be formed if the rain stayed in the place where it fell. From this point of view, then, observed amounts of rainfall, or other physical quantities, can be used in a manner analogous to terrain elevation measurements.

Other more abstract variables, which are based on average values for given areas, can also be observed and measured as though the amounts involved were equivalent to terrain elevations. Measures of population density, average incomes, average housing values, ratios of crop land to total land area, and the percentage of farms with tractors are examples. Such variables are often treated as areal averages and mapped by choropleth methods, as was discussed in the previous chapter. At times, however, such variables are mapped by using the same techniques that are used to represent physical surfaces.

The concepts used for mapping the physical surface of the earth provide a model for the mapping of other distributions. The locational component, in all cases, is readily related to the system of latitude and longitude, or any other reference system. The measurement component, on the other hand, varies. In the case of the physical surface, the measurement is the elevation of the surface, above some datum, at that particular location. In the case of other physical phenomena, however, the measurements tend to be absolute amounts, such as Celsius degrees or centimeters of rain. When more abstract distributions are shown, a great variety of measures are used, as the listing of sample topics suggests. In general, ratio data are required for the production of maps of surfaces. At times, however, the process of generalization leads to the elimination of detail, so that the result is equivalent to what would be obtained by using ordinal data—the use of layer tints to show elevation zones is an example.

The general techniques of surface representation are described separately in this chapter. Each of the various techniques has particular strengths and weaknesses; some are suitable for presenting actual measurements and others are more effective in providing a visual impression of the shape of the surface. It is common, therefore, for a combination of methods to be used on a single map. In particular, the techniques that have a strong visual impact are often combined with the less visually effective techniques that are more suited for designating specific values. Hachures or hill shading, for example, may be combined with layer tints, or spot values and isolines with hill shading. Combinations such as this allow the advantages of the different techniques to reinforce one another. Although some of the more common combinations of techniques are mentioned, no attempt is made to list all of the combinations which are used from time to time.

Because of the amount of work that has been devoted to the development of techniques for representing terrain surfaces, many of the examples that follow are presented in those terms. There is nothing inherent in most of these techniques, however, that limits them to portraying the physical terrain; in general, a great variety of data can be represented by the use of the same techniques used to represent topographic relief. Despite the interest in showing three-dimensional information on a flat piece of paper, and the value of the process, surface representation presents a difficult challenge for the cartographer. The purpose of this chapter is to discuss a variety of methods that are used to meet this challenge.

SPOT VALUES

The simplest form of surface representation is the use of *spot values* to indicate the measurements that apply at particular points on the surface. A spot value is a small symbol that marks the reference point; the symbol is combined with a number that indicates the value associated with it (Fig. 10.1). Such measurements must be specified in relation to some starting value or datum. In the case of terrain, the datum for the measurement is often mean sea level; in the case of other surfaces, the datum is often a value of zero.

When terrain is represented, some spot values (spot heights) are located at points that are physically monumented benchmarks on the ground. Others are located at unmonumented but important locations such as hilltops, mountain passes, bottoms of depressions, and road intersections. On navigational charts, depth soundings are spot values that show the depth of the water and reveal the location

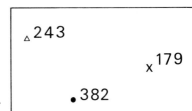

Figure 10.1   Typical spot value symbols.

of channels and of navigational hazards. On maps that show other types of variables, each spot value is located at the observation point where the particular measurement was taken.

Spot values are simple; they are also very accurate for the specific points that are chosen. They do not give a graphic effect of shape, however, nor do they give any indication of the values that exist at locations between the designated points. Because of this limitation, a map viewer cannot easily acquire a good impression of the characteristics of the surface from spot values alone. It is important, therefore, that the placement of spot values be carefully selected in order to give as reliable an indication as possible of the general nature of the surface. In general, spot values are most useful as a means of supplementing one of the other methods of surface representation.

ISOLINES

Isolines are imaginary lines that join points of equal value. Several terms are used to refer to different types of isolines; because these terms tend to fall in and out of fashion, or to be used interchangably, it is very difficult at times to keep them separated. The term *isoline,* for example, is used here to refer to the general class of imaginary lines joining points of equal value, but the terms *isarithm* and *isogram* are sometimes used for the same purpose.

The most easily recognized type of isoline, called an *isometric* line, is based on the measurement of selected points in a *continuous distribution.*[1] A continuous distribution is exemplified by such physical phenomena as the undulation of the earth's surface, the amount of precipitation that falls from place to place, or the temperature observed at different locations. The distinguishing characteristic of such surfaces is that they exist everywhere—even if they are not measured everywhere—and they exist in a continuous form. That is, along a line between point A, which has an elevation of 100 m, and point B, which has an elevation of 200 m, every point has a measurable elevation, either higher or lower. It is not possible, furthermore, for any points to exist whose elevation could not be measured.

An *isopleth,* on the other hand, is an isoline that joins points of equal values that are based on ratios computed for areas. Lines joining points of equal population density are representative of this type. When an average is computed for a region, its value must be arbitrarily assigned to a specific location—the center of the region, for example. It is obvious, however, that if one were to take an observation at the particular point selected, there would be no way to directly observe the abstract concept of population density. In addition, the surface that is represented is not continuous—values between the selected points cannot be observed, and there may be abrupt changes or gaps in values. In the case of the population

[1]The definitions of *isometric lines* and *isopleths* are based on J. Ross Mackay, "Some Problems and Techniques in Isopleth Mapping," *Economic Geography,* 27, no. 1 (January 1951), 1–9.

density in a metropolitan area, for example, there is no necessity for intermediate density values to exist between the high values of the urbanized areas and the low values of the rural areas, or even between different density levels within the urbanized areas. In such a situation the inclusion of a series of intermediate isopleths, which indicate a transition from high to low, is misleading because the value differences are, in reality, abrupt and discontinuous. When this occurs, the intermediate values are sometimes omitted, which is something that could not happen in the case of a contour map of the terrain. It may be more satisfactory, then, to use a different type of map, such as a choropleth, dasymetric, or dot map, to portray such a distribution.[2]

The techniques used for drawing the two types of isolines are virtually identical; it is the basis on which the surface is defined that distinguishes the two types.

In addition to the terms already mentioned, a seemingly endless array of special terms is used to identify isolines that are applied to particular measures. Thus, there are *contours* (elevations), *isobaths* (submarine depths), *isotherms* (temperatures), *isohyets* (rainfall), *isobars* (barometric pressure), *isochrones* (time), and many others. These terms are simply used as a matter of convenience so that long explanatory phrases need not be repeated every time a particular type of line is mentioned. For purposes of this discussion, the distinction between these categories of isolines is not important because they are all treated in the same manner once the data are acquired.

Control Points and Centroids

The process of contouring a surface requires the establishment of *control points*. In a terrain survey the control points are the benchmarks, whose horizontal location and elevation are known. The development of the contour plot based on such a survey is relatively straightforward. In the case of other data, such as rainfall figures, the location of the observation stations is used as the location of the control points. Here, the assumption is that the observations taken at each station reveal the general pattern of the distribution of the phenomenon. It is normally assumed, for example, that the amount of rainfall that occurs midway between two observation stations is the average of the amount that falls at the two stations.

When data are reported as areal averages, however, there is no specific location to which the information is tied. If a county produces a total of 100,000 kg of wheat within an area of 1000 ha for example, the average production figure is 100 kg/ha. This is an artificial figure, however, that does not have a specific location in space—there is no benchmark at which the 100 kg/ha value is located. In such a case, it may still be reasonable to produce an isopleth map but, in order to do so, it is necessary to establish a control point (*centroid*) for each region and to assign the value calculated for the region to that point.

---

[2]Some authors strongly discourage the use of isopleths; see, for example, David Unwin, *Introductory Spatial Analysis* (New York: Methuen, Inc., University Paperbacks, 1981), p. 158. The technique is widely accepted, however, so it is included here along with this cautionary comment.

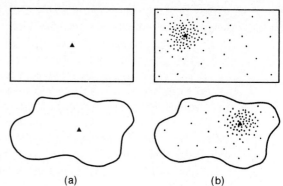

Figure 10.2   Locating centroids: (a)
Geometric center; (b) Center of grav-
ity.   (a)   (b)

The simplest way of defining a control point for an areal average is to place
it at the *geometric center* of the zone to which it refers [Fig. 10.2(a)]. This is not
always the most reasonable approach, however. It may be the case, for instance,
that the principal production area in the previous example is located in the northeast
corner of the county. The control point, therefore, is more logically located if it is
shifted toward the area of concentration; this is called the *center of gravity* concept.
The idea is to find a point that represents the center of the mass of the distribution
rather than the geometric center of the region [Fig. 10.2(b)]. On the other hand, if
the distribution is relatively uniform, the geometric center is a satisfactory location
for the control point.

Plotting Isolines

The most common isoline, as already suggested, is the contour. In the past, contours
were actually surveyed if an accurate line was needed. Today, the derivation of
contours from aerial photography provides a particularly quick and accurate method
of drawing contours (see Chapter 4). In the case of "imaginary" values, where
direct survey or the use of aerial photography does not apply, isolines are drawn
on the basis of control points and a set of logical rules. After the locations of the
control points are determined, lines are drawn joining points of equal value. This
is done by *interpolating* between the control points, using a method called *logical
contouring*.

Logical contouring is based on the assumption that there is a constant, *uniform slope* between each pair of control points. If this is the case, the contour lines
that represent the slopes pass between the control points at logical, predictable
points—hence the term *logical contouring*. The procedures used for logical contouring apply equally well to the plotting of other types of isolines, with the exception that certain clues to placement that are provided by a knowledge of terrain
characteristics are absent for the other types. Such aspects as the generally rare
occurrence of depressions and the tendency for slopes to grade into one another
rather than to change abruptly, serve as general guides for the plotting of contours.

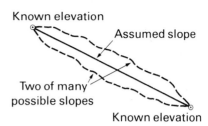

Figure 10.3 Possible slope relationships between two control points.

The more common existence of sharp breaks, with little or no transition, and the lack of any physical limitations on shapes, make the plotting of other isolines more directly dependent on the data.

The logical contouring technique for plotting isolines requires drawing straight lines connecting each control point to its *nearest neighbors*. These lines represent the paths of *cross sections* joining the pairs of control points. In the absence of information to the contrary, the assumption is made that the slope along each cross section is uniform (Fig. 10.3). If an isoline is desired at a value of 10, for example, and two adjacent control points have values of 9 and 11, respectively, it is apparent that the 10 contour will cross the slope line halfway between the two control points. Other isolines are established by similar proportional interpolation procedures (Fig. 10.4).

Other interpolation methods are also used; these usually involve considering a larger portion of the information about the surface than just the value of the adjoining control point. These methods are particularly facilitated by computer techniques that make it possible systematically (and quickly) to take into account the values of more than one neighboring point. The assumption involved, when this is done, is that considering more information about the surface allows a better estimate of the elevation at any given interpolated point.

Isoline Interval

The difference between the values associated with successive isolines is the *isoline interval*. In the case of a terrain map, for example, this interval is called the *contour interval* and is the difference in elevation between two adjoining contours. The se-

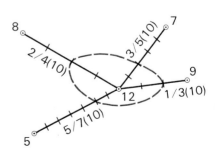

Figure 10.4 Proportional interpolation of values between control points.

lection of the isoline interval is the most important aspect of the design of an isoline map. This is because the horizontal spacing between isolines indicates the relative slope of the surface [Fig. 10.5(a)].

The isoline interval is ideally selected so that, in flat areas, the isolines are close enough together to indicate the slope of the surface. In steep areas, on the other hand, the isolines need to be far enough apart so that other information on the map is not hidden by a clutter of isolines. The isoline interval that is selected, therefore, is a compromise chosen to suit the variation in slope within the area being mapped. If the interval is selected so that the spacing between isolines is not too spread out, an experienced map reader can acquire a rather good understanding of the general shape of the surface from the isoline pattern.

The interval between isolines on any single map is usually constant; at times, however, a variable isoline interval is used. On terrain maps, the variable interval is used to accommodate large variations in surface slope; the wider interval is used in the areas of steep slope and a closer one is used in flatter areas. The interval is more often varied when other types of surfaces are involved, especially when there is a large number of occurrences at either end of the data distribution. Particular care is needed when a variable interval is used, however, because of its effect on the interpretation of the shape of the surface. As already mentioned, when a constant interval is used, the horizontal spacing between isolines provides a clue to the relative steepness of slopes in different areas. If the interval varies, on the other hand, the same horizontal spacing between isolines does not mean the same vertical difference; thus the determination of shape becomes very difficult [Fig. 10.5(b)].

Because isolines are continuous lines, they provide a more comprehensive

Figure 10.5   Relationship between slope and spacing of isolines: (a) Equal vertical interval between isolines allows interpretation of slope by examination of horizontal spacing between isolines. (b) Variable vertical interval between isolines confuses interpretation of slope.

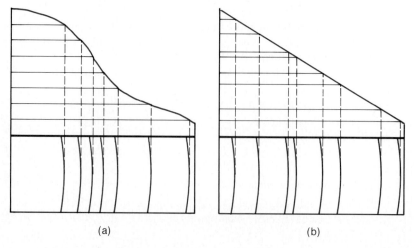

(a)   (b)

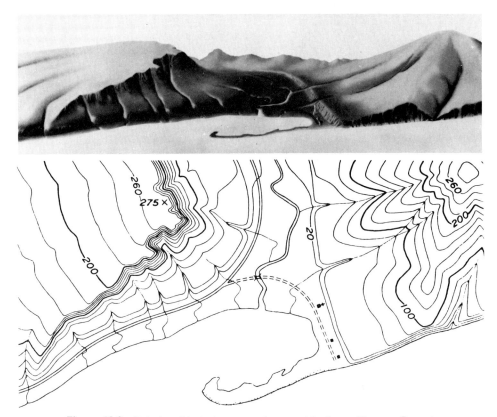

Figure 10.6   Relationship between surface and isolines. (Source: Department of the Interior, U. S. Geological Survey.)

method of displaying a surface than do spot values. The curvature of the lines provides the map viewer with a more graphic impression of the shape of the surface (Fig. 10.6). When isolines are used, however, it is not possible for the map user to determine an exact value for every point on the map. It is possible, on the other hand, to estimate values, even for points that are not located directly on an isoline. The accuracy of such estimates depends on the isoline interval and the variability of the surface. If the surface is quite regular, for example, a point whose horizontal location is halfway between two isolines can reasonably be expected to have a value halfway between that of the two isolines. If the surface is irregular, however, such an estimate can be in considerable error because the point might actually lie anywhere between the two values or, depending on the accuracy of the representation, even beyond those values.

Isolines are often supplemented by spot values. This combination has the advantage that the general shape of the surface is indicated by the isolines, whereas the values at significant locations on the surface are specified by the spot values, even though they are not located on an isoline.

LAYER TINTS

The area between two isolines can be thought of as a value zone within which all locations have values below the value of the upper isoline and above the value of the lower one. On a *layer-tinted map,* each value zone is indicated by printing a distinctive color or tone between the bounding isolines in order to make the zones clearly visible (Plate 9).

The truth of the assumption that the values within a given zone all fall within the limits established by the isolines depends, in part, on the accuracy of the original mapping. It also depends on the scale and level of generalization of the final map. The smaller the scale of the map the greater the generalization, which increases the likelihood of including significantly higher or lower values within a value zone.

The main disadvantage of layer-tinted maps is that they do not differentiate internal variations within each layer. There is, therefore, no direct way to know whether there is considerable local variation in values in one region, which is shown by a particular layer tint, as compared with the local variation in another region, which is shown by the same tint.

Layer tints are sometimes printed in gray values, with the darker tones usually used to represent higher values. When colors are used, a progression of hues is often used. This progression typically starts with cool greens and yellows in the lower elevations. Warmer oranges, browns, and reds are then used in the upper elevations and white is often reserved for the very highest elevations. The idea behind these color choices is that the warm colors in the upper elevations will appear to advance toward the eye, whereas the cool colors in the lower elevations will retreat. The overall effect of these relatively advancing or retreating colors should be to give a feeling of three dimensions. Unfortunately, there is little evidence that the colors actually yield such a three-dimensional effect. Layer tints are useful, however—map users tend to recognize their meaning because they are so frequently encountered on wall maps and in atlases.

Terrain Representation

On small-scale physical maps, such as those typically found in atlases, *form lines* are used instead of contours to outline the elevation zones. Form lines are very generalized contours and therefore serve to give only a general impression of the elevation zones within a region; there may be considerable elevation variation within what appears to be a zone of uniform elevation.

When terrain is being represented, the color sequence that has been described has the potential for misinterpretation. In particular, there may be a tendency to associate the colors with climatic and vegetation characteristics instead of elevation; green, for example, is often associated with moisture and green vegetation. Thus, when a green lowland color is printed in Death Valley, a region not noted for its green vegetation, the potential for confusion exists.

ILLUMINATED ISOLINES

The technique of *illuminated isolines* involves a modification of the usual isoline map.[3] In this method, the isolines are drawn as though they were illuminated by a light source shining from the upper left corner of the map. The overall effect of light and shadow on the isolines gives a strong feeling of three dimensions.

The impression of illumination of the isolines is obtained through the use of two values of one color plus white. The overall map area is covered with an intermediate value of gray or of a basic color such as blue. The isolines on the side oriented toward the light source are shown as white lines against the intermediate background, in order to give the impression that a light is shining on them. The isolines on the side away from the source, on the other hand, are shown as dark lines, as though they are in shadow (Fig. 10.7).

An advantage of the illuminated isolines, in addition to the visual effect of relief, is that the isolines can be read in the usual way. The possibility of measuring

Figure 10.7   Illuminated isolines. [Reprinted from Kitirô Tanaka "The Relief Contour Method of Representing Topography on Maps," *Geographical Review,* 40, no. 3 (July 1950), 444–56, with the permission of the American Geographical Society.]

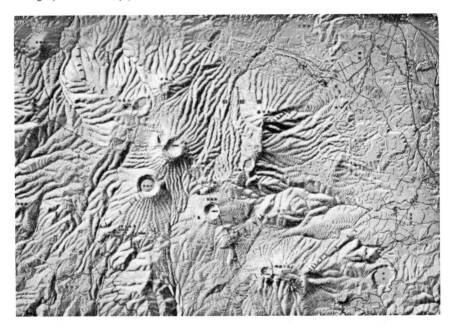

[3]The original application of this technique was to the representation of physical relief: Kitirô Tanaka, "The Relief Contour Method of Representing Topography on Maps," *The Geographical Review,* 40, no. 3 (July 1950), 444–56. As with other techniques, however, it may also be applied to the representation of other surfaces.

and estimating values is retained. Unfortunately, however, the technique gives the unrealistic impression that the surface is divided into layers rather than being made up of continuous slopes.

PLANIMETRICALLY CORRECT INCLINED CONTOURS

The technique of *planimetrically correct inclined contours* is based on drawing a series of profiles through a surface.[4] The usual profile is drawn as a vertical cross section through a surface (Fig. 10.8). When the method of inclined contours is used, however, the profiles are traced on a series of inclined planes. Taken together, these profiles depict an apparent surface that is a representation of the surface variations in the mapped area. The impression conveyed is a view of the surface from a vantage point located in front of the mapped area and above it [Fig. 10.9(d)].

The method has the advantage of quite simple and rapid construction. A series of closely spaced horizontal guide lines is first drawn over an isoline map [Fig. 10.9(a) and (b)]. The spacing between these lines is based on the slope of the planes on which the profiles are drawn. The greater the distance between lines the greater the slope of the planes and the greater the exaggeration of the apparent surface variation. The readings referred to in this section should be consulted for further information regarding the selection of the slope and the spacing of the profiles.

Figure 10.8   Relationship between isolines and profile.

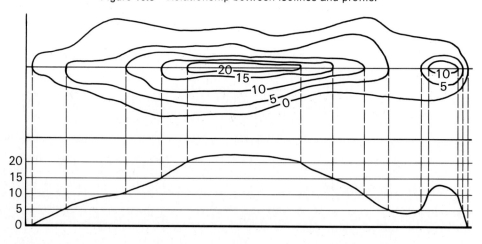

[4]See Arthur H. Robinson and Norman J. W. Thrower, "A New Method of Terrain Representation," *Geographical Review,* 47, no. 4 (October 1957), 507–20. See also, Kitirô Tanaka, "The Orthographical Relief Method of Representing Hill Features on a Topographical Map," *Geographical Journal,* 79 (1932), 213–19. The approach taken here is that the method is useful for the general representation of surfaces. Professor Robinson has already made this suggestion in "The Cartographic Representation of the Statistical Surface," *International Yearbook of Cartography,* 1 (1961), 53–63.

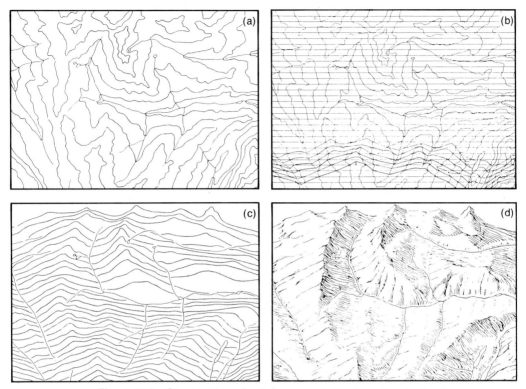

Figure 10.9 Construction of relief representation based on inclined contours. See text for explanation. [Adapted from Arthur H. Robinson and Norman J. W. Thrower, "A New Method of Terrain Representation," *Geographical Review,* 47, no. 4 (October 1957), 507–20, with the permission of the American Geographical Society.]

The horizontal guidelines are drawn on an overlay, so that the base map remains intact. The drawing of the profiles is done on the same overlay, usually in a different color, in order to avoid confusion. The first profile is started at the intersection of one of the horizontal lines with lowest-valued isoline. A line is drawn connecting this initial point with the intersection of the next higher horizontal line with the next higher-valued isoline. When the profile crosses a lower-valued isoline, on the other hand, the line is drawn on a downward slope. This process is continued until the profile is completed. Additional profiles are drawn, with one profile for every horizontal line, until the entire map area has been treated.

The final step is to trace, on a second overlay, only the profiles themselves. The map features are then added, in their correct planimetric position, by tracing from the base map [Fig. 10.9(c)].

When the drawing is completed, the effect obtained is of a three-dimensional surface viewed from a vantage point located at an angle above the surface. Despite the apparently angled view, however, all of the map features remain in their proper planimetric location. This means that none of the map features are hidden or displaced, so the completed drawing can be used in the same manner as an ordinary map. The lack of planimetric displacement is in contrast to block diagrams and physiographic diagrams, discussed later in this chapter. There is, however, a problem involved in the interpretation of slopes because "neither the density of the traces nor their angle from the horizontal is a strict indication of the declivity of the surface."[5]

Computer programs are now available to create inclined contour maps automatically (see Chapter 11). This should make it more feasible to use the method, because the computer speeds up the plotting process as well as producing a more consistent and accurate plot. The use of computers and plotters makes it easier to experiment with various settings to find the most effective spacing of profiles and angle of view for a particular area.

HACHURES

In the historical development of terrain representation, the technique known as *hachuring* is noteworthy, even though it is seldom used on modern maps. Hachuring involves the systematic drawing of lines that are placed to "run with the slope" of the surface being represented. In the case of a physical terrain surface, for example, each individual hachure line traces down the slope in the same direction as water would flow if it were dropped on the surface. In addition, the length of the hachures varies inversely with the degree of slope. That is, on a steep slope, the hachures are short, just as the contours on such a slope would be closely spaced. On a flat slope, where the contours would be farther apart, the hachures are longer lines.

In one version of the hachuring technique (called the Lehmann system), the width of the hachures is also varied. In this system, the lines are wide where the slope is steep and are narrow where it is flat. This works well, in concert with the variations in length, to give a feeling of three dimensions to the map. In another version, the width of the hachures is varied in order to give a shadow effect. In this case, the lines on the presumed shadow slope are wider than those on the presumed illuminated slope, giving the effect of shadows (Fig. 10.10).

One problem with hachuring is that the mass of lines conflicts with the other detail on the map. Two methods are used to reduce this conflict. First, white spaces (windows) are provided around the symbols and lettering, so that they are more easily read. Second, the hachures are printed in a lighter color, such as gray or brown. Both approaches reduce the conflict of the hachures with the other map detail but, at the same time, slightly reduce the effectiveness of the terrain representation.

[5]Theodore M. Oberlander, "A Critical Appraisal of the Inclined Contour Technique of Surface Representation," *Annals of the Association of American Geographers,* 58, no. 4 (December 1968), 802–13. This article should be consulted for suggestions on how to deal with this problem.

Figure 10.10 Hachures. (Portion of French Hydrographic Chart.)

Even though a well-done hachuring job gives an excellent representation of a surface, especially in areas with considerable undulation, the technique is little used today. This is partly because of the problems mentioned in the previous paragraph. The process is also very time-consuming and demanding, and requires that workers have considerable training and practice to do it effectively. Even if workers are trained in the technique, therefore, its cost is prohibitive for most applications.

VACUUM-FORMED MAPS

Individual *three-dimensional models* are sometimes built to effectively represent the terrain of a region. Such models are typically constructed in *layers*. Each layer is cut to the shape of the contour of the elevation it represents. The individual layers are then aligned, one over the other, and built up to create the three-dimensional relief. The steplike appearance that results is often smoothed with a modeling material so that a more realistic, smooth slope is created. Because of the specialized techniques involved in their construction, as well as their relative expense and rarity, terrain models are not described in detail here. *Vacuum-formed maps* are commonly produced, however, which are, in all respects, three-dimensional models of the surfaces to be shown. Although terrain surfaces are most commonly represented (Fig. 10.11), other surfaces can be modeled just as easily.

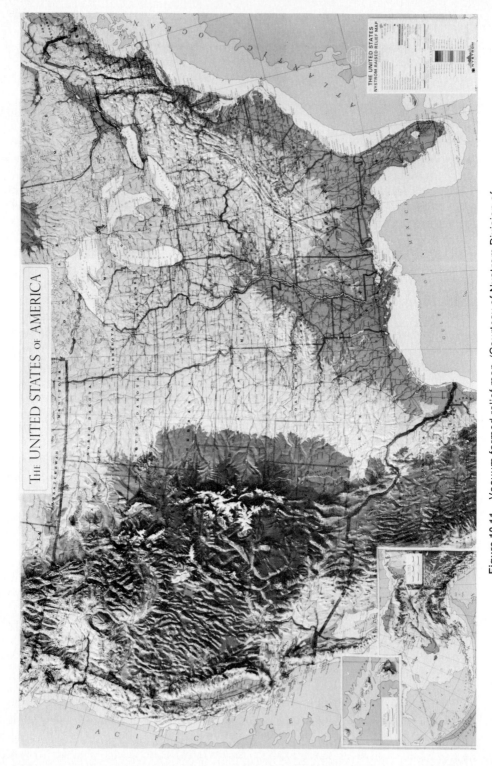

Figure 10.11 Vacuum-formed relief map. (Courtesy of Nystrom Division of Carnation Co.)

The production of vacuum-formed maps involves printing a map of the desired region in the normal manner, except that the printing is done on a sheet of plastic instead of on paper. This printed sheet is placed over a three-dimensional model of the surface that is to be shown. This model is constructed to the same horizontal scale as the map. The printed sheet is then heated and air is evacuated from behind it, so that a vacuum is formed between the sheet and the relief model. The resulting air pressure on the surface of the sheet, which is easily deformed when heated, presses it down over the model. When the sheet cools, it retains the three-dimensional shape of the model.

In the case of a terrain map, it is usual for the relief model used in the vacuum-forming process to be constructed with some *vertical exaggeration*. That is, the vertical scale is greater than the horizontal scale. Vertical exaggeration is usually necessary in order to obtain sufficient relief to give a visually satisfactory effect. If the vertical scale is the same as the horizontal scale, the elevation of even major terrain features usually appears to be very slight in comparison to their horizontal extent. The vertical exaggeration varies from map to map, even between maps of the same horizontal scale and, at times, even in different areas of the same map. This variation occurs because of differences in the amount of relative relief in different areas. Generally, less exaggeration is needed in areas of greater relief, whereas more is needed in areas that are relatively flat. The amount of vertical exaggeration that is used is usually determined on the basis of experience and judgment. Ideally, several samples of the particular area that is being represented are tested, each with a different amount of exaggeration, before a final selection is made. Similarly, a vertical scale suitable for other surfaces is usually selected on the basis of experimentation.

Vacuum-formed maps are very literal graphic representations of surfaces. They are somewhat awkward to use for many traditional purposes, such as tracing information, measuring distances, and so on, and are more difficult to store than is a flat map. They do, however, provide an excellent, easily understood graphic display.

HILL SHADING

It is possible to produce flat maps that give the effect of three dimensions by photographing an obliquely illuminated model from overhead. The image of the shadows cast on the model, when printed over a base map, gives a strong general impression of the shape of the surface that is represented. In practice, an actual model is seldom used, for several reasons. First, there is the factor of the time and expense involved in creating the model itself. In addition, however, the shadows cast on the model do not create a uniformly effective result. Features that are aligned with the light source appear too subdued, for example, whereas those that run perpendicular to a line from the light source are exaggerated. Also, shadows sometimes fall across depressions onto slopes that are facing the light source, creating a somewhat confusing image. Finally, the fact that the photograph is a per-

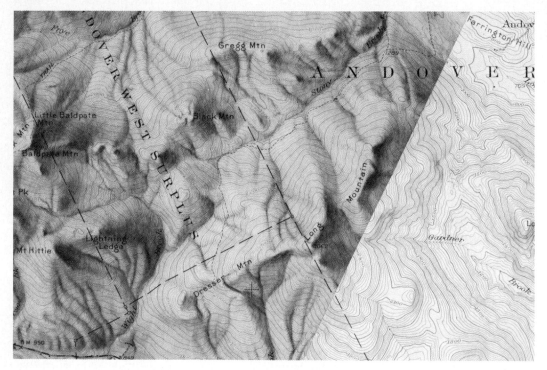

Figure 10.12 The right-hand portion of this illustration shows a contour version of a standard USGS topographic map. Hill shading has been added to the left-hand portion of the same map.

spective view, rather than an orthographic view, also works against the use of a photograph of a model. Because of these difficulties, the effect of shadow on an undulating surface is most often obtained by a technique called *hill shading* instead of by using a photograph of a model.[6]

When hill shading is to be included on a map, an additional separation drawing is produced as part of the production process. On this drawing, the effect of a surface is created by the use of continuous-tone shading that simulates shadows. The shading is usually done with an airbrush, although pencil, charcoal, or other materials are also used. The shading is usually done on a paper or plastic overlay, which is placed over an isoline drawing. Alternatively, a blue line image of the isolines is applied to a sheet of drawing paper; the blue lines are bleached away after the shading is done. When it is completed, the shaded drawing is photographed on a halftone negative. The negative is used to produce a plate that is printed in combination with the linework used for the other map features (Fig. 10.12).

Hill shading is normally done as though the light source is located above the upper left corner of the map. This general orientation is used so that the shadows

---

[6]A number of terms are used for this approach, including *shaded relief, terrain shading*, and *plastic shading*.

appear to fall toward the viewer. If the shadows are allowed to fall away from the viewer the result is a so-called *pseudoscopic effect;* that is, the elevations look like depressions and the depressions look like elevations. This is the same phenomenon encountered in the stereoscopic viewing of aerial photographs, and the reasons for it are not well understood.

The general effect of a hill-shaded drawing is similar to the effect of shadows cast by a model. The shading does not, however, exactly duplicate the behavior of actual shadows. One of the differences is that, in hill shading, the shadows from a high point are not cast across a depression onto the slope on the opposite side, even when the depression is narrow and deep, as they would be if actual shadows were being cast. Another difference is that hill shading allows a shifting of the light source. Although the main source of light is assumed to be the upper left corner of the map, the direction may be varied somewhat to improve the rendering of the surface features that run parallel with the orientation of the lighting source. In this case, the apparent source is shifted so that effective shading is produced. This type of variation is difficult to achieve by shifting the actual source of light on a model. For this reason, as well as for reasons of time and cost of construction, hill-shaded maps are often an improvement on photographs of terrain models.

BLOCK DIAGRAMS

A *block diagram* is a pictorial representation of a surface, drawn from a viewpoint in space (Fig. 10.13). The viewpoint, however, is from an angle and is not the vertical viewpoint of a map. Although the oblique angle of view allows a three-dimensional impression to be obtained, it has the disadvantage that it introduces planimetric displacement of the features on the diagram. The top of an elevation, for example, appears to be shifted away from its map location. Another disadvantage of an oblique viewing angle is that elevated features on the diagram hide from view those portions of the area that are located behind them.

Because of planimetric displacement, and the hidden areas that occur, the selection of the viewpoint, both in terms of altitude and direction of view, is an important element in planning each diagram. Some angles of view are more effective than others for a particular region, because of the shape of the surface and because different areas become visible or hidden as the viewpoint changes. The backs of elevated areas are blocked from view, for example, as are portions of features behind them, and the specific areas that are hidden must be chosen with the purpose of the diagram in mind. Computer methods are available for the creation of block diagrams. When they can be utilized, these methods have the great advantage that any desired point of view can be quickly and easily tested by changing the instructions to the computer (see Chapter 11).

For ease of drawing, many block diagrams utilize an isometric construction method. The isometric approach has an unfortunate result, however, because it causes the block to appear to tilt up at the back [Fig. 10.14(a)]. For this reason, the more realistic perspective view is sometimes preferred [Fig. 10.14(b)]. In perspective,

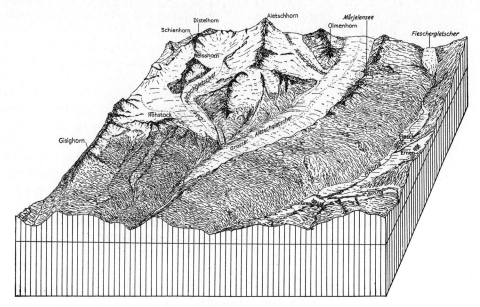

Figure 10.13 Block diagram of a typical portion of the Swiss Alps. [Source: Armin K. Lobeck, *Geomorphology, An Introduction to the Study of Landscapes* (New York: McGraw-Hill, 1939), with permission of the publisher.]

more distant points are relatively smaller, and the lines taper toward the vanishing points, thus removing the appearance of tilt that occurs in an isometric view.

If terrain is being represented, it is frequently necessary to exaggerate the vertical scale of a block diagram in order to make the apparent relief visually significant. The amount of vertical exaggeration that is needed depends on the local relief and the scale of the diagram; it is usually determined by experimentation with the particular area being shown, as is the case with vacuum-formed maps. The final selection of the vertical scale of any diagram, whether it represents terrain or an

Figure 10.14 Comparison between isometric and perspective blocks.

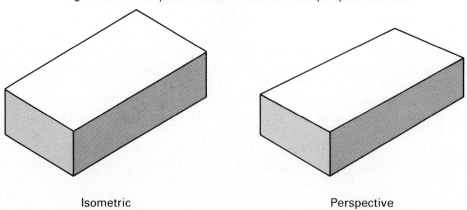

Isometric   Perspective

abstract surface, is made on the basis of a subjective judgment as to what is effective. Computer methods also allow flexible testing of different vertical exaggerations.

Method

The process of drawing an isometric block diagram without computer assistance is relatively straightforward and is described here. The perspective method is briefly compared to it.

First, the area to be drawn is selected and outlined on the source map. This area is viewed from one of its corners, which is selected so that important features are not hidden in the final view. A reference grid is drawn over the map and an isometric version of the same grid is prepared on a separate drawing sheet [Fig. 10.15(a) and (b)]. The map view is then transferred onto the isometric view, using the method of similar figures (see Chapter 5).

A construction overlay is needed next. On this overlay, the highest-valued isoline is traced from the isometric view [Fig. 10.15(c)]. The overlay is then shifted upward along the vertical axis by the correct amount to account for the vertical distance to the next isoline. The amount of shift is chosen to provide the desired vertical scale. When the overlay is in the new position, the next isoline is traced. This process is continued until all of the isolines are transferred. As the isolines are drawn, any hidden lines that are encountered are omitted. Finally, details such as roads, rivers, and any other features that are desired are added to the drawing.

If the isoline network is dense enough, a three-dimensional effect is obtained without additional drawing. Adding slope lines or shadows usually enhances the effect, however [Fig. 10.15(d)]. The amount of work done at this stage, and the effect obtained, depends on the artistic ability of the person doing the drawing.

Perspective block diagrams use the same basic approach as isometric ones. In perspective, however, the network of squares is drawn with reference to either one or two vanishing points, using standard perspective drawing techniques. Because both the horizontal and vertical scales decrease from the front of the perspective diagram to the back, it is more difficult to plot the correct location of the terrain features on a perspective drawing. Although perspective block diagrams have a more realistic appearance, they have the same drawbacks as the isometric version—planimetric displacement and blocking of a portion of the surface.

PHYSIOGRAPHIC DIAGRAMS

Physiographic diagrams, or *landform maps,* are pictorial techniques used for the representation of relief, especially on small-scale maps.[7] These diagrams are designed to represent the relief features in a relatively generalized way, but with an

---

[7]Erwin J. Raisz, "The Physiographic Method of Representing Scenery on Maps," *Geographical Review,* 21, no. 2 (April 1931), 297–304. Although these techniques could be used for the representation of other types of surfaces, the idea does not seem to be worth pursuing. For this reason, physiographic diagrams are presented specifically in terms of terrain representation.

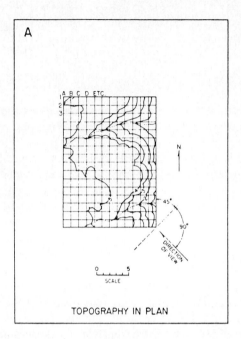

TOPOGRAPHY IN PLAN

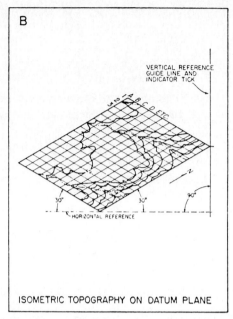

ISOMETRIC TOPOGRAPHY ON DATUM PLANE

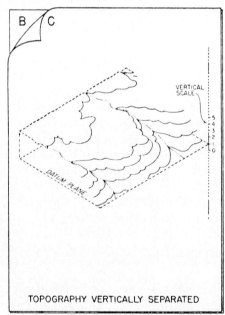

TOPOGRAPHY VERTICALLY SEPARATED

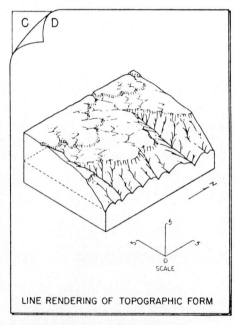

LINE RENDERING OF TOPOGRAPHIC FORM

Figure 10.15 Construction of isometric block diagram. [Reprinted from John R. Stacy, "Terrain Diagrams in Isometric Projection—Simplified," *Annals of the Association of American Geographers,* 48, no. 3 (September 1958), 232–6, with permission.]

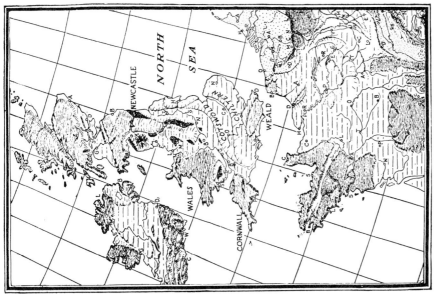

Figure 10.16 Physiographic diagrams: (a) France. [Reprinted from Erwin J. Raisz, "The Physiographic Method of Representing Scenery on Maps," *Geographical Review*, 21, no. 2 (April 1931), 297–304, by courtesy of the American Geographical society.] (b) The coastal plain of England and France. [Source: Armin K. Lobeck, *Geomorphology, An Introduction to the Study of Landscapes* (New York: McGraw-Hill, 1939), with permission of the publisher.]

345

effect that gives an impression of realism. The drawing is done from a bird's-eye viewpoint, as though the observer were located above the terrain, looking down on it obliquely. The goal is not to represent the actual individual features but, rather, to classify the types of terrain found in an area and to portray it by the use of standardized and simplified symbols (Fig. 10.16).

This type of drawing contains a basic contradiction, which is that the features themselves are shown from an *oblique* point of view even though they are drawn on a planimetric base. This combination, of course, could not actually occur in nature—it is a form of artistic license. One additional problem with terrain drawing is that some of the terrain is hidden behind other features, as also happens on block diagrams. The extent to which this characteristic is important is a function of the type of terrain involved and the point of view selected. Despite its problems, a well-done terrain drawing is an effective form of representation.

Suggested Readings

KEATES, J. S., "Techniques of Relief Representation," *Surveying and Mapping,* 21, no. 4, (December 1961), 459–63.

LOBECK, ARMIN KOHL, *Block Diagrams* (2nd ed.). Amherst, Mass.: Emerson-Trussell Book Co., 1958.

MACKAY, J. ROSS, "Some Problems and Techniques in Isopleth Mapping," *Economic Geography,* 27, no. 1 (January 1951), 1–9.

———, "An Analysis of Isopleth and Choropleth Class Intervals," *Economic Geography,* 31, no. 1 (January 1955), 71–81.

OBERLANDER, THEODORE M., "A Critical Appraisal of the Inclined Contour Technique of Surface Representation," *Annals of the Association of American Geographers,* 58, no. 4 (December 1968), 802–13.

RAISZ, ERWIN J., "The Physiographic Method of Representing Scenery on Maps," *Geographical Review,* 21 (1931), 297–304.

ROBINSON, ARTHUR H., "The Cartographic Representation of the Statistical Surface," *International Yearbook of Cartography,* 1 (1961), 53–63.

———, and NORMAN J. W. THROWER, "A New Method of Terrain Representation," *Geographical Review,* 47, no. 4 (October 1957), 507–20.

SLOANE, ROSCOE C., and JOHN M. MONTZ, *Elements of Topographic Drawing* (2nd ed.). New York and London: McGraw-Hill Book Co. Inc., 1943.

STACY, J. R., "Terrain Diagrams in Isometric Projection—Simplified," *Annals of the Association of American Geographers,* 48, no. 3 (September 1958), 232–36.

TANAKA, KITIRÔ, "The Orthographical Relief Method of Representing Hill Features on a Topographical Map," *Geographical Journal,* 79 (1932), 213–19.

————, "The Relief Contour Method of Representing Topography on Maps," *Geographical Review,* 40, no. 3 (July 1950), 444–56.

YOELI, PINHAS, "Relief Shading," *Surveying and Mapping,* 19, no. 2 (June 1959), 229–32.

11

Computer-Assisted Cartography

The computer "revolution" is now a major factor in the field of cartography. In many ways, computer-assisted cartographic techniques are in their infancy and problems of cost, lack of specialized equipment, lack of expertise, and so on, have frequently prevented their widespread use. Nevertheless, as these problems are overcome, the scope of computer applications is increasing rapidly. It is, therefore, both desirable and necessary for cartographers to develop an understanding and appreciation of some of the possibilities that are, and will be, available. The uses discussed here are not the limited computational uses that are commonly thought of in connection with computers. Instead, they involve the use of the computer as a means of acquiring, storing, and manipulating map information, as well as of producing the maps themselves.

As computer techniques come to be applied more extensively to cartography, the power and capabilities of the computer will be used to solve many of the traditional cartographic problems. The computer is a new, powerful, and flexible tool that has been added to the more traditional pen, ink, and paper that the cartographer has used for generations. It has the potential to enhance the role of the cartographer in many ways, because the computer may be used to accomplish some of the more mundane tasks associated with cartography, leaving the cartographer free to spend his or her time and effort on the more creative aspects. The speed of computer techniques, for example, often allows the cartographer to test several potential solutions to a particular problem—a luxury that was often not available with traditional techniques. Even this simple advantage should result in the production of more effective maps.

The use of computers in map production provides opportunities for increasing the speed, flexibility, and accuracy of many aspects of the mapping process. This chapter presents an overview of the role of the computer in cartography, drawing on the background of the more traditional approaches discussed in the preceding chapters. The field of computers, including the applications of computers to cartography, is changing so rapidly that this discussion cannot hope to fully encompass the field, nor can it offer descriptions of every one of the very latest techniques, equipment, and applications. The descriptions that are provided, therefore, are divorced, insofar as possible, from specific pieces of equipment or systems; they are presented in the barest form, so that the principles involved are the focus of the discussion. If the principles are understood, the specifics can be fitted into the over-all framework with a minimum of difficulty.

OVERVIEW OF ELECTRONIC DATA PROCESSING

Before one can understand and appreciate the application of computers to car-tographic processes it is necessary to have a basic idea of the operation of *electronic data processing* (EDP) systems. These systems involve two distinct entities: *hardware* and *software.* Hardware consists of a variety of equipment, such as input, output, and storage devices. Software, on the other hand, consists of the instructions, programs, and data that are devised by (or furnished to) the user and entered into the computer in order to accomplish the required processing and to produce the desired output.

An EDP system consists of four main components (Fig. 11.1). The central component of the system is known as the *central processing unit* (CPU). The CPU is divided into three subcomponents: the *arithmetic logic unit,* the *control section,* and the *main memory.* The remaining components are the *peripheral devices*: the *input unit, output unit,* and *secondary memory.*

The general functions of these components are as follows. The input component provides the means by which data and instructions are transmitted to the main mem-ory, where they are stored, as directed by the control section. Depending on the manipulations required for a particular job, data are pulled from and stored in the main memory (and the secondary memory, if additional space is needed), and are subjected to various transformations in the arithmetic logic unit. Upon completion of these operations, the final result is transferred from memory to the output com-ponent, where it is made available to the user.

Figure 11.1 Relationship between components of a typical EDP system.

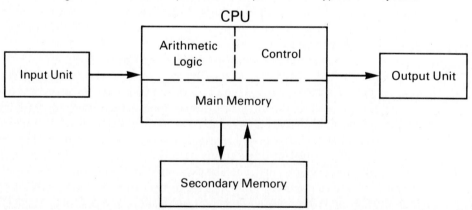

Peripheral Devices

A variety of input, output, and storage devices may be connected to the CPU and this section describes those devices that are particularly useful in cartographic applications. The devices used in a specific application are selected on the basis of the types of information to be handled, the form of output needed by the user, and the characteristics of the particular computer system that is being utilized.

Input devices translate the data and the control programs that are provided by the user into a form that can be accepted by the CPU. Output devices, on the other hand, communicate to the user the results of the manipulations that the computer has carried out, based on the data and instructions provided. Some devices serve both an input and an output function.

One of the main advantages gained by using computer techniques in cartographic applications is that both data and programs may be saved for later use and do not have to be newly created for every project. This is a very powerful advantage that allows a maximum amount of flexibility, as well as saving a great deal of time when a variety of final maps is needed, each based on selected portions of the existing data. Storage devices provide a means of retaining processed information for future use.

Card devices   Data or instructions may be *punched* into Hollerith cards (the type of computer card that is frequently encountered in daily usage, such as computerized billings). This is done with a punching device that looks and operates much like an electric typewriter. There may be as many as 80 columns on each card, and each column may contain one or more punches. In each column, the location of one or more punches stands for a specific letter, number, or symbol. A series of these cards is fed into a special reader that translates the punches into electronic impulses and transmits the data or instructions contained on the cards to the CPU. Card punch output devices produce punched cards of the same type under the control of the computer.

The same cards that are used to input a particular program or set of data, or that are produced as the output from a program, are also a means of storing information from one use to the next. In fact, for a number of years, punched cards were the principal means of storing information. While they are still used, other models have become predominant. This is partly because the card decks that are needed to store a large amount of data are very bulky and awkward to handle, and are rather fragile (hence all the well-known admonitions against folding, punching, stapling, and mutilating). The process of reading the cards and loading the information they contain into the computer is also comparatively time-consuming, even with high-speed readers.

Information may also be stored on cards, similar to punched cards, that have a strip of magnetic tape along one edge. The information is electronically recorded on the tape instead of being punched into the card. This type of card, which is not too common, has characteristics similar to those of punched cards, with the exception that changes can be made in the stored data by deleting from or adding to the magnetic record.

Paper-tape devices Data or instructions can be punched into a roll of "ticker tape" by a special punch and the tape fed into a reading device. Each letter, number, or symbol is represented by a particular pattern of punches in the tape. These patterns are converted into electronic form and are transmitted to the computer in the same manner as are the patterns on punched cards, although the patterns themselves are different. Paper-tape output punches are similar to card punches but they produce punched paper tapes rather than cards.

The general characteristics of punched paper tapes as a storage mode are very similar to the characteristics of punched cards. They are relatively slow and inconvenient as compared with other modes, and their use is becoming less frequent.

Terminals Instead of creating punched cards or tapes, a computer user may type the desired data or instructions on a special *terminal* that communicates directly with the computer. This type of input device consists of a typewriterlike device that has a keyboard and a printer for recording entries. The printer also prints the output from the computer. A terminal is usually used in what is called an *interactive mode*. In this mode the operator enters data or instructions, communicating directly with the computer, and the computer then uses the terminal to record any output or other information that is produced. The operator can then react to the output and make changes or corrections in data or instructions directly from the terminal and can observe the resulting change in output—hence the term *interactive*.

In place of the printed form of input and output, some terminals display information on a televisionlike *cathode ray tube* (CRT), which is particularly useful for working with maps or other graphic matter (Fig. 11.2). In addition to using a keyboard, some CRT terminals allow the use of a *light pen* to enter information or instructions. This is accomplished in one of two ways. In one use of the light pen the operator traces a desired outline on the CRT screen, which acts essentially as a drawing board, and the traced line then shows on the screen. If desired, the tracing on the screen of the CRT can be transferred to the CPU for processing. The results can be printed out by a line printer, plotter, or other *hard-copy* output device, or can be directly converted to coordinates and stored for later use. Another use of the light pen involves touching designated spots on the screen. These spots, which are called a *menu,* have been coded to indicate particular instructions. These instructions are used to manipulate the image on the screen, altering the scale, for example, or to control the operation of the computer.

One difficulty with CRT output is that when the display is turned off the image is lost and, of course, there is no direct way to view the output without the use of the CRT. Various devices are available to capture the ephemeral CRT display for more permanent storage. It is possible, for example, to instruct the computer to route the information currently being shown on the CRT through an alternative output device, such as a line printer or a plotter. The result is a permanent record called, in computer parlance, *hard copy*. It is also possible to photograph the image

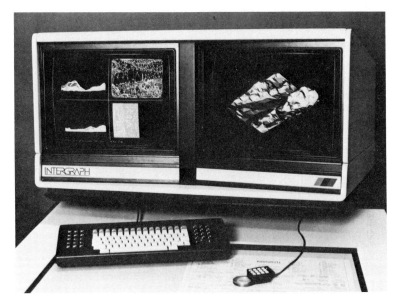

Figure 11.2 Cathode ray tube (CRT) terminal. (Courtesy of Intergraph Corporation.)

displayed on a CRT. Prints are made from the resulting negative and are used in the same way as any other form of hard copy. Although black-and-white CRTs are the most common, color units are also available.

Line printers   *Line printers* are output devices that produce a printed sheet of typewriterlike output. There are a number of types of line printers, but the chief characteristic of all of them is that the output is produced as separate characters (letters, numbers, or symbols) that are printed, side by side, one row at a time, in the same manner as the letters on a printed page.

The simplest and earliest form of line printer was an electric typewriter linked with the computer. This arrangement was very slow in relation to the output capacity of even the slowest computers. Since the early use of electric typewriters, a variety of machines have been introduced to allow the speed of production of printed output to more nearly keep pace with the computational capabilities of the computer. For example, chain printers, daisy wheel printers, printers that print in alternate directions so that a carriage return is not required, ink jet printers, dot matrix printers, and printers that create their images electrostatically have been devised. The detail of the operation of these printing devices is not important for our purposes. What is important is that, whatever the mechanical or electrical device used, the symbol-by-symbol appearance of the output remains. The limitations of such devices for cartographic purposes are discussed later in this chapter. Printing heads with special symbols can be used in place of those conventionally found on a typewriter, however, and can produce a more effective map output.

Plotters   A *plotter* is an output device that draws a two-dimensional line image, under the control of the computer or of a computer-generated tape. There are two general types of plotters: flatbed and drum. Because plotters are able to draw line plots, and are not limited to the letters and symbols produced by line printers, they (along with CRTs) are particularly useful in cartographic applications. These devices are described in greater detail in the section on output processing.

Computer output microfilm (COM)   Specialized devices have been developed to record images directly on microfilm. A typical device of this type moves a focused laser beam across the film, under computer direction. The action of the light beam on the film forms a photographic image that is developed and utilized in conventional fashion in the reproduction of a finished map. The image produced may be a line image, a window, or a letter or symbol. By producing a sequence of such negatives, it is even possible to produce a set of color separations from which to print a color map. This type of device is also discussed in more detail later in this chapter.

Magnetic tapes   Data or programs may be stored in magnetic form on reels of special recording *tape.* When the information is needed, the appropriate tape is mounted on a reading device (tape drive) and the material stored on the tape is copied into the internal computer memory or is used to operate an *off-line* device, such as a plotter. One advantage of this form of storage, as compared with cards and paper tapes, is that the reading and transfer process is much more rapid, so that expensive computer time is conserved. Another advantage is that it is compact, so that a number of data files or programs may be stored on a single tape.

It is also possible to search fairly quickly through a tape to read selected files or portions of files. This search process is more difficult with cards or paper tapes, which must be read into memory in their entirety before any selection or manipulation can be carried out. A disadvantage of magnetic tapes, however, is the fact that the files are necessarily recorded on the tape in *sequential* fashion and searches for the files must also be sequential. If one desired file is recorded at the beginning of the tape, for example, and another is recorded near the end of the same tape, all of the tape separating the two files is scanned as the search for the second file is carried out. Even though the tape moves at quite high speed, a considerable amount of expensive computer time is expended during the search process.

Disk storage   Data and programs may also be stored on *magnetic disks.* These disks, which resemble phonograph records in appearance, are coated with electromagnetic material similar to that used on magnetic tapes. The information is recorded in concentric *tracks* on the disk, and the tracks are divided into *sectors,* so that a great deal of information can be recorded on a single disk. A major advantage of disk storage, as compared to storage on magnetic tape, is that the search for a particular file is done by moving directly to the appropriate track and sector, without the necessity of working sequentially. For this reason, disks are referred to as *random access* or *direct access* storage devices.

Other storage modes　A number of other means of data storage exist, either in fully developed or experimental form, including what are called solid-state memories. For purposes of this discussion, however, there is no need to examine them because the use of one rather than the other has little effect on the types of cartographic tasks that can be performed. The greatest differences are in terms of increases in the amount of information stored and the speed with which it is placed into or retrieved from storage. Developments such as this tend to decrease the unit cost and increase the availability of computer technology and therefore have an indirect influence on the use of such techniques in cartography.

Programming

A number of *programming languages* are used to provide processing instructions to the computer: BASIC, FORTRAN, COBOL, and PL/1, to name a few. Each of these languages has a structure that makes it more or less suitable for particular needs and for particular systems. In the present context, however, it is not necessary to understand such complexities. All that we need to keep in mind is that the user (or a programmer working for the user) provides instructions to the EDP system that will allow the input, processing, and output of a variety of data, using a number of devices, and that these are selected to best fit a particular purpose.

In the early years of the development of computer techniques in cartography, the hardware that was available placed definite limits on the types of applications that could be carried out. This was particularly true of the output devices. Typically, for example, line printers were used to produce output and the quality of the product that could be obtained using the printers was severely limited. As faster, more accurate, more flexible, and less expensive output devices have become available, the main bar to increasingly sophisticated applications has been the shortage of software—that is, of specialized programs capable of taking the data that are the raw materials of maps, such as locational coordinates and census information, and converting them into meaningful map form. As more highly developed and universally applicable software is produced, this difficulty will decline in importance.

INPUT PROCESSING

Perhaps the most fundamental cartographic task for which a computer system can be utilized is the drawing of a simple outline map. Nevertheless, this basic task involves a number of considerations. An examination of these considerations provides a useful introduction to the use of computers in cartography.

Assume, then, that we wish to produce the base map shown in Fig. 11.3(a), using computer techniques. The first task is to create a file of locational information that is *machine readable*; that is, information in a form that allows it to be read into the computer system and stored there for later manipulation and retrieval. For introductory purposes, we shall assume that the map to be produced is not a part

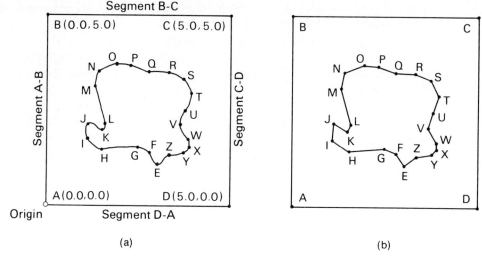

Figure 11.3 (a) Image to be digitized. (b) Digitized image.

of a larger map series and, therefore, does not have to be related to an external reference or grid system.

Coordinate Systems

The simplest form of *coordinate system* that can be used is a traditional *Cartesian grid*. This is an *x-y* coordinate system in which both horizontal and vertical distances are measured from an arbitrary origin.

The first decision involved in setting up this coordinate system is to select the units for the measurement of distances. One choice is to use the actual distances that would be measured on the ground (or from a map, using the correct map scale). An existing grid system, such as state plane coordinates, that is already plotted on many maps provides a convenient framework for this approach. If actual distances are used it is a simple matter to convert them to whatever scale ratio is desired, when a map is produced, using the computer to perform the necessary calculations. A second choice is to measure distances directly from the map, using inches, centimeters, or other convenient units. Some software systems require the use of such measurements, so there may be no practical choice in the matter. A third choice is to use latitude and longitude to designate location. This has the advantage of allowing the map to be related to the worldwide latitude and longitude system.

The second decision that must be made is to determine the location of the origin of the system. This choice is based on a selection from the eight possible combinations of the following variables:[1]

[1]Thomas K. Peucker, *Computer Cartography,* Resource Paper No. 17, Commission on College Geography (Washington, D.C.: Association of American Geographers, 1972), p. 56. The decision is already made in the case of geographical coordinates.

1. Because each point will be defined by a pair of coordinates, it is possible to code either the *x*- or the *y*-coordinate first.
2. The system origin may be either to the west or to the east of the area to be mapped.
3. The system origin may be either to the south or to the north of the area to be mapped.

The selection of the origin location is conditioned by the computer system being utilized. One commonly used system, for example, codes the *y*-coordinate first and has its origin at the north and west. This system is designed to use a line printer to produce its output. The printing starts in the northwest (upper left) corner and proceeds across each row, in order from top to bottom, and ends in the southeast (lower right) corner. The *y*-coordinate is needed first, in order to identify the line on which a symbol is to be printed. The *x*-coordinate is then needed to identify the column in which the symbol is to be printed.

Other systems, particularly those using line plotters, may require a southwest origin, with the *x*-coordinate first, and the *y*-coordinate second, because of the plotting sequence. Other combinations may be used simply for the convenience of the cartographer if the system does not impose specific requirements. Whatever combination is in use, it is obviously necessary for all the input to be done consistently or a great deal of confusion will result. For example, a mirror image of the desired map is produced if the origin is established to the east of the mapped area when an origin to the west is required.

Digitizing the Image

Once the coordinate system is established, the lines that make up the map are converted into numerical form. In this example, the lower left-hand corner of the neatline is the origin. This is convenient because the point is at the edge of the area to be mapped and all the map locations can be designated as positive valued horizontal (*x*) and vertical (*y*) coordinates. For the sake of simplicity, map distances in centimeters are used for measurement purposes.

Given these assumptions, the following steps are involved in digitizing the map image shown in Fig. 11.3(a). First, point *A*, which is the origin itself, is recorded as a pair of decimal numbers: 0.0,0.0. Three additional pairs of coordinates are recorded to represent the remaining corners of the neatline. Proceeding in a clockwise direction from the origin, the required coordinates are as follows: for point *B*, 0.0,5.0; for point *C*, 5.0,5.0; and for point *D*, 5.0,0.0.

The coordinates of the neatline corners also describe the path of the neatline itself. That is, each of the pairs of coordinates that designate a corner also designate the beginning of one of the four segments of the neatline and the end of another. The vertical line on the left (*AB*) begins at 0.0,0.0 and ends at 0.0,5.0; the horizontal line at the top (*BC*) begins at 0.0,5.0 and ends at 5.0,5.0; and so on. Plotting each pair of coordinates and joining the plotted points in sequence results in the reproduction of the original square neatline. Furthermore, the path of the neatline is described, numerically, by the coordinate string: 0.0,0.0; 0.0,5.0; 5.0,5.0; 5.0,0.0; 0.0,0.0. Note that the string begins and ends at the origin. This is necessary or the final segment (*DA*) will not be described and therefore would not be plotted.

The idea of describing the path of a straight line, or a series of straight lines, by the use of a string of locational coordinates is called vector digitizing. It can be extended to the description of irregular or curved lines. This requires establishing a series of coordinates that follow the path of the irregular line. The coordinates are then joined by straight-line segments, which together approximate the path of the original line. The irregular coastline of the island in Fig. 11.3(a), for example, is shown in Fig. 11.3(b) by lines that connect the coordinates of the points at which the original line "significantly" changed direction. The coordinates of regular curves (such as circles) are similarly established, either at points computed on the basis of the mathematical formula that describes the particular curve required, or at points plotted along the curve as it is drawn on the source map.

Because vector lines are defined by *coordinate strings,* it is obvious that some of the intricacies of the original line may be lost in the digitizing plotting process. This difficulty is overcome, to some extent, by increasing the number of coordinates used to describe each line, so that the resulting shorter *straight-line segments* come closer to representing the path of the original line. Conceivably, if the number of segments could be greatly increased, the original line would be almost perfectly represented. As a practical matter, however, it is necessary to decide how much detail is needed and to select the coordinate locations accordingly. This selection process will be discussed in more detail later; for the moment it is sufficient to understand that map lines, whether straight, regularly curved, or irregular, can be put into a numerical form that is ultimately used in the computer.

Digitizing Processes

Map information is converted into digital form by a number of methods. If the map to be reproduced is small and relatively simple, it is feasible to select the desired points individually and to manually prepare lists of coordinates defining each line on the map as a vector, as already described. The lists are then converted into computer inputs, either by punching appropriate cards or tapes or by entering the data through a CRT terminal.

If the map is larger and more complex, the task of measuring, listing, and recording the map coordinates quickly becomes burdensome. For this reason, various means of at least partially automating the task have been developed. Three of these approaches are described here.

Cursor and digitizing table   A *digitizing table* consists of a large flat surface that incorporates an electronic detection system. This system is used to locate the features that are to be digitized. In recently developed systems the points on the table surface are located to an accuracy of ±0.0005 in.

In order to use the digitizer, the source map is mounted on the table [Fig.

(a)

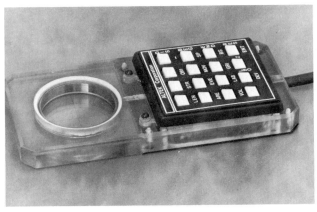

Figure 11.4 Manual digitizing equipment: (a) Table (Courtesy of Summagraphics Corporation.); (b) Cursor (Courtesy of Altek Corporation.)

(b)

11.4(a)] and an appropriate point is selected as the origin, based on the considerations already discussed. A special *cursor,* which is connected to a recording device, is then placed on the surface of the map [Fig. 11.4(b)]. Typically, this cursor consists of a transparent disk, approximately 1 in. in diameter, held within a metal ring. In the center of the disk is a target, such as a fine cross hair, which is used as a line tracer. The cross hair is first aligned over the designated point of origin and the system is activated. This step establishes the origin as the point of reference for the measurement of coordinate locations within the map area. Other control points, such as the corners of the map sheet, or the coordinates of limiting lines of latitude and longitude, may also be digitized at this time. They are used if the individual map has to be related to other maps that cover the same area or adjoining areas.

The cursor is then moved to a starting point on one of the map lines and, thence, along the line itself.

The initial location of the cursor on the line is detected by the electronic system and the coordinate information is fed into the recording terminal in digital form. This location is in terms of map distance units but, if desired, can be converted to latitude and longitude, or ground distance units. Then, as the cursor is moved over the surface, its changing location is continuously and automatically recorded. Coordinates are spaced a set distance apart or, alternatively, are based on the location of the cursor at given time intervals. In the latter case, the spacing is close together when the cursor is moving slowly (presumably along a relatively complex line) and is farther apart when it is moving rapidly (along a smoother line). When the line has been traced from beginning to end, which is achieved quite quickly compared to the manual method of digitizing coordinates, the recording terminal will have stored, either on punched cards or on magnetic tape, a sequence of coordinate locations that describe the course of the traced line. Each line is also given an appropriate label, so that railroads, for example, are distinguished from highways, and both are separated from coastlines.

As is discussed further, below, the recording of a stream of coordinates spaced at very close intervals may provide much more information than is needed for plotting purposes. Provision is made, therefore, for using the cursor in a mode that permits the operator to record selected points rather than automatically recording the whole stream of points. In this mode, the operator aligns the cursor cross hair over each desired point on the line and presses a switch that causes the coordinates of the point to be recorded. The cursor is then moved to successive points that are also individually recorded. The same technique is used to record individual points, such as survey control points, that are to be mapped.

Regardless of the mode used, the results obtained by using the digitizing table are very similar to those obtained by using the hand recording technique, but it is a much quicker and, in most cases, more accurate method.

Floating arm graphic digitizer   The *floating arm graphic digitizer* utilizes a stylus that is mounted on a freely movable arm suspended over a flat surface. The stylus is guided manually along the lines, or to individual points that are to be digitized, and their location is recorded on the basis of the geometry of the suspension system, which is monitored by a small computer.

Automatic digitizing   There are two principal types of *automatic digitizers: line following* and *raster scanning*. In the past, both types have suffered from the problem that they require very clean, separated source maps. Such separations are expensive to prepare. They were needed, however, because the scanner cannot distinguish between similar features, like roads and railroads, for example. The simplest way to deal with this difficulty was to place features that were to be symbolized differently on the final map onto separate overlays so they could be recorded and stored as separate records. Other methods are now available in some systems to circumvent this preseparation requirement.

The scanner depends on the detection of light transmitted through the source document, or reflected from it, to identify the location of a line; it cannot distinguish between a random mark and a map feature. If any extraneous marks exist, they will be recorded as though they were part of the linework. If this occurs, the unwanted coordinates are eliminated through an *editing* process before the data is used for mapping purposes.

One rather unique problem connected with automatic digitizers is that the lines on the separations are usually very coarse in relation to the resolution accuracy of the digitizer. It is difficult, therefore, for the scanner to determine the center of the lines being recorded. Because of this, it is often necessary to institute an editing step that reduces and smoothes each line to a single stream of coordinates.

Line-following scanner   One type of *optical scanner* semi-automatically locks onto and traces the outline of a data zone, providing a record of the coordinates as it moves along the line [Fig. 11.5(a)].

In order to use this device, the linework of the map that is to be digitized is first recorded as a black line image on a film negative. The operator of the scanner, using a large-screen monitor to observe what is happening in the system, directs a focused laser beam to a point on the first line that is to be recorded. The laser beam then moves automatically from its starting position along the route of the line. The system detects the line by means of the change in the intensity of light as the laser beam moves from the darkened area of the film and strikes the open portion of the image. Using a combination of programmed logic and operator control, the laser beam, which moves in a back and forth scanning motion, continues to follow the line upon which it is focused until it returns to its starting point. This scanning process proceeds very rapidly.

As the scanning continues, the coordinates that describe the line are determined by the computer, which also acts as a control unit for the process. The coordinates are established through a calculation based on the changing angle of the mirrors used to direct the laser beam onto the image. In this particular system, the coordinates of the line are recorded in increments that are usually at an interval of 0.002 to 0.003 in. on the original map. When the path of the first line is completed, the operator checks the image to be certain that the line was correctly followed—any necessary changes are made by the operator from the control console. In one system, the image of the line that has been digitized is removed from the viewing screen by a second laser beam so that a constant check is kept on the recording process. The laser beam is then moved to a point on the next line and the recording process is continued. These steps are repeated until all the desired lines are recorded. A recording device of this type is very rapid and accurate.

Raster scan digitizer   There are two types of *raster scan digitizers*: drum and flatbed. The *flatbed* type has a large, flat, glass table on which the separated film positive image is placed [Fig. 11.5(b)]. The image is then scanned, using a computer-controlled focused light beam and detector. The scanning is done in a predetermined pattern rather than by following individual image lines (Fig. 11.6). Each unit area, or *pixel,* on the separation is checked to determine whether or not an image is present. If an image is present, that fact is recorded. Lines are not, therefore, recorded as a sequence of coordinates as they are in vector digitizing. Instead, they are recorded as individual elements that collectively represent a continuous line.

A *drum* type of raster scanner has a cylindrical drum on which the original is placed [Fig. 11.5(c)]. As the drum rotates, a scanning head determines the presence

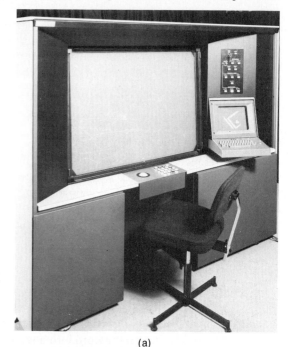

Figure 11.5 Automated digitizing equipment: (a) Line-following scanner (Courtesy of Laser-Scan International Inc.); (b) Raster scan digitizing table (Courtesy of Broomall Industries, Inc.); (c) Color drum scanner (Courtesy of Scitex America Corp.)

(a)

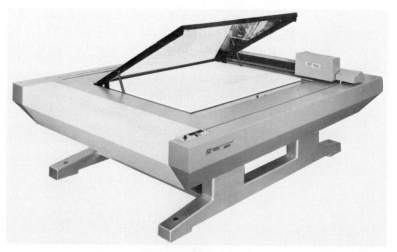

(b)

(c)

Figure 11.5 (*cont.*)

or absence of an image in each pixel. Preseparated images are most easily dealt with on drum scanners, as well as on flatbed scanners. More recent models, however, allow the separation of a multicolor original image. In this type of system, several colors or shades of gray can be selected and the scanner will determine the color of the image in each pixel instead of just the presence or absence of the image. In this manner, all the black images, for example, are recorded in a separate record from the green images, and so on. Further processing is carried out semi-automatically to convert the *raster* record into a *vector* record and to distinguish different features of the same color from one another if either step is required.

If a raster type display is to be produced on a CRT screen or on certain types of printers, no further processing is necessary. In such a display, pixels that contain

Figure 11.6 Sequence of raster scan digitizing.

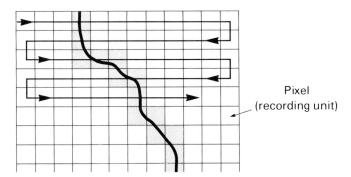

Pixel
(recording unit)

an image are displayed and those that do not contain an image are not, so that a duplicate of the original raster image is produced. If a vector type of output is required, such as is obtained from most plotters, the tape record of the image is edited, using a special software routine, in order to convert the information regarding the individual pixels into information regarding the lines or vectors that make up the image. This *raster-to-vector conversion* has been a time-consuming and expensive step that has tended to reduce the usability of raster mode data. Recently, however, the speed of conversion has been improved, so that the conversion is much less of a problem than in the past and high-speed raster scan machinery is becoming increasingly important.

Storage and Editing

Digitized map data, however if it generated, must be retained for future use because it is obviously impractical to determine and record the data anew each time a map is to be constructed. In fact, the concept of *storage* and *retrieval* is essential to a practical application of computer assistance because of the time and expense involved in creating a usable data file. It is estimated that 75 to 80 percent of the cost of producing computer maps is involved in the input, editing, and correction of the cartographic data base so that future applications will be free from data errors. These costs must usually be spread over multiple uses in order to bring the average cost of each use to a practical level. Depending on the type of equipment available, the coordinate pairs that describe the location of map features are punched into cards, or are recorded directly onto a magnetic tape or disk, so that they are stored for future use.

Coordinate data files may contain a variety of errors, the nature of which depends, in part upon the type of digitizing system in use. Certain points may be omitted, for example, other points may be located inaccurately, or extraneous points may be recorded. These errors may result in omitting some parts of the map, in mapping other areas twice, or in drawing a line that suddenly takes a sharp jog to one side or another of its correct path. Editing is necessary in order to remove these errors from the files prior to use.

Data density   As was already suggested, the number of data points obtained from the digitizing process, particularly from the stream mode of an automated system, may exceed the number of points needed for a particular purpose. This may be true either because there is more information than is needed at the scale at which the map is to be reproduced, or because the type of output device to be utilized cannot plot the information at a level of resolution equal to the close spacing of the points. It is important, therefore, to eliminate unnecessary data in order to reduce storage capacity needs and to speed up the output process, thereby reducing costs. Preferably, the editing is done in such a way that the character of the line to be represented is retained. This implies the use of editing criteria that go beyond the simple, arbitrary deletion of a certain percentage of the stored coordinates. This problem is discussed further in the section on filtering.

Classes

As with conventional cartography, the types of phenomena that are mapped using computer-assisted techniques occur at points in space, are linear in form, or occupy areas or regions. These categories were discussed in detail in Chapter 9. In the case of computer-assisted cartography, the means of encoding each of these types of occurrence is adapted to the particular type that is being handled.

Points Many features that appear on maps, such as buildings, benchmarks, or even cities or towns, occur at specific points in space, or in such relatively small areas that on small-scale maps their locations may be treated as points. In such cases, it is sufficient simply to identify the points by the use of their coordinates, using the appropriate coordinate system.

Lines Lines are used to record the locations of many features, such as roads, rivers, and coastlines. Depending on the characteristics of the line that is to be recorded (whether it is straight, regularly curved, or irregular), its path may be designated and recorded by the coordinate string method already discussed.

An alternative means of defining irregular lines utilizes a method called *chain encoding*. In this method, the location of an initial point is established and a square locational grid is superimposed on it. The lines on this grid are spaced a distance apart that is appropriate to the scale of the map and to the level of resolution of the equipment which is available. From the center of the locational grid there are eight adjoining points to which it is possible to move in one step. Each point is located at the crossing point of two of the grid lines that adjoin the center point. The points are each identified by a number, ranging from 0 to 7 [Fig. 11.7(a)]. A move to point 2, for example, would result in a movement of one step in a vertical direction. A move to point 5, however, would be to the diagonal corner that is one step down and one to the left. Once a move has been made, the locational grid is recentered over the new location and the next move is defined in the same way.

The chain encoding method of representing an irregular mapped line is shown in Fig. 11.7 (b). Assume that the portion of the mapped line from X to Y is to be represented. Because of the limitation to grid square units, then, the point X' is the nearest defined point from which the plot can begin. Starting from X', the first move is one space to the right, as is the second. Then, a move up and to the right is needed, followed by a horizontal move to the right, and so on. The path of the line from X' to Y', then, is described as: 0,0,1,0,2,0,7,6,5 (each step, in this case, is one unit long). Depending on the irregularity of the line on the map, the coded line necessarily represents only an approximation of the actual line; the finer the grid spacing the closer the fit of the coded line to the actual line.

Zones Many types of phenomena, such as crop regions, political units, physiographic provinces, and climatic zones, cover smaller or larger areas on the earth's surface. The boundaries of these regions or zones must be defined adequately, so that they can be accurately mapped. For computer-assisted mapping purposes the definition is done either by describing the path of the outline around the zone or

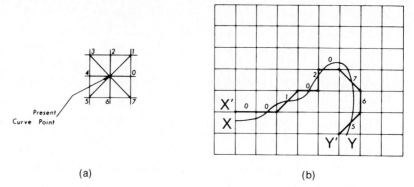

(a)   (b)

Figure 11.7 Chain encoding. [Source: Thomas Peucker, *Computer Cartography*, Resource Paper No. 17, Commission on College Geography (Washington: D.C.: Association of American Geographers, 1972), with permission.]

by describing the area occupied by the zone. An explanation of the differences between these two approaches follows.

When the *zone outline* approach is used, the path of the line that surrounds the zone is defined and is used as the limit to the zone. This is done in one of two ways. In the first method, the outline of each zone within the map area is recorded using either the incremental coordinate [Fig. 11.8(a)] or the chain encoding [Fig. 11.8(b)] techniques described above.

In the second method of defining map zones, *boundary points and pointers* are used. This means that the corners of the zone boundaries, and the points where two or more zone boundaries join, are established and their coordinate locations are recorded. The zones *A, B,* and *C* are identified in Fig. 11.9(a), for example. The corner points of zone *A* are the points at which the boundary changes direction: numbers 1, 2, 10, 9, 8, and 7. The joining points, on the other hand, are numbers 5, 9, and 6. Notice that some points are only corner points (such as 1 and 2), some are only joining points (4 and 5), and some are both (9). A numerical list of boundary points is established and the coordinates of each point are recorded [Fig. 11.9(b)].

Based on the same diagram, the *pointer arrays* that establish the boundaries for each zone are defined by designating in sequence the numbers of the appropriate boundary points. The boundary points for region *A,* for example, are 1, 2, 5, 10, 9, 8, 7, 4, and 1 [Fig. 11.9(c)]. The first and last boundary points are identical; in order to close the outline of the region, the plot must end at the same point from which it started. When a plot is desired, the appropriate region is identified by its label. The computer then identifies the first boundary point of the region, as listed in the pointer array; for region *A,* this is point 1. This identifying label is then used to locate the point in the coordinate array where the grid coordinates are located and this information is recorded. After this is done, the computer moves to the next point in the pointer array (point 2, in region *A*) and uses its identifying label to locate its coordinates in the coordinate table. After these coordinates are recorded,

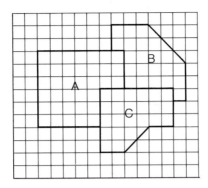

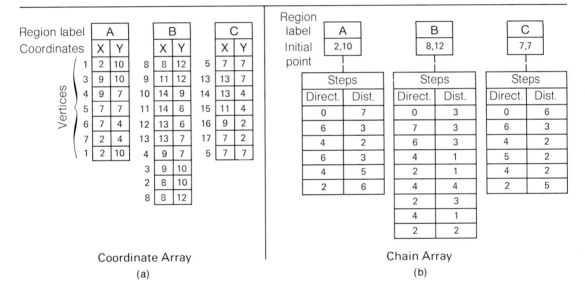

Coordinate Array

Region label	A			B			C		
Coordinates	X	Y		X	Y		X	Y	
Vertices 1	2	10	8	8	12	5	7	7	
3	9	10	9	11	12	13	13	7	
4	9	7	10	14	9	14	13	4	
5	7	7	11	14	6	15	11	4	
6	7	4	12	13	6	16	9	2	
7	2	4	13	13	7	17	7	2	
1	2	10	4	9	7	5	7	7	
			3	9	10				
			2	8	10				
			8	8	12				

(a)

Chain Array

Region label	A		B		C	
Initial point	2,10		8,12		7,7	
Steps	Direct.	Dist.	Direct.	Dist.	Direct.	Dist.
	0	7	0	3	0	6
	6	3	7	3	6	3
	4	2	6	3	4	2
	6	3	4	1	5	2
	4	5	2	1	4	2
	2	6	4	4	2	5
			2	3		
			4	1		
			2	2		

(b)

Figure 11.8   Zone outline encoding: (a) Coordinate sequence. (b) Chain array.

the above sequence is repeated until the outline of the region is completed. The signal for completion is the repetition of the initial label in the pointer array. Once the full list of coordinates is obtained, plotting proceeds as with any other coordinate string.

The method of boundary points and pointers has the advantage that the coordinates of each boundary point are only established once. This not only saves computer storage space, it also eliminates coordinate measurement errors. Such errors are often introduced in the zone outline approach, for example. This is because that method records the coordinates of each boundary point each time it is encountered. Point 9, for example, is a boundary point for all three regions. If slightly different coordinates are recorded during the process of tracing the outline of each

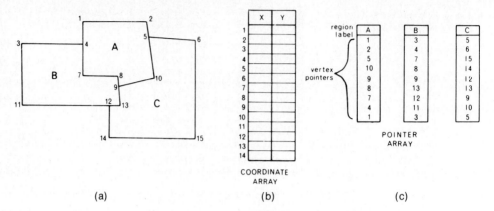

(a)   (b)   (c)

Figure 11.9 Boundary points and pointers. [Source: Thomas Peucker, *Computer Cartography,* Resource Paper No. 17, Commission on College Geography (Washington: D.C.: Association of American Geographers, 1972), with permission.]

region, the fact that it is a single point is lost and an editing process is necessary to be certain that the point is identically recorded in all three regions.

A technique that has been dubbed *skeleton encoding* is also used to define map zones. In this technique, each zone is defined by designating a set of *rhombi* (oblique-angled equilateral parallelograms with opposite sides equal). The outlines of these rhombi, taken together, establish the outer limits of the zone that is being defined. In Figure. 11.10, for example, the outer line, which surrounds all of the rhombi, is the outline of the zone that is to be defined. Each individual rhombus, numbered 0 through 3, contributes to the overall shape of the zone to the extent that a portion of its outline forms a portion of the outer line around the zone. (In this example, the rhombi are diamond-shaped, but other shapes are utilized, depending on the irregularity of the zone outline.) Each rhombus is easily defined by recording the coordinates of its corners. This technique has the advantage that lines

Figure 11.10 Skeleton encoding. [Source: Thomas Peucker, *Computer Cartography,* Resource Paper No. 17, Commission on College Geography (Washington: D.C.: Association of American Geographers, 1972), with permission.]

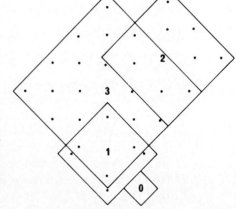

forming a common boundary between zones are always consistently defined, thus avoiding errors that would result in gaps or overlaps between the zones.

Cartographic Data Bases

Because of the considerable time, effort, and expense involved in the preparation and editing of any extensive file of locational coordinates, it is frequently advantageous to utilize already prepared files. This is especially true when relatively large and complex maps must be converted to digital form.

Various public and private agencies (such as the Harvard University Laboratory for Computer Graphics, the Central Intelligence Agency, and the Census Bureau) have produced machine-readable files that provide the coordinates of coastlines, rivers, boundaries of countries, states, and counties, and other features, using standardized formats and specified standards of accuracy. In order to capitalize on the investment made in these files, many of the producers have made them available for purchase. When such files are available, the cartographer should consider using them, instead of creating new files, because of the potential for saving time and money, as well as the accuracy of the products.

A major consideration in deciding whether or not to use prepared *cartographic data bases* is the compatibility of the available data base with the particular mapping system being utilized. The determination of compatibility must take into account both hardware and software considerations. If the user is not familiar with the technical aspects of computer applications, appropriate computer center personnel should be asked to evaluate compatability in terms of the tape format that is used, the density of the coding on the tape, the encoding procedures, and other technical considerations. The naive user should not assume, simply because a particular data base is available on magnetic tape, that it will be immediately usable; it is quite possible that extensive revision will be necessary.

The level of detail of the prepared data base must also be appropriate to the map scale and to the type of output device being used. If the map scale is to be relatively large, a data base that does not contain considerable detail will produce a map that lacks a convincing appearance, or that is inaccurate. If, however, the map scale is to be relatively small, or if the resolution capability of the output device is not great, the amount of detail may exceed what is needed for the final map. In the former case, there is little or nothing that can be done to improve the data base and its use may have to be foregone. In the latter case, it may be possible to edit the data base to obtain an appropriate level of detail, as discussed in the section on generalization and detail, below. If editing is necessary, however, it is obvious that the costs of using the prepared data base will be increased.

Centroid Files

If an isarithmic map is to be produced, based on data reported by region, it is necessary to select points within each region to represent the presumed point locations of the data. These points, which are called *centroids,* are used as the control points for the logical contouring of the map. The required centroid locations may be established by simply specifying the geometric center of the region, or the location may be weighted in relation to the distributional characteristics of the data, as was discussed in Chapter 9.

Prepared centroid files are available in conjunction with some cartographic data bases. When they are available, the user must consider the approach that was taken in establishing the centroids in order to evaluate their potential usefulness for the particular purposes at hand. It would generally not be appropriate, for example, to use centroids based on population distribution criteria for the mapping of agricultural features.

Data Banks

A *data bank* is the computer equivalent of a table of data that provides the user with information about certain aspects of a region. A typical example is the familiar census table that lists the characteristics of the population of a region, although the contents of a particular data bank may range from statistics regarding agricultural production, to rainfall data, economic production information, or, literally, any other type of information.

A data bank may have to be prepared by the user from primary or secondary sources, or a suitably prepared data bank may be available from an agency such as the Bureau of the Census. Whatever its source, the information in a data bank must be made available to the mapping program in such a way that each item of data is unambiguously related to its appropriate map location. The coordination of the data with the locations may be accomplished by either a sequential or a random listing.

In a *sequential system,* the records in the data bank and the coordinates of the related locations are listed in the same sequence in their separate files. When the data are used, the computer simply reads through both files in order, relating the first set of locational coordinates with the first item of data, the second set of coordinates with the second item of data, and so on. Obviously, it is absolutely necessary that the correct listing sequence be maintained in both the coordinate file and the data bank. Because there is no simple means of checking the relationship between the two files other than their sequence, hopeless confusion will result if the sequence is lost.

In a *random system,* each record in the data bank has a name that identifies its location. The mapping program retrieves data from the appropriate record, as required, by use of its name. In this type of file, the sequence of the coordinate listings does not have to be the same as the sequence of the data because the name establishes the relationship. This type of file is more flexible than the sequential file and is especially useful when certain locations are to be excluded on some occasions and included on others.

OUTPUT PROCESSING

Plotting

Plotting involves the translation of digital data into visible form on some sort of permanent medium, like paper or film. These plots are usually performed off-line. That is, a tape containing the digital information for the map is produced by the computer and the tape is then read by the plotter's control unit and the actual plotting is carried out.

The plotters available for producing map output are limited to drawing very short horizontal or vertical straight-line segments to connect the designated coordinate points. Depending on the length of the segments that can be drawn, lines that are not perfectly horizontal or vertical may acquire a jagged, stair-step appearance (Fig. 11.11). The greater the *resolution* capability of the plotter (that is, the shorter the line segments it can draw) the less the problem—as the jogs in the line become smaller, a point is reached at which the eye is no longer able to distinguish them and the line appears to be smooth. Some plotters, today, move in increments as small as 40 μm, so jagged lines need no longer be a problem.

The two main types of plotters are flatbed plotters and drum plotters. The results obtained from each of the two types are essentially similar.

Flatbed plotter On a *flatbed plotter,* as the name implies, the output is produced on a sheet of paper, drafting plastic, sensitized photographic film, or other suitable material that is fastened to a flat-surfaced stationary table. A movable *plotting head,* which can hold a pen, a pencil, a scribing tip, or a pinpoint light source, is mounted above the plotting surface. Its position is precisely controlled in both the x and y directions by motor-driven gears. A bar is mounted across the width of the table and moves along the table in the x direction. The plotting head is mounted on this bar so that it moves, independently, in the y direction [Fig. 11.12(a)].

To start a plot, the head is moved to the position that represents the coordinates of the starting point of the line to be plotted. This movement is controlled by programmed instructions that read the required information from the cartographic data bank describing the map that is to be drawn. The pencil, or other tool, which

Figure 11.11 Effect of plotting increments on appearance of diagonal lines.

Smooth lines   Jagged plot

(a)

(b)

Figure 11.12 Plotters: (a) Flatbed (Courtesy of Kern Systems, Inc.); (b) Drum (Courtesy of Houston Instrument.)

is mounted in the head, is then lowered into contact with the plotting surface (a pinpoint light source will not actually touch the surface). After the starting point is located, the head is automatically moved to the coordinates of the second point on the line and, as the plotting tool moves, it traces a line connecting the two points. This process continues as successive coordinates are read from the output tape and the plotting tool continuously traces the line that connects the points. At the end of the line, the head is raised, moved to the starting point of the next line, lowered into plotting position, and the process is repeated until the plot is complete.

For some purposes, a scribing tool is used in place of a pen-type plotter. The result is a scribed separation the same as those described in Chapter 7. Similarly, on some machines a pinpoint light source can be used to create a photographic image when that is required.

Drum plotter   *Drum plotters* work in a manner very similar to the operation of flatbed plotters except that the paper moves around the drum in the *x* direction and the plotting head moves along the axis of the drum in the *y* direction [Fig. 11.12(b)]. Each line is plotted independently, so the paper moves backward and forward as required to reach the starting and ending points.

Transformations

Once cartographic data bases and informational data banks are available in edited, machine-readable form, they may be used to produce a large variety of map output. The ability of the computer to manipulate digital information can be brought into play, so that an almost endless variety of operations can be carried out, each of which will result in a change in the mapped output. Following are examples of some of the types of transformations the computer can be called upon to perform.

Scale   One of the simplest changes that can be made in an existing digitized map is a change in scale. This requires the systematic increase or decrease in the values of the recorded coordinates in proportion to the ratio between the original scale and the new scale. Assume, for example, that the source map was at a scale of 1:100,000, and it is desired to produce a map at a scale of 1:50,000. All that is required is to double the value of each coordinate prior to plotting the map. If this is done, a point located 2.5 in. east and 3.0 in. north of the origin on the original map will be plotted 5.0 in. east and 6.0 in. north of the origin on the enlarged map.

Projection   As was discussed in Chapter 2, map projections are defined by mathematical formulae. Using the formulae for a given projection, the latitude and longitude of a point on the earth's surface can be converted to Cartesian coordinates which are then used to plot the point. It is then a relatively simple matter to recompute the plotting location of the points in the cartographic data base to allow any desired change in projection aspect or type.

Generalization and detail   As we have pointed out, the level of detail contained in a map must be appropriate to the system being used for the production of the map, as well as to the map scale. It may therefore be desirable to generalize the map by reducing the number of data points in the file, thereby reducing plotting time and required storage capacity, while retaining sufficient detail to produce a satisfactory image. These goals are met either by *simplification* or by *filtering* of the coordinate file.

The process of simplification involves the elimination of data points on the basis of systematic selection. Every second point, for example, (or every *n*th point)

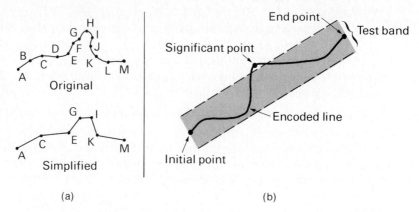

Figure 11.13   (a) Effect of arbitrary elimination of data points. (b) Filtering approach to generalization of a line.

is retained and all other points eliminated. This is obviously an arbitrary approach to the problem of eliminating superfluous coordinates. Indeed, it may eliminate points that are important to the definition of the shape of a line and that should therefore be retained. Figure 11.13(a) illustrates the type of problem that occurs if coordinate files are edited in this manner. Points that are not needed, on the other hand, may be retained. Because of the frequently unsatisfactory results obtained from this arbitrary approach, the use of a filtering technique is usually favored.

Filtering involves establishing criteria to determine whether or not a particular coordinate location is needed in the set of coordinates used to describe a line. In this approach, each point is checked to determine its relationship to the rest of the line. If it contributes "significantly" to the definition of the shape of the line, the point is retained; if it does not, it is eliminated.

The number of points eliminated depends on the complexity of the line being represented, as well as on the standard that is established to determine whether or not the points should be retained. If the line being represented is a straight line, for example, the original set of points, which could be a large number if the line were long, could be reduced to two—the initial point and the end point. The inclusion of any coordinates other than those of the end points would not increase the accuracy of the output. In this case, the intermediate coordinates should be eliminated by the editing program.

In more general terms, intermediate coordinates are eliminated whenever their inclusion does not change the direction of a line plot significantly. One way of achieving this is to use a procedure that checks the *geometric significance* of each data point.[2] If the point being tested falls within a *test band* it is eliminated. If it falls outside the band, on the other hand, it provides additional information about

[2]See, for example, David H. Douglas and Thomas K. Peucker, "Algorithms for the Reduction of the Number of Points Required to Represent a Digitized Line or Its Caricature," *The Canadian Cartographer,* 10, no. 2 (December 1973), 112–22.

the line and is retained [Fig. 11.13(b)]. The width of the test band, and hence the level of detail to be retained, is adjusted to suit the map scale and the resolution capacity of the output device.

Compilation

Cartographic data bases and informational data banks may be brought together to produce a desired map in a manner similar to the compilation procedures used for conventional maps (see Chapter 5). The flexibility and speed of this process, once the information is available in machine-readable form, makes it possible to economically create a variety of approaches to a given mapping problem. This often permits the testing of more possible map solutions than has typically been the case using the relatively time-consuming conventional compilation techniques. It also often permits the final production of a greater variety of maps than has been feasible previously, because of the speed and relatively low cost of map preparation once the compilation is completed.

Map compilation using computer-assisted techniques typically involves the selective combination of one or more cartographic data bases with information from one or more data banks. The particular files to be used are selected from the total list of files available to the cartographer. The files are also edited as desired, and trial outputs are reviewed.

Revision

An existing cartographic data base is revised by changing appropriate sets of coordinates within the data base. Assume, for example, that a railroad has been realigned since the original data base was prepared. All that need be done to update the base is to determine the coordinates of the point at which the new alignment departs from the old, and to determine the new coordinates from that point to the point at which the new alignment rejoins the old (or, if it does not rejoin, the point at which it leaves the map). The coordinates that define the old alignment are then deleted from the file and are replaced by the coordinates of the new alignment. When the railroad route is next plotted, the new alignment will be produced. It is also, of course, perfectly feasible to retain both the old and the new alignments as separate elements in the file, so that either or both can be used as desired.

It is, perhaps, more difficult to describe the flexibility of handling and revising cartographic data bases than it is to actually carry out the revisions. Ultimately, the applications are limited only by the imagination and creativity of the cartographer, although hardware or software shortcomings may be short-term obstacles in particular cases.

Symbolization and Lettering

Instructions for producing standardized symbols, letters, and numbers may be included in the computer software. Typically, files of required symbols, place names, and other words are prepared along with their locational coordinates. As the output is produced, the plotter or other output device inserts the symbols and names at the correct locations. There are frequently problems with this process because the words or symbols will overlap other portions of the map or one another. It is often necessary, therefore, to run one or more preliminary plots in order to make any required adjustments before the final plot is run.

Because of the relative difficulty of placing computer-generated symbols and lettering,[3] conventional techniques such as those described in Chapter 6 are frequently used, even on computer-assisted maps. Transfer type, preset type, and transfer symbols may be applied directly to the plotted hard-copy output or to an overlay, and final reproduction then proceeds in the normal manner.

APPLICATIONS

Many different types of maps are produced by computer techniques and brief descriptions of some of these are provided in this section. It must be recognized, however, that new applications are continually being developed; those presented here are simply suggestive of the wide variety that can and ultimately will be produced.

Choropleth Maps

In a choropleth map, each zone has a symbol applied to it. The symbols that are used are determined on the basis of the data values associated with each of the zones. Typically, the zones are counties, states, or other entities with already defined boundaries.

In order to produce a computer-assisted choropleth map, the outlines of the zones are defined as a set of *x-y* coordinate values. These coordinates are either measured and coded by the user, or they are obtained from an existing geographic data bank. In addition, the data values associated with each zone are recorded in machine-readable form. Again, these data are coded and supplied by the user or are obtained from a suitable data bank.

When necessary information has been supplied, the computer divides the range of data into the desired number of categories and assigns each zone to the appropriate value range. The symbols assigned are then printed out, along with the outlines of the data zones. In addition, the printed map contains any desired labels and marginal information.

If a line printer is used to produce the map, the gray values are obtained by using the same letters, numbers, and symbols that are employed for ordinary computer output (Fig. 11.14).[4] By printing individual symbols in each space, or by ov-

---

[3]For a discussion of progress in this regard, and for further references, see Stephen A. Hirsch, "An Algorithm for Automatic Name Placement Around Point Data," *The American Cartographer,* 9, no. 1 (April 1982), 5–17.

[4]In this case, the term *conformant* is used instead of the more usual term *choropleth* to describe the map type.

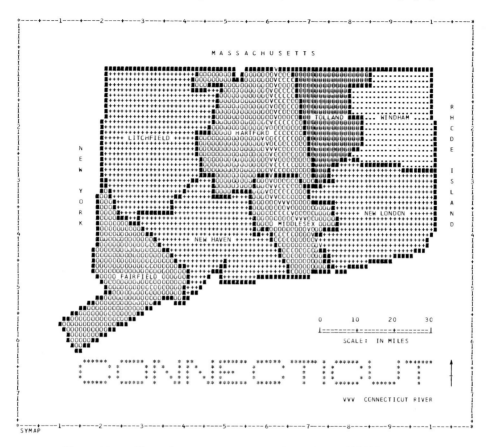

Figure 11.14 Choropleth map produced by line printer. (SYMAP computer program. Courtesy of Laboratory for Computer Graphics & Spatial Analysis, Harvard Graduate School of Design.)

erprinting various combinations of symbols, an impression of a gray value is obtained. The strength of the gray value is varied from light to dark and, as is usual, the darker grays are associated with the greater values. It is also possible to photograph a choropleth map from a CRT in either black and white or color (Plate 10).

Flatbed or drum plotters are also used to produce choropleth maps. The main characteristic of the choropleth technique remains, however, because the data are mapped according to preexisting zones, such as administrative areas. Depending on the data value associated with each zone, the plotter produces a map on which a series of patterns are drawn to provide shading values (Fig. 11.15). In this case, however, the gray-tone scale is produced by drawing a sequence of patterns in which the density of line spacing produces darker or lighter values.

TELEPHONES PER HUNDRED PERSONS

■ 8 – 58
▧ 3 – 8
▨ 2 – 3
▫ 1 – 2
□ 0 – 1

PRODUCED BY THE CALFORM PROGRAM

Figure 11.15 Choropleth map produced by pen-and-ink plotter. (CAL-FORM computer program. Courtesy of Laboratory for Computer Graphics & Spatial Analysis, Harvard Graduate School of Design.)

Prisms

When data are available for regions rather than for points, it is often not appropriate to plot a continuous surface to represent the data. Instead, each zone is treated as a homogeneous area, as in a choropleth map. The elevation of each zone, then, is varied in relation to the data value associated with it. The effect is to make each data zone the equivalent of a bar in a bar graph (Fig. 11.16).

Surface Representation

Data surfaces are often presented in three-dimensional form, using computer-assisted techniques. In order to accomplish this, data are provided assigning values to specific locations within the area being mapped, as was described in Chapter 10. A surface is then computed, based on these values, with the elevation of each point

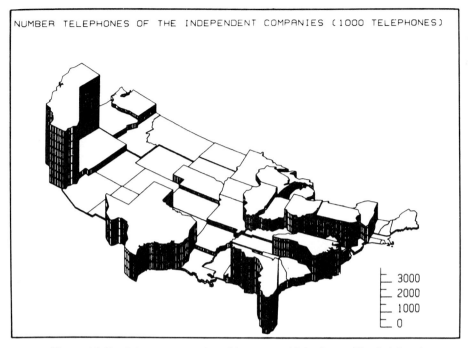

NUMBER TELEPHONES OF THE INDEPENDENT COMPANIES (1000 TELEPHONES)

3000
2000
1000
0

Figure 11.16 Prism map produced by pen-and-ink plotter. The height of each prism is proportional to the data value associated with that zone. (ODYSSEY program. Courtesy of Laboratory for Computer Graphics & Spatial Analysis, Harvard Graduate School of Design.)

related to the value of the data at that point. The design of the final output based on this computed surface may take a variety of forms.

Isolines   The methods used to provide the data necessary to produce a computer-assisted isoline map are similar to those used to produce choropleth maps, as are the methods used to print or plot the final product. The method of analyzing and presenting the data is quite different, however.

As was discussed in the previous chapter, isoline maps are drawn as a means of representing a set of data that occurs over a continuous surface (Fig. 11.17 and Plate 11). In the case of a computer-assisted isoline map, the initial data specifies the locations of the control points and the value associated with each point; these points may not be arranged in any particular pattern. The computer program uses these data points to interpolate values for a regularly spaced grid of control points by means of a logical contouring technique. In some programs, different weightings are applied during the interpolation process—greater weight may be given to nearby points, and lesser weight to more distant points, for example. The program then determines points within the control network that correspond to the desired isoline

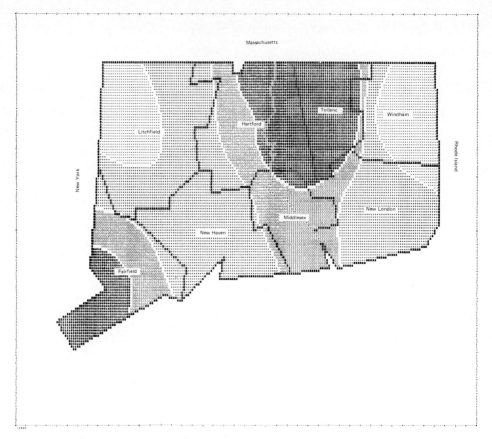

Figure 11.17   Isarithmic map produced by line printer. (SYMAP computer program. Courtesy of Laboratory for Computer Graphics & Spatial Analysis, Harvard Graduate School of Design.)

values. When the final map is produced, the isolines are plotted in accordance with the locations determined by the interpolation procedures.

If a plotter is used to produce the final map, the isolines are drawn in the usual manner. If a line printer is used, they are created by printing a special symbol at each point along the path of the line. If gray values are applied to the areas between the isolines, in the manner of layer tints, the isolines are indicated by leaving the points along their paths blank.

Proximal maps   The methods that are used to produce *proximal* maps are basically the same as those used to produce isoline maps. When a proximal map is produced, however, zones are mapped instead of contours (Fig. 11.18).

The zones in a proximal map are not based on preexisting boundaries, as are those in a choropleth map. Instead, each point within the map area is individually evaluated, using the nearest neighbor method. In this approach, a search process is

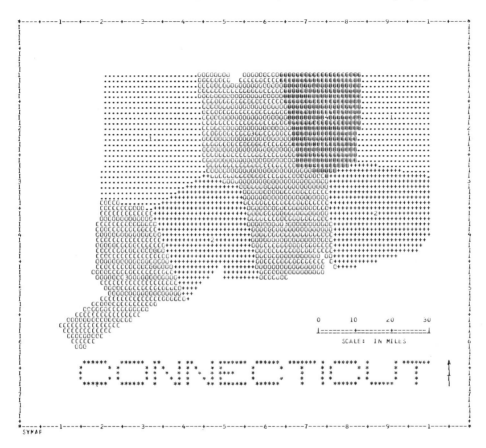

Figure 11.18   Proximal map produced by line printer. (SYMAP computer program. Courtesy of Laboratory for Computer Graphics & Spatial Analysis, Harvard Graduate School of Design.)

carried out around each point that is to be mapped. In essence, this involves locating the data point nearest to the point to be mapped. When this nearest-neighbor data point is located, the point being mapped is assigned the same value and is plotted accordingly. Thus, when the map is printed, it presents a set of equal-valued polygons with each polygon centered on one of the data points.

Perspective diagrams   Oblique perspective views of a region may be produced to represent a data surface (Fig. 11.19; see also Fig. 4.31). In this approach, the surface is represented as it would appear from a particular viewpoint in space. The desired viewpoint is specified by selecting the viewer's altitude above the surface, distance from the area being viewed, and direction of view. The surface itself is frequently represented by plotting lines drawn along the tops of a series of profiles that pass through the data surface.

When a perspective plot is produced, some portions of the scene are likely to

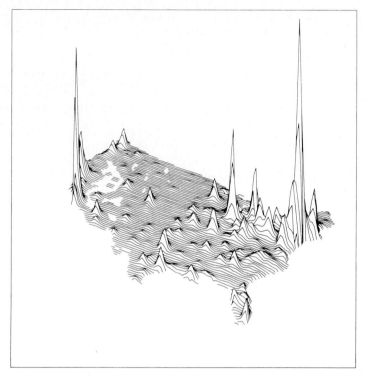

Figure 11.19   Perspective diagram (ASPEX computer program. Courtesy of Laboratory for Computer Graphics & Spatial Analysis, Harvard Graduate School of Design.)

be out of sight from the selected viewpoint. A valley, for example, may be visible when viewed from the northeast but may disappear behind a hill when viewed from the southwest. When this occurs, a special computational routine, or *algorithm,* determines which lines are hidden and deletes them from the scene.

Perspective plots are often developed on a CRT screen, operating interactively. When this is done, the person using the program defines the viewpoint to be used—including the altitude, azimuth, and angle of view. The viewpoint is then adjusted in order to provide the best appearance, depending on the particular arrangement of high and low points involved. In addition, the distance of the viewpoint from the scene is adjusted to obtain the desired scale. Finally, if desired, a technique called *windowing* is used to select a particular portion of the scene for viewing.

If the selection of viewpoint and scale cannot be carried out interactively, it is necessary to select an initial viewpoint and to produce a plotted copy of the map. Any necessary adjustment of the viewpoint is then made and another plot is produced. This process is continued until a satisfactory result is obtained; the advantage of an interactive approach in simplifying and speeding up the selection process is apparent.

When the desired configuration has been developed, the output is plotted on a flatbed or drum plotter, or is photographed from the CRT screen.

Gray values   A value surface may also be represented by printing a range of gray tones on the map (Fig. 11.20). In this approach, the tone at each point is varied

Figure 11.20 Gray values produced by plotting variable dot sizes. Each hexagonal dot is proportional to the data value of the surface at that point. [Reproduced from Richard E. Groop and Paul Smith. "A Dot Matrix Method of Portraying Continuous Statistical Surfaces," *The American Cartographer,* 9, no. 2 (October 1982), 123–30, with permission of the authors and the publisher.]

from white, where the values are lowest, to black, where they are highest. When this is done, each surface point has a gray tone that is proportional to its corresponding data value.

In this example, the appropriate hexagonal symbols are plotted at a large scale, with the size of the symbols computed on the basis of the data value associated with each point. The plot is then photographically reduced to provide an apparently continuously changing gray tone.

Hill shading Hill shading is an appropriate method of representing a continuous data surface, as was discussed in Chapter 10, and computer-assisted techniques are also used to generate such maps. In the color representation shown in Plate 12, values for slope, flatness, and reflectance have been computed for each point on the surface, based on initial elevation data. The computed values are then used to produce an image on the CRT. In this image, each elevation point is represented by a range of values of different colors, displayed in a group of four adjacent pixels. The values of the individual colors each represent a particular attribute of the surface; elevations are depicted in red, steepness of slope in blue, flatness in green, and reflectance in yellow. The colors are not mixed on the screen but, as in a color halftone image, the viewer sees an image in which the four colors blend to form a multicolor representation.

Analysis

Rather than simply presenting choropleth or isoline representations of spatial data, various analysis techniques may be applied to the data. Maps are then produced on the basis of the analysis, rather than on the initial data alone.

Figure 11.21 Linear trend surface (left) and the actual surface (right) viewed in the direction of maximum trend slope. [Reproduced from Mark S. Monmonier, "Viewing Azimuth and Map Clarity," *Annals of the Association of American Geographers,* 68, 2 (June 1978), 180–95, with permission.]

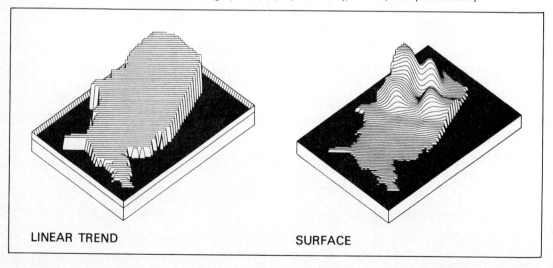

LINEAR TREND   SURFACE

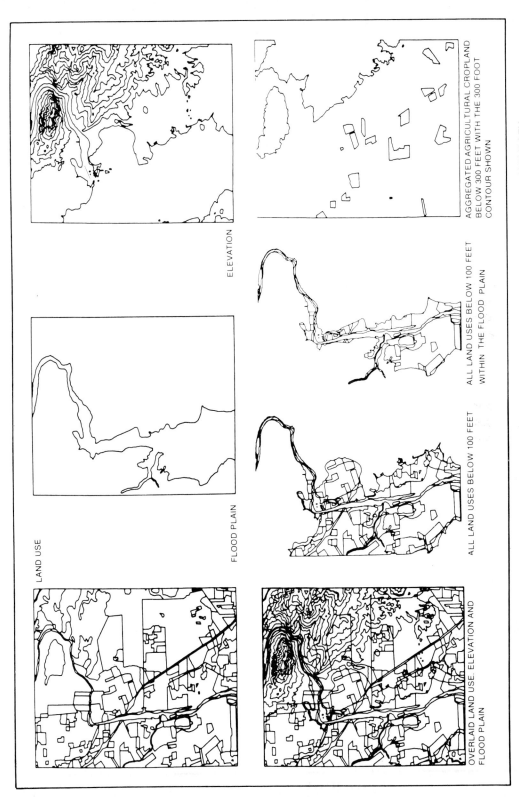

Figure 11.22 Use of polygon overlay technique to determine land-use and elevation combinations. (ODYSSEY program. Courtesy Laboratory for Computer Graphics & Spatial Analysis, Harvard Graduate School of Design).

LAND USE

FLOOD PLAIN

ELEVATION

AGGREGATED AGRICULTURAL CROPLAND BELOW 300 FEET WITH THE 300 FOOT CONTOUR SHOWN

ALL LAND USES BELOW 100 FEET WITHIN THE FLOOD PLAIN

ALL LAND USES BELOW 100 FEET

OVERLAID LAND USE, ELEVATION AND FLOOD PLAIN

Trend surface   The surface that results from mapping the range of values of a given variable is usually more or less complex and undulating. One type of analysis that can be done of such surfaces involves something akin to averaging—that is, the underlying general shape of the surface is determined in terms of a mathematically defined surface of greater or lesser complexity. For example, although a surface exhibits a considerable amount of undulation, it may be generally tilted down from a high point at one end. The simplest way to represent such a surface, then, would be to show it as a generalized flat plane, sloping from the high to the low ends (Fig. 11.21). When this is done, the plane is called a *trend surface*.

Trend surface maps graphically depict a mathematical surface that has been fitted to a set of data points and their data values. Because a plane would seldom do justice to representing a surface of any complexity, more complicated mathematical surfaces are frequently used. Those details of the surface characteristics that are not represented by the trend surface are called residuals. Maps of residual values are also often constructed in order to assist in the analysis of the characteristics of a surface.[5]

Polygon overlay   Another form of manipulation that is efficiently done using computer techniques is called *polygon overlay*. In this approach, maps of a variety of topics are converted into digital form (digitizing in raster form is particularly suitable for this purpose). The individual areas on each map, then, are simply polygons with specified characteristics. Depending on the needs of the particular application, two or more selected sets of polygons are mathematically overlaid on one another. Wherever the originally defined polygons coincide, a new polygon is created which has all of the characteristics of each of the original polygons (Fig. 11.22). This technique is useful, for example, when an analysis is being done to locate zones that are suitable for economic development or to identify commercial land-use zones that lie within a river's flood plain. Alternatively, sets of polygons based on different definitions may be aggregated to show areas that have one or another of a desired set of characteristics.

Suggested Readings

BAXTER, RICHARD, "A Computer File and Data Structure for Manipulating Digital Outlines of Polygons," *Geo-Processing,* 1, no. 3 (November 1980), 243–55.

BRASSEL, KURT, "A Model for Automatic Hill-Shading," *The American Cartographer,* 1, no. 1 (April 1974), 15–27.

BURKHARD, BRUCE R., "Cartographic Base Files at Lawrence Berkeley Laboratory: 1979 Inventory," in *Cartographic Data Bases and Software: Plus Cadastral Data Bases,* Harvard Library of Computer Graphics, 1980 Mapping Collec-

---

[5]Additional information regarding trend surface analysis and the analysis of residuals is provided in Mark S. Monmonier, *Computer-Assisted Cartography: Principles and Prospects* (Englewood Cliffs, N.J.: Prentice-Hall, Inc., 1982), pp. 52–55.

tion, vol. 13, 11–46. Cambridge, Mass.: Harvard Laboratory for Computer Graphics and Spatial Analysis, 1981. A listing of cartographic base files maintained at a large computer center. Provides information regarding area covered, form and contents of the file, and the contact person at the laboratory.

CALDWELL, DOUGLAS R., "Design Principles and Automated Choropleth Mapping," in *How to Design an Effective Graphics Presentation,* Harvard Library of Computer Graphics, 1980 Mapping Collection, vol. 17, 5–6. Cambridge, Mass.: Harvard University, Laboratory for Computer Graphics and Spatial Analysis, 1981.

DOUGLAS, DAVID H., and THOMAS K. PEUCKER, "Algorithms for the Reduction of the Number of Points Required to Represent a Digitized Line or Its Caricature," *The Canadian Cartographer,* 10, no. 2 (December 1973), 112–22.

Harvard Library of Computer Graphics, Various Titles. Cambridge, Mass.: Harvard University, Laboratory for Computer Graphics and Spatial Analysis, 1979 and later. Comprehensive series of publications illustrating a great variety of applications of computer graphics, including maps. For example, vol. 14 (1981), *Computer Graphics Hardware.*

MONMONIER, MARK S., *Computer-Assisted Cartography: Principles and Prospects.* Englewood Cliffs, N.J.: Prentice-Hall, Inc., 1982. Thorough coverage of the field of computer-assisted cartography.

PEQUET, DONNA J., "Raster Processing: An Alternative Approach to Automated Cartographic Data Handling," *The American Cartographer,* 6, no. 2 (October 1979), 129–39.

PETRIE, G., "Hardware Aspects of Digital Mapping," *Photogrammetric Engineering and Remote Sensing,* 47, no. 3 (March 1981), 307–20.

PEUCKER, THOMAS K., *Computer Cartography,* Resource Paper No. 17. Washington, D.C.: Association of American Geographers, Commission on College Geography, 1972.

TAYLOR, D. R. FRASER, ed., *The Computer in Contemporary Cartography.* Vol. 1 of *Progress in Contemporary Cartography.* New York: John Wiley & Sons, 1980.

TOBLER, WALDO R., "Automation in the Preparation of Thematic Maps," *The Cartographic Journal,* 2, no. 1 (June 1965), 32–38.

UTANO, JACK J., *Digitizing: Its Application in Mapping,* Technical Report No. 4, Department of Geography, University of Akron. Akron, Ohio: The University of Akron, Laboratory for Cartographic and Spatial Analysis, 1979.

YOELI, PINHAS, "Computer-Aided Relief Presentation by Traces of Inclined Planes," *The American Cartographer,* 3, no. 1 (April 1976), 75–85.

Appendix A

Dimensions of the Reference Ellipsoid

LENGTH OF DEGREES OF LATITUDE AND LONGITUDE GEODETIC REFERENCE SYSTEM 1980 ELLIPSOID*

	Kilometers per degree	
Latitude	Latitude†	Longitude‡
0	110.574	111.319
1	110.575	111.303
2	110.576	111.252
3	110.577	111.168
4	110.580	111.050
5	110.583	110.899
6	110.586	110.714
7	110.591	110.495
8	110.596	110.243
9	110.601	109.958
10	110.608	109.639
11	110.615	109.288
12	110.622	108.903
13	110.630	108.485
14	110.639	108.034
15	110.649	107.551
16	110.659	107.034
17	110.669	106.486
18	110.680	105.905
19	110.692	105.292
20	110.704	104.647
21	110.717	103.970
22	110.730	103.262

Latitude	Latitude†	Longitude‡
23	110.744	102.523
24	110.758	101.752
25	110.773	100.950
26	110.788	100.118
27	110.804	99.255
28	110.819	98.362
29	110.836	97.439
30	110.852	96.486
31	110.869	95.504
32	110.887	94.493
33	110.904	93.453
34	110.922	92.385
35	110.941	91.288
36	110.959	90.164
37	110.978	89.012
38	110.996	87.832
39	111.015	86.626
40	111.035	85.394
41	111.054	84.135
42	111.073	82.851
43	111.093	81.541
44	111.112	80.206
45	111.132	78.847
46	111.151	77.463
47	111.171	76.056
48	111.190	74.625
49	111.210	73.172
50	111.229	71.696
51	111.248	70.198
52	111.267	68.678
53	111.286	67.137
54	111.305	65.576
55	111.324	63.994
56	111.342	62.393
57	111.360	60.772
58	111.378	59.133
59	111.395	57.475
60	111.412	55.800
61	111.429	54.107
62	111.446	52.398
63	111.462	50.673
64	111.477	48.932
65	111.493	47.176
66	111.507	45.405
67	111.522	43.620
68	111.536	41.822
69	111.549	40.010
70	111.562	38.187
71	111.574	36.351
72	111.586	34.504

Latitude	Latitude†	Longitude‡
73	111.598	32.647
74	111.608	30.779
75	111.618	28.902
76	111.628	27.016
77	111.637	25.121
78	111.645	23.219
79	111.653	21.310
80	111.660	19.393
81	111.666	17.471
82	111.672	15.544
83	111.677	13.611
84	111.682	11.675
85	111.685	9.735
86	111.688	7.791
87	111.691	5.846
88	111.693	3.898
89	111.694	1.949
90	111.694	0.000

*The ellipsoid has the following parameters: $a = 6378137.000$; $f = 298.2572221$

†Length of a degree of arc centered on the latitude named.

‡Length of a degree of arc along the latitude named.

Source: Computed from data supplied by National Geodetic Survey.

Appendix B

Selected Suppliers of Graphic Arts Equipment and Materials

Agfa-Gevaert, Inc.
275 North Street
Teterboro, NJ 07608

Artype Inc.
3530 Work Drive
P.O. Box 7151
Fort Meyers, FL 33901

Charvoz-Carsen Corp.
5 Daniel Rd.
Fairfield, NJ 07006

The Craftint Manufacturing Co.
1615 Collamer Ave.
Cleveland, OH

Direct Reproduction Corp.
P.O. Box 356, Van Brunt Station
Brooklyn, NY 11215

E. I. DuPont deNemours and Co.
Photoproducts Dept.
Wilmington, DE

Eastman Kodak Co.
Graphics Markets Division
Rochester, NY 14650

Faber-Castell Corp.
41 Dickerson St.
Newark, NJ 07107

General Photo Products Co., Inc.
10 Paterson Ave.
Newton, NJ 07860

Graphic Products Corp.
Rolling Meadows, IL 60008

Koh-I-Noor Rapidograph Inc.
100 North St.
Bloomsbury, NJ 08804

Kratos/Keuffel & Esser Co.
20 Whippany Road
Morristown, NJ 07960

Letraset USA
40 Eisenhower Dr.
Paramus, NJ 07652

Munsell Color
2441 N. Calvert St.
Baltimore, MD 21218

Para-Tone, Inc.
P.O. Box 645
Countryside, IL 60525

J. S. Staedler, Inc.
P.O. Box 68
Montville, NJ 07045

Prestype, Inc.
194 Veteran's Blvd.
Carlstadt, NJ 07072

Varigraph, Inc.
Box 690
Madison, WI 53701

Wood-Regan Co.
15 Label Ave.
Montclair, NJ 07042

Index

Multicolor Map Production

Typical workflow using scribing
and photomechanical techniques

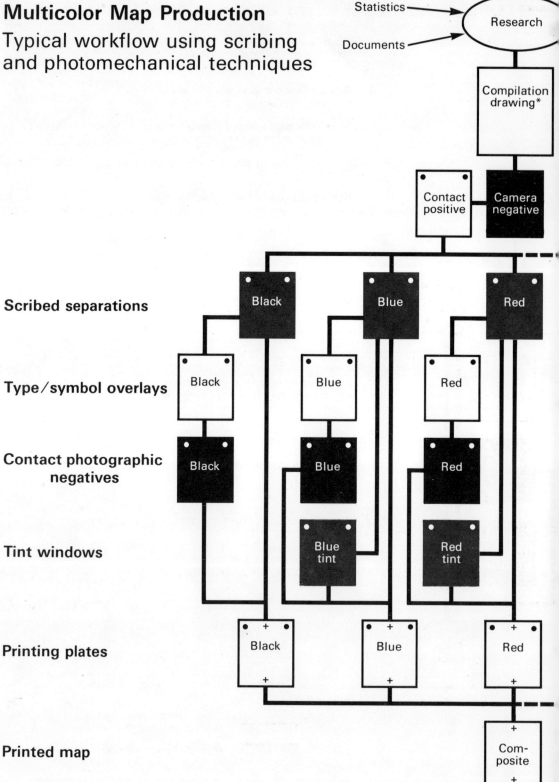

Statistics

Documents

Research

Compilation drawing*

Contact positive

Camera negative

Scribed separations

Black   Blue   Red

Type/symbol overlays

Black   Blue   Red

Contact photographic negatives

Black   Blue   Red

Tint windows

Blue tint   Red tint

Printing plates

Black   Blue   Red

Printed map

Composite